SIR.G.KNELLER PINX.   ENG.D BY GIMBER.

SIR ISAAC NEWTON.

HARPER'S FAMILY LIBRARY

Printed by R. Miller.

THE

LIFE

OF

SIR ISAAC NEWTON.

BY

DAVID BREWSTER, LL.D. F.R.S.

Ergo vivida vis animi pervicit, et extra
Processit longe flammantia mœnia mundi;
Atque omne immensum peragravit mente animoque.
Lucret. lib. i. l. 73.

The Birthplace of Newton.

NEW-YORK:

PRINTED AND PUBLISHED BY J. & J. HARPER,

NO. 82 CLIFF-STREET.

1831.

TO

THE RIGHT HONOURABLE

LORD BRAYBROOKE.

THE kindness with which your lordship intrusted to me some very valuable materials for the composition of this volume has induced me to embrace the present opportunity of publicly acknowledging it. But even if this personal obligation had been less powerful, those literary attainments and that enlightened benevolence which reflect upon rank its highest lustre would have justified me in seeking for it the patronage of a name which they have so justly honoured.

DAVID BREWSTER.

Allerly, June 1st, 1831.

PREFACE.

As this is the only Life of Sir Isaac Newton on any considerable scale that has yet appeared, I have experienced great difficulty in preparing it for the public. The materials collected by preceding biographers were extremely scanty; the particulars of his early life, and even the historical details of his discoveries, have been less perfectly preserved than those of his illustrious predecessors; and it is not creditable to his disciples that they have allowed a whole century to elapse without any suitable record of the life and labours of a master who united every claim to their affection and gratitude.

In drawing up this volume, I have obtained much assistance from the account of Sir Isaac Newton in the Biographia Britannica; from the letters to Oldenburg, and other papers in Bishop Horsley's edition of his works; from Turnor's Collections for the History of the Town and Soke of Grantham; from M. Biot's excellent Life of Newton in the Biographie Universelle; and from Lord King's Life and Correspondence of Locke.

Although these works contain much important information respecting the Life of Newton, yet I have been so fortunate as to obtain many new materials of considerable value.

To the kindness of Lord Braybrooke I have been indebted for the interesting correspondence of Newton, Mr. Pepys, and Mr. Millington, which is now published for the first time, and which throws much light upon an event in the life of our author that has recently acquired an unexpected and a painful importance. These letters, when combined with those which passed between Newton and Locke, and with a curious extract from the manuscript diary of Mr. Abraham Pryme, kindly furnished to me by his collateral descendant Professor Pryme of Cambridge, fill up a blank in his history, and have enabled me to delineate in its true character that temporary indisposition which, from the view that has been taken of it by foreign philosophers, has been the occasion of such deep distress to the friends of science and religion.

To Professor Whewell, of Cambridge, I owe very great obligations for much valuable information. Professor Rigaud, of Oxford, to whose kindness I have on many other occasions been indebted, supplied me with several important facts, and with extracts from the diary of Hearne in the Bodleian Library, and from the original correspondence between Newton and Flamstead, which the president of Corpus Christi College had for this purpose committed to his care; and Dr. J. C. Gregory, of Edinburgh, the descendant of the illustrious inventor of the reflecting telescope, allowed me to use his unpublished account of an autograph manuscript of Sir Isaac Newton, which was found among the papers of David Gregory, Savilian Professor of Astronomy at Oxford, and which throws some light on the history of the Principia.

I have been indebted to many other friends for the communication of books and facts, but especially to Sir William Hamilton, Bart., whose liberality in promoting literary inquiry is not limited to the circle of his friends.

D. B.

Allerly, June 1st, **1831.**

CONTENTS.

B

Page

LIFE

OF

SIR ISAAC NEWTON.

CHAPTER I.

The Pre-eminence of Sir Isaac Newton's Reputation—The Interest attached to the Study of his Life and Writings—His Birth and Parentage—His early Education—Is sent to Grantham School—His early Attachment to Mechanical Pursuits—His Windmill—His Waterclock—His Selfmoving Cart—His Sundials—His Preparation for the University.

THE name of Sir Isaac Newton has by general consent been placed at the head of those great men who have been the ornaments of their species. However imposing be the attributes with which time has invested the sages and the heroes of antiquity, the brightness of their fame has been eclipsed by the splendour of his reputation; and neither the partiality of rival nations, nor the vanity of a presumptuous age, has ventured to dispute the ascendency of his genius.   The philosopher,* indeed, to whom posterity will probably assign the place next to Newton, has characterized the *Principia* as pre-eminent above all the productions of human intellect, and has thus divested of extravagance the contemporary encomium upon its author,

Nec fas est propius mortali attingere Divos.
                                                                    HALLEY.
So near the gods—man cannot nearer go.

* The Marquis La Place.—See *Système du Monde*, p. 336.

The biography of an individual so highly renowned cannot fail to excite a general interest. Though his course may have lain in the vale of private life, and may have been unmarked with those dramatic events which throw a lustre even round perishable names, yet the inquiring spirit will explore the history of a mind so richly endowed,—will study its intellectual and moral phases, and will seek the shelter of its authority on those great questions which reason has abandoned to faith and hope.

If the conduct and opinions of men of ordinary talent are recorded for our instruction, how interesting must it be to follow the most exalted genius through the incidents of common life;—to mark the steps by which he attained his lofty pre-eminence; to see how he performs the functions of the social and the domestic compact; how he exercises his lofty powers of invention and discovery; how he comports himself in the arena of intellectual strife; and in what sentiments, and with what aspirations he quits the world which he has adorned.

In almost all these bearings, the life and writings of Sir Isaac Newton abound with the richest counsel. Here the philosopher will learn the art by which alone he can acquire an immortal name. The moralist will trace the lineaments of a character adjusted to all the symmetry of which our imperfect nature is susceptible; and the Christian will contemplate with delight the high-priest of science quitting the study of the material universe,—the scene of his intellectual triumphs,—to investigate with humility and patience the mysteries of his faith.

Sir Isaac Newton was born at Woolsthorpe, a hamlet in the parish of Colsterworth, in Lincolnshire, about six miles south of Grantham, on the 25th December, O. S., 1642, exactly one year after Galileo died, and was baptized at Colsterworth on the 1st January, 1642–3. His father, Mr. Isaac Newton, died at the early age of thirty-six, a little more than a year after the death of his father Robert Newton, and only a few months after his marriage to Harriet Ayscough, daughter of James Ayscough of Market Overton in Rutlandshire. This lady was accordingly left in a state of pregnancy, and appears to have given a premature birth to her only and posthumous child. The helpless infant thus ushered into the world was of such an extremely diminutive size,* and seemed of so perishable a frame, that two women who were sent to Lady Pakenham's at North Witham, to bring some medicine to strengthen him, did not expect to find him alive on their return. Providence, however, had otherwise decreed; and that frail tenement which seemed scarcely able to imprison its immortal mind was destined to enjoy a vigorous maturity, and to survive even the average term of human existence. The estate of Woolsthorpe, in the manor-house of which this remarkable birth took place, had been more than a hundred years in the possession of the family, who came originally from Newton in Lancashire, but who had, previous to the purchase of Woolsthorpe, settled at Westby, in the county of Lincoln. The manor-house, of which we have given an engraving, is situated in a beautiful little valley, remarkable for its copious wells of pure spring water, on the west side of the river Witham, which has its origin in the neighbourhood, and commands an agreeable prospect to the east towards Colsterworth. The manor of Woolsthorpe was worth only 30*l.* per annum; but Mrs. Newton possessed another small estate at Sewstern,† which raised the annual value of their property to about 80*l.*; and it is probable that the cultivation of the little farm on which she resided

---

* Sir Isaac Newton told Mr. Conduit, that he had often heard his mother say that when he was born he was so little that they might have put him into a quart mug.

† In Leicestershire, and about three miles south-east of Woolsthorpe.

somewhat enlarged the limited income upon which
she had to support herself, and educate her child.

For three years Mrs. Newton continued to watch
over her tender charge with parental anxiety; but
in consequence of her marriage to the Reverend
Barnabas Smith, rector of North Witham, about a
mile south of Woolsthorpe, she left him under the
care of her own mother. At the usual age he was
sent to two day-schools at Skillington and Stoke,
where he acquired the education which such semi-
naries afforded; but when he reached his twelfth
year he went to the public school at Grantham,
taught by Mr. Stokes, and was boarded at the house
of Mr. Clark, an apothecary in that town. According to information which Sir Isaac himself gave to
Mr. Conduit, he seems to have been very inattentive
to his studies, and very low in the school. The
boy, however, who was above him, having one day
given him a severe kick upon his stomach, from
which he suffered great pain, Isaac laboured inces-
santly till he got above him in the school, and from
that time he continued to rise till he was the head
boy. From the habits of application which this
incident had led him to form, the peculiar character
of his mind was speedily displayed. During the
hours of play, when the other boys were occupied
with their amusements, his mind was engrossed with
mechanical contrivances, either in imitation of something which he had seen, or in execution of some
original conception of his own. For this purpose
he provided himself with little saws, hatchets, ham-
mers, and all sorts of tools, which he acquired the
art of using with singular dexterity. The principal
pieces of mechanism which he thus constructed
were a windmill, a waterclock, and a carriage put in
motion by the person who sat in it. When a windmill was erecting near Grantham on the road to
Gunnerby, Isaac frequently attended the operations
of the workmen, and acquired such a thorough

knowledge of the machinery that he completed a working model of it, which excited universal admiration. This model was frequently placed on the top of the house in which he lodged at Grantham, and was put in motion by the action of the wind upon its sails. Not content with this exact imitation of the original machine, he conceived the idea of driving it by animal power, and for this purpose he enclosed in it a mouse which he called the miller, and which, by acting upon a sort of treadwheel, gave motion to the machine. According to some accounts, the mouse was made to advance by pulling a string attached to its tail, while others allege that the power of the little agent was called forth by its unavailing attempts to reach a portion of corn placed above the wheel.

His waterclock was formed out of a box which he had solicited from Mrs. Clark's brother. It was about four feet high, and of a proportional breadth, somewhat like a common houseclock. The index of the dialplate was turned by a piece of wood, which either fell or rose by the action of dropping water. As it stood in his own bedroom he supplied it every morning with the requisite quantity of water, and it was used as a clock by Mr. Clark's family, and remained in the house long after its inventor had quitted Grantham.* His mechanical carriage was a vehicle with four wheels, which was put in motion with a handle wrought by the person who sat in it, but, like Merlin's chair, it seems to have been used only on the smooth surface of a floor, and not fitted to overcome the inequalities of a road. Although

---

* "I remember once," says Dr. Stukely, "when I was deputy to Dr. Halley, secretary at the Royal Society, Sir Isaac talked of these kind of instruments. That he observed the chief inconvenience in them was, that the hole through which the water is transmitted being necessarily very small, was subject to be furred up by impurities in the water, as those made with sand will wear bigger, which at length causes an inequality in time."—Stukely's Letter to Dr. Mead.—Turnor's *Collections*, p. 177.

Newton was at this time " a sober, silent, thinking
lad," who scarcely ever joined in the ordinary games
of his schoolfellows, yet he took great pleasure in
providing them with amusements of a scientific
character. He introduced into the school the flying
of paper kites ; and he is said to have been at great
pains in determining their best forms and proportions, and in ascertaining the position and number
of the points by which the string should be attached.
He made also paper lanterns, by the light of which
he went to school in the winter mornings, and he
frequently attached these lanterns to the tails of
his kites in a dark night, so as to inspire the country
people with the belief that they were comets.

In the house where he lodged there were some
female inmates in whose company he appears to have
taken much pleasure. One of these, a Miss Storey,
sister to Dr. Storey, a physician at Buckminster,
near Colsterworth, was two or three years younger
than Newton, and to great personal attractions she
seems to have added more than the usual allotment
of female talent. The society of this young lady
and her companions was always preferred to that
of his own schoolfellows, and it was one of his most
agreeable occupations to construct for them little
tables and cupboards, and other utensils for holding
their dolls and their trinkets. He had lived nearly
six years in the same house with Miss Storey, and
there is reason to believe that their youthful friendship gradually rose to a higher passion ; but the
smallness of her portion and the inadequacy of his
own fortune appear to have prevented the consummation of their happiness. Miss Storey was afterward twice married, and under the name of Mrs.
Vincent, Dr. Stukely visited her at Grantham in 1727,
at the age of eighty-two, and obtained from her
many particulars respecting the early history of our
author. Newton's esteem for her continued un-
abated during his life. He regularly visited her when

he went to Lincolnshire, and never failed to relieve her from little pecuniary difficulties which seem to have beset her family.

Among the early passions of Newton we must recount his love of drawing; and even of writing verses. His own room was furnished with pictures drawn, coloured, and framed by himself, sometimes from copies, but often from life.* Among these were portraits of Dr. Donne, Mr. Stokes, the master of Grantham school, and King Charles I. under whose picture were the following verses.

> A secret art my soul requires to try,
> If prayers can give me what the wars deny.
> Three crowns distinguished here, in order do
> Present their objects to my knowing view.
> Earth's crown, thus at my feet I can disdain,
> Which heavy is, and at the best but vain.
> But now a crown of thorns I gladly greet,
> Sharp is this crown, but not so sharp as sweet;
> The crown of glory that I yonder see
> Is full of bliss and of eternity.

These verses were repeated to Dr. Stukely by Mrs. Vincent, who believed them to be written by Sir Isaac, a circumstance which is the more probable, as he himself assured Mr. Conduit, with some expression of pleasure, that he "excelled in making verses," although he had been heard to express a contempt for poetical composition.

But while the mind of our young philosopher was principally occupied with the pursuits which we have now detailed, it was not inattentive to the movements of the celestial bodies, on which he was destined to throw such a brilliant light. The imperfections of his waterclock had probably directed his thoughts to the more accurate measure of time which the motion of the sun afforded. In the yard of the

* Mr. Clark informed Dr. Stukely that the walls of the room in which Sir Isaac lodged were covered with charcoal drawings of birds, beasts, men, ships, and mathematical figures, all of which were very well designed.

house where he lived, he traced the varying movements of that luminary upon the walls and roofs of the
buildings, and by means of fixed pins he had marked
out the hourly and half-hourly subdivisions. One
of these dials, which went by the name of *Isaac's
dial*, and was often referred to by the country people
for the hour of the day, appears to have been drawn
solely from the observations of several years; but
we are not informed whether all the dials which he
drew on the wall of his house at Woolsthorpe, and
which existed after his death, were of the same
description, or were projected from his knowledge
of the doctrine of the sphere.

Upon the death of the Reverend Mr. Smith in the
year 1656, his widow left the rectory of North
Witham, and took up her residence at Woolsthorpe
along with her three children, Mary, Benjamin, and
Hannah Smith. Newton had now attained the
fifteenth year of his age, and had made great progress in his studies; and as he was thought capable
of being useful in the management of the farm and
country business at Woolsthorpe, his mother, chiefly
from a motive of economy, recalled him from the
school at Grantham. In order to accustom him to
the art of selling and buying, two of the most important branches of rural labour, he was frequently
sent on Saturday to Grantham market to dispose
of grain and other articles of farm produce, and to
purchase such necessaries as the family required.
As he had yet acquired no experience, an old trust-
worthy servant generally accompanied him on these
errands. The inn which they patronised was the
Saracen's Head at West Gate; but no sooner had
they put up their horses than our young philosopher
deserted his commercial concerns, and betook himself to his former lodging in the apothecary's garret,
where a number of Mr. Clark's old books afforded
him abundance of entertainment till his aged guardian had executed the family commissions, and an-

nounced to him the necessity of returning. At other times he deserted his duties at an earlier stage, and intrenched himself under a hedge by the way-side, where he continued his studies till the servant returned from Grantham. The more immediate affairs of the farm were not more prosperous under his management than would have been his marketings at Grantham. The perusal of a book, the execution of a model, or the superintendence of a waterwheel of his own construction, whirling the glittering spray from some neighbouring stream, absorbed all his thoughts when the sheep were going astray, and the cattle were devouring or treading down the corn.

Mrs. Smith was soon convinced from experience that her son was not destined to cultivate the soil, and as his passion for study, and his dislike for every other occupation increased with his years, she wisely resolved to give him all the advantages which education could confer. He was accordingly sent back to Grantham school, where he continued for some months in busy preparation for his academical studies. His uncle, the Reverend W. Ayscough, who was rector of Burton Coggles, about three miles east of Woolsthorpe, and who had himself studied at Trinity College, recommended to his nephew to enter that society, and it was accordingly determined that he should proceed to Cambridge at the approaching term.*

* "One of his uncles," says M. Biot, "having one day found him under a hedge with a book in his hand and entirely absorbed in meditation, took it from him, and found that he was occupied in the solution of a mathematical problem. Struck with finding so serious and so active a disposition at so early an age, he urged his mother no longer to thwart him, and to send him back to Grantham to continue his studies." I have omitted this anecdote in the text, as I cannot find it in Turnor's Collections, from which M. Biot derived his details of Newton's infancy, nor in any other work.

C

CHAPTER II.

Newton enters Trinity College, Cambridge—Origin of his Propensity for Mathematics—He studies the Geometry of Descartes unassisted—Purchases a Prism--Revises Dr. Barrow's Optical Lectures—Dr. Barrow's Opinion respecting Colours.--Takes his Degrees—Is appointed a Fellow of Trinity College —Succeeds Dr. Barrow in the Lucasian Chair of Mathematics.

To a young mind thirsting for knowledge, and ambitious of the distinction which it brings, the transition from a village school to a university like that of Cambridge,—from the absolute solitude of thought to the society of men imbued with all the literature and science of the age,—must be one of eventful interest. To Newton it was a source of peculiar excitement. The history of science affords many examples where the young aspirant had been early initiated into her mysteries, and had even exercised his powers of invention and discovery before he was admitted within the walls of a college; but he who was to give philosophy her laws did not exhibit such early talent; no friendly counsel regulated his youthful studies, and no work of scientific eminence seems to have guided him in his course. In yielding to the impulse of his mechanical genius, his mind obeyed the laws of its own natural expansion, and, following the line of least resistance, it was thus drawn aside from the strongholds with which it was destined to grapple.

When Newton, therefore, arrived at Trinity College, he brought with him a more slender portion of science than falls to the lot of ordinary scholars; but this state of his acquirements was perhaps not unfavourable to the development of his powers. Unexhausted by premature growth, and invigorated by healthful repose, his mind was the better fitted to make those vigorous and rapid shoots which soon covered with foliage and with fruit the genial soil to which it had been transferred.

Cambridge was consequently the real birthplace of Newton's genius. Her teachers fostered his earliest studies;—her institutions sustained his mightiest efforts;—and within her precincts were all his discoveries made and perfected. When he was called to higher official functions, his disciples kept up the pre-eminence of their master's philosophy, and their successors have maintained this seat of learning in the fulness of its glory, and rendered it the most distinguished among the universities of Europe.

It was on the 5th of June, 1660, in the 18th year of his age, that Newton was admitted into Trinity College, Cambridge, during the same year that Dr. Barrow was elected professor of Greek in the university. His attention was first turned to the study of mathematics by a desire to inquire into the truth of judicial astrology; and he is said to have discovered the folly of that study by erecting a figure with the aid of one or two of the problems of Euclid. The propositions contained in this ancient system of geometry he regarded as self-evident truths; and without any preliminary study he made himself master of Descartes's Geometry by his genius and patient application. This neglect of the elementary truths of geometry he afterward regarded as a mistake in his mathematical studies, and he expressed to Dr. Pemberton his regret that "he had applied himself to the works of Descartes, and other algebraic writers, before he had considered the elements of Euclid with that attention which so excellent a writer deserved.* Dr. Wallis's Arithmetic of Infinites, Saunderson's Logic, and the Optics of Kepler were among the books which he had studied with care. On these works he wrote comments during their perusal;

* Pemberton's *View of Sir Isaac Newton's Philosophy.* Pref.

and so great was his progress, that he is reported to
have found himself more deeply versed in some
branches of knowledge than the tutor who directed
his studies.

Neither history nor tradition has handed down to
us any particular account of his progress during the
first three years that he spent at Cambridge. It
appears from a statement of his expenses, that in
1664 he purchased a prism, for the purpose, as has
been said, of examining Descartes's theory of colours; and it is stated by Mr. Conduit, that he soon
established his own views on the subject, and detected the errors in those of the French philosopher.
This, however, does not seem to have been the case.
Had he discovered the composition of light in 1664
or 1665, it is not likely that he would have withheld
it, not only from the Royal Society, but from his
own friends at Cambridge till the year 1671. His
friend and tutor, Dr. Barrow, was made Lucasian
Professor of Mathematics in 1663, and the optical
lectures which he afterward delivered were published
in 1669. In the preface of this work he acknowledges his obligations to his colleague, Mr. Isaac
Newton,* for having revised the MSS., and corrected
several oversights, and made some important sug-
gestions. In the twelfth lecture there are some observations on the nature and origin of colours,
which Newton could not have permitted his friend
to publish had he been then in possession of their
true theory. According to Dr. Barrow, *White* is
that which discharges a copious light equally clear
in every direction; *Black* is that which does not
emit light at all, or which does it very sparingly.
Red is that which emits a light more clear than
usual, but interrupted by shady interstices. *Blue* is
that which discharges a rarified light, as in bodies
which consist of white and black particles arranged

* Peregregiæ vir indolis ac insignis peritiæ.—*Epist ad. Lect.*

alternately. *Green* is nearly allied to blue. *Yellow* is a mixture of much white and a little red; and *Purple* consists of a great deal of blue mixed with a small portion of red. The blue colour of the sea arises from the whiteness of the salt which it contains, mixed with the blackness of the pure water in which the salt is dissolved; and the blueness of the shadows of bodies, seen at the same time by candle and daylight, arises from the whiteness of the paper mixed with the faint light or blackness of the twilight. These opinions savour so little of genuine philosophy that they must have attracted the observation of Newton, and had he discovered at that time that white was a mixture of all the colours, and black a privation of them all, he could not have permitted the absurd speculations of his master to pass uncorrected.

That Newton had not distinguished himself by any positive discovery so early as 1664 or 1665, may be inferred also from the circumstances which attended the competition for the law fellowship of Trinity College. The candidates for this appointment were himself and Mr. Robert Uvedale; and Dr. Barrow, then Master of Trinity, having found them perfectly equal in their attainments, conferred the fellowship on Mr. Uvedale as the senior candidate.

In the books of the university, Newton is recorded as having been admitted sub-sizer in 1661. He became a scholar in 1664. In 1665 he took his degree of Bachelor of Arts, and in 1666, in consequence of the breaking out of the plague, he retired to Woolsthorpe. In 1667 he was made Junior Fellow. In 1668 he took his degree of Master of Arts, and in the same year he was appointed to a Senior Fellowship. In 1669, when Dr. Barrow had resolved to devote his attention to theology, he resigned the Lucasian Professorship of Mathematics in favour of Newton, who may now be considered

as having entered upon that brilliant career of discovery the history of which will form the subject of
some of the following chapters.

―――――

CHAPTER III.

*Newton occupied in grinding Hyperbolical Lenses—His first Experi-
ments with the Prism made in 1666—He discovers the Composition of
White Light, and the different Refrangibility of the Rays which compose it—Abandons his Attempts to improve Refracting Telescopes, and
resolves to attempt the Construction of Reflecting ones—He quits Cambridge on account of the Plague—Constructs two Reflecting Telescopes
in 1668, the first ever executed—One of them examined by the Royal Society, and shown to the King—He constructs a Telescope with Glass
Specula—Recent History of the Reflecting Telescope—Mr. Airy's
Glass Specula—Hadley's Reflecting Telescopes—Short's—Herschel's
—Ramage's—Lord Oxmantown's.*

THE appointment of Newton to the Lucasian
chair at Cambridge seems to have been coeval with
his grandest discoveries. The first of these of
which the date is well authenticated is that of the
different refrangibility of the rays of light, which he
established in 1666. The germ of the doctrine of
universal gravitation seems to have presented itself
to him in the same year, or at least in 1667; and "in
the year 1666 or before"* he was in possession of
his method of fluxions, and he had brought it to such
a state in the beginning of 1669, that he permitted
Dr. Barrow to communicate it to Mr. Collins on the
20th of June in that year.

Although we have already mentioned, on the authority of a written memorandum of Newton himself, that he purchased a prism at Cambridge in 1664,
yet he does not appear to have made any use of it,
as he informs us that it was in 1666 that he "pro-

―――――

* See Newton's Letter to the Abbe Conti, dated February 26, 1715-16,
in the *Additamenta Comm. Epistolici.*

cured a triangular glass prism to try therewith the celebrated phenomena of colours."* During that year he had applied himself to the grinding of "optic glasses, of other figures than spherical," and having, no doubt, experienced the impracticability of executing such lenses, the idea of examining the phenomena of colour was one of those sagacious and fortunate impulses which more than once led him to discovery. Descartes in his *Dioptrice*, published in 1629, and more recently James Gregory in his *Optica Promota* published in 1663, had shown that parallel and diverging rays could be reflected or refracted, with mathematical accuracy, to a point or focus, by giving the surface a parabolic, an elliptical, or a hyperbolic form, or some other form not spherical. Descartes had even invented and described machines by which lenses of these shapes could be ground and polished, and the perfection of the refracting telescope was supposed to depend on the degree of accuracy with which they could be executed.

In attempting to grind glasses that were not spherical, Newton seems to have conjectured that the defects of lenses, and consequently of refracting telescopes, might arise from some other cause than the imperfect convergency of rays to a single point, and this conjecture was happily realized in those fine discoveries of which we shall now endeavour to give some account.

When Newton began this inquiry, philosophers of the highest genius were directing all the energies of their mind to the subject of light, and to the improvement of the refracting telescope. James Gregory of Aberdeen had invented his reflecting telescope. Descartes had explained the theory and exerted himself in perfecting the construction of the common refracting telescope, and Huygens had not

* Newtoni *Opera*, tom. iv. p. 205, Letter to Oldenburg.

only executed the magnificent instruments by which
he discovered the ring and the satellites of Saturn,
but had begun those splendid researches respecting
the nature of light, and the phenomena of double
refraction, which have led his successors to such
brilliant discoveries.   Newton, therefore, arose when
the science of light was ready for some great accession, and at the precise time when he was required to propagate the impulse which it had received
from his illustrious predecessors.

The ignorance which then prevailed respecting
the nature and origin of colours is sufficiently apparent from the account we have already given of
Dr. Barrow's speculations on this subject.   It was
always supposed that light of every colour was
equally refracted or bent out of its direction when
it passed through any lens or prism, or other refracting medium; and though the exhibition of colours
by the prism had been often made previous to the
time of Newton, yet no philosopher seems to have
attempted to analyze the phenomena.

When he had procured his triangular glass prism,
a section of which is shown at ABC, (*fig.* 1,) he

Fig. 1.

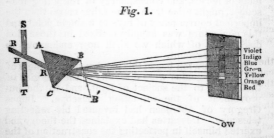

made a hole H in one of his window-shutters, SHT,
and having darkened his chamber, he let in a convenient quantity of the sun's light RR, which, pass-

ing through the prism ABC, was so refracted as to
exhibit all the different colours on the wall at MN,
forming an image about five times as long as it was
broad. "It was at first," says our author, " a very
pleasing divertisement to view the vivid and intense
colours produced thereby," but this pleasure was
immediately succeeded by surprise at various circumstances which he had not expected. According to
the received laws of refraction, he expected the
image MN to be circular, like the white image at W,
which the sunbeam RR had formed on the wall
previous to the interposition of the prism; but when
he found it to be no less than five times larger than
its breadth, it "excited in him a more than ordinary
curiosity to examine from whence it might proceed.
He could scarcely think that the various thickness of
the glass, or the termination with shadow or darkness, could have any influence on light to produce such
an effect: yet he thought it not amiss first to examine
those circumstances, and so find what would happen
by transmitting light through parts of the glass of
divers thicknesses, or through holes in the window
of divers bignesses, or by setting the prism without
(on the other side of ST), so that the light might
pass through it and be refracted before it was terminated by the hole; but he found none of these circumstances material. The fashion of the colours
was in all those cases the same."

Newton next suspected that some unevenness in
the glass, or other accidental irregularity, might
cause the dilatation of the colours. In order to try
this, he took another prism BCB', and placed it in
such a manner that the light RRW passing through
them both might be refracted contrary ways, and
thus returned by BCB' into that course RRW, from
which the prism ABC had diverted it, for by this
means he thought the regular effects of the prism
ABC would be destroyed by the prism BCB, and the
irregular ones more augmented by the multiplicity

of refractions. The result was, that the light which
was diffused by the first prism ABC into an oblong
form, was reduced by the second prism BCB′ into a
circular one W, with as much regularity as when it
did not pass through them at all; so that whatever
was the cause of the length of the image MN, it did
not arise from any irregularity in the prism.

Our author next proceeded to examine more criti-
cally what might be effected by the difference of the
incidence of the rays proceeding from different parts
of the sun's disk; but by taking accurate measures
of the lines and angles, he found that the angle of
the emergent rays should be 31 minutes equal to the
sun's diameter, whereas the real angle subtended by
MN at the hole H was 2° 49′. But as this computation was founded on the hypothesis, that the sine of
the angle of incidence was proportional to the sine
of the angle of refraction, which from his own experience he could not imagine to be so erroneous as
to make that angle but 31′, which was in reality 2°
49′, yet "his curiosity caused him again to take up
his prism" ABC, and having turned it round in both
directions, so as to make the rays RR fall both with
greater and with less obliquity upon the face AC, he
found that the colours on the wall did not sensibly
change their place; and hence he obtained a decided
proof that they could not be occasioned by a difference in the incidence of the light radiating from different parts of the sun's disk.

Newton then began to suspect that the rays, after
passing through the prism, might move in curve lines,
and, in proportion to the different degrees of curvature, might tend to different parts of the wall; and
this suspicion was strengthened by the recollection
that he had often seen a tennis-ball struck with an
oblique racket describe such a curve line. In this
case a circular and a progressive motion is communicated to the ball by the stroke, and in consequence
of this, the direction of its motion was curvilineal

so that if the rays of light were globular bodies, they might acquire a circulating motion by their oblique passage out of one medium into another, and thus move like the tennis-ball in a curve line. Notwithstanding, however, "this plausible ground of suspicion," he could discover no such curvature in their direction, and, what was enough for his purpose, he observed that the difference between the length MN of the image, and the diameter of the hole H, was proportional to their distance HM, which could not have happened had the rays moved in curvilineal paths.

These different hypotheses, or suspicions, as Newton calls them, being thus gradually removed, he was at length led to an experiment which determined beyond a doubt the true cause of the elongation of the coloured image. Having taken a board with a small hole in it, he placed it behind the face BC of the prism, and close to it, so that he could transmit through the hole any one of the colours in MN, and keep back all the rest. When the hole, for example, was near C, no other light but the red fell upon the wall at N. He then placed behind N another board with a hole in it, and behind this board he placed another prism, so as to receive the red light at N, which passed through this hole in the second board. He then turned round the first prism ABC so as to make all the colours pass in succession through these two holes, and he marked their places on the wall. From the variation of these places, he saw that the *red* rays at N were less refracted by the second prism than the *orange* rays, the *orange* less than the *yellow*, and so on, the *violet* being more refracted than all the rest.

Hence he drew the grand conclusion, *that light was not homogeneous, but consisted of rays, some of which were more refrangible than others.*

As soon as this important truth was established, Sir Isaac saw that a lens which refracts light exactly

like a prism must also refract the differently coloured
rays with different degrees of force, bringing the
violet rays to a focus nearer the glass than the red
rays. This is shown in *fig.* 2, where LL is a convex lens, and S, L, SL rays of the sun falling upon it

Fig. 2.

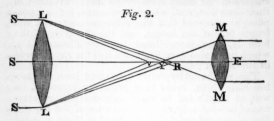

in parallel directions. The violet rays existing in
the white light SL being more refrangible than the
rest, will be more refracted or bent, and will meet at
V, forming there a violet image of the sun. In like
manner the yellow rays will form an image of the
sun at Y, and so on, the red rays, which are the least
refrangible, being brought to a focus at R, and there
forming a red image of the sun.

Hence, if we suppose LL to be the object-glass of
a telescope directed to the sun, and MM an eye-glass
through which the eye at E sees magnified the image
or picture of the sun formed by LL, it cannot see
distinctly all the different images between R and V.
If it is adjusted so as to see distinctly the *yellow*
image at Y, as it is in the figure, it will not see distinctly either the *red* or *violet* images, nor indeed any
of them but the yellow one. There will consequently be a distinct yellow image, with indistinct
images of all the other colours, producing great confusion and indistinctness of vision. As soon as Sir
Isaac perceived this result of his discovery, he abandoned his attempts to improve the refracting tele-

scope, and took into consideration the principle of re-flection; and as he found that rays of all colours were reflected regularly, so that the angle of reflection was equal to the angle of incidence, he concluded that, upon this principle, *optical instruments might be brought to any degree of perfection imaginable*, provided a reflecting substance could be found which could polish as finely as glass, and reflect as much light as glass transmits, and provided a method of communicating to it a parabolic figure could be obtained. These difficulties, however, appeared to him very great, and he even thought them insuperable when he considered that, as any irregularity in a reflecting surface makes the rays deviate five or six times more from their true path than similar irregularities in a refracting surface, a much greater degree of nicety would be required in figuring reflecting specula than refracting lenses.

Such was the progress of Newton's optical discoveries, when he was forced to quit Cambridge in 1666 by the plague which then desolated England, and more than two years elapsed before he proceeded any farther. In 1668 he resumed the inquiry, and having thought of a delicate method of polishing, proper for metals, by which, as he conceived, "the figure would be corrected to the last," he began to put this method to the test of experiment. At this time he was acquainted with the proposal of Mr. James Gregory, contained in his *Optica Promota*, to construct a reflecting telescope with two concave specula, the largest of which had a hole in the middle of the larger speculum, to transmit the light to an eye-glass;* but he conceived that it would be

* M. Biot, in his Life of Newton, has stated that Newton was preceded in the invention of the reflecting telescope by Gregory, *but probably without knowing it.* It is quite certain, however, that Newton was acquainted with Gregory's invention, as appears from the following avowal of it. "When I first applied myself to try the effects of reflection, Mr. Gregory's *Optica Promota* (printed in the year 1663) having fallen into my hands, where there is an instrument described with a hole

D

an improvement on this instrument to place the eye-glass at the side of the tube, and to reflect the rays to it by an oval plane speculum. One of these instruments he actually executed with his own hands; and he gave an account of it in a letter to a friend, dated February 23d, 1668–9, a letter which is also remarkable for containing the first allusion to his discoveries respecting colours. Previous to this he was in correspondence on the subject with Mr. Ent, afterward Sir George Ent, one of the original council of the Royal Society, an eminent medical writer of his day, and President of the College of Physicians. In a letter to Mr. Ent he had promised an account of his telescope to their mutual friend, and the letter to which we now allude contained the fulfilment of that promise. The telescope was six inches long. It bore an aperture in the large speculum something more than an inch, and as the eye-glass was a plano-convex lens, whose focal length was one-sixth or one-seventh of an inch, it magnified about forty times, which, as Newton remarks, was more than any six-foot tube (meaning refracting telescopes) could do with distinctness. On account of the badness of the materials, however, and the want of a good polish, it represented objects less distinct than a six-feet tube, though he still thought it would be equal to a three or four feet tube directed to common objects. He had seen through it Jupiter distinctly with his four satellites, and also the horns or moon-like phases of Venus, though this last phenomenon required some niceness in adjusting the instrument.

Although Newton considered this little instru-

in the midst of the object-glass, to transmit the light to an eye-glass placed behind it, I had thence an occasion of considering that sort of construction, and found their disadvantages so great, that I saw it necessary before I attempted any thing in the practice to alter the design of them, and place the eye-glass at the side of the tube rather than at the middle." —*Letter to Oldenburg*, May 4th, 1672.

ment as in itself contemptible, yet he regarded it as an "epitome of what might be done;" and he expressed his conviction that a six-feet telescope might be made after this method, which would perform as well as a sixty or a hundred feet telescope made in the common way; and that if a common refracting telescope could be made of the "purest glass exquisitely polished, with the best figure that any geometrician (Descartes, &c.) hath or can design," it would scarcely perform better than a common telescope. This, he adds, may seem a paradoxical assertion, yet he continues, "it is the necessary consequence of some experiments which I have made concerning the nature of light."

The telescope now described possesses a very peculiar interest, as being the first reflecting one which was ever executed and directed to the heavens. James Gregory, indeed, had attempted, in 1664 or 1665, to construct his instrument. He employed Messrs. Rives and Cox, who were celebrated glass-grinders of that time, to execute a concave speculum of six feet radius, and likewise a small one; but as they had failed in polishing the large one, and as Mr. Gregory was on the eve of going abroad, he troubled himself no farther about the experiment, and the tube of the telescope was never made. Some time afterward, indeed, he "made some trials both with a little concave and convex speculum," but, "possessed with the fancy of the defective figure, he would not be at the pains to fix every thing in its due distance."

Such were the earliest attempts to construct the reflecting telescope, that noble instrument which has since effected such splendid discoveries in astronomy. Looking back from the present advanced state of practical science, how great is the contrast between the loose specula of Gregory and the fine Gregorian telescopes of Hadley, Short, and Veitch, —between the humble six-inch tube of Newton and the gigantic instruments of Herschel and Ramage.

The success of this first experiment inspired Newton with fresh zeal, and though his mind was now
occupied with his optical discoveries, with the elements of his method of fluxions, and with the ex-
panding germ of his theory of universal gravitation,
yet with all the ardour of youth he applied himself
to the laborious operation of executing another reflecting telescope with his own hands. This instrument, which was better than the first, though it lay
by him several years, excited some interest at Cambridge ; and Sir Isaac himself informs us, that one
of the fellows of Trinity College had completed a
telescope of the same kind, which he considered as
somewhat superior to his own. The existence of
these telescopes having become known to the Royal
Society, Newton was requested to send his instrument for examination to that learned body. He accordingly transmitted it to Mr. Oldenburg in December, 1671, and from this epoch his name began to
acquire that celebrity by which it has been so peculiarly distinguished.

On the 11th of January, 1672, it was announced
to the Royal Society that his reflecting telescope
had been shown to the king, and had been examined
by the president, Sir Robert Moray, Sir Paul Neale,
Sir Christopher Wren, and Mr. Hook. These gentlemen entertained so high an opinion of it, that, in
order to secure the honour of the contrivance to its
author, they advised the inventor to send a drawing
and description of it to Mr. Huygens at Paris. Mr.
Oldenburg accordingly drew up a description of it
in Latin, which, after being corrected by Mr. Newton, was transmitted to that eminent philosopher.
This telescope, of which the annexed is an accurate
drawing, is carefully preserved in the library of the
Royal Society of London, with the following inscription :—

" *Invented by Sir Isaac Newton and made with his
own hands,* 1671."

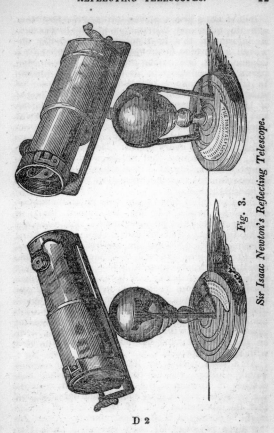

Fig. 3.

Sir Isaac Newton's Reflecting Telescope.

It does not appear that Newton executed any other reflecting telescopes than the two we have mentioned. He informs us that he repolished and greatly improved a fourteen-feet object-glass, executed by a London artist, and having proposed in 1678 to substitute glass reflectors in place of metallic specula, he tried to make a reflecting telescope on this principle four feet long, and with a magnifying power of 150. The glass was wrought by a London artist, and though it seemed well finished, yet, when it was quicksilvered on its convex side, it exhibited all over the glass innumerable inequalities, which gave an indistinctness to every object. He expresses, however, his conviction that nothing but good workmanship is wanting to perfect these telescopes, and he recommends their consideration "to the curious in figuring glasses."

For a period of fifty years this recommendation excited no notice. At last Mr. James Short of Edinburgh, an artist of consummate skill, executed about the year 1730 no fewer than six reflecting telescopes with glass specula, three of fifteen inches, and three of nine inches in focal length. He found it extremely troublesome to give them a true figure with parallel surfaces; and several of them when finished turned out useless, in consequence of the veins which then appeared in the glass. Although these instruments performed remarkably well, yet the light was fainter than he expected, and from this cause, combined with the difficulty of finishing them, he afterward devoted his labours solely to those with metallic specula.

At a later period, in 1822, Mr. G. B. Airy of Trinity College, and one of the distinguished successors of Newton in the Lucasian chair, resumed the consideration of glass specula, and demonstrated that the aberration both of figure and of colour might be corrected in these instruments. Upon this ingenious principle Mr. Airy executed more than one telescope, but though the result of the experiment was such as to excite hopes of ultimate success, yet the construction of such instruments is still a desideratum in practical science.

Such were the attempts which Sir Isaac Newton made to construct reflecting telescopes; but notwithstanding the success of his labours, neither the philosopher nor the practical optician seems to have had courage to pursue them. A London artist, indeed, undertook to imitate these instruments; but Sir Isaac informs us, that "he fell much short of what he had attained, as he afterward understood by discoursing with the under workmen he had employed." After a long period of fifty years, John Hadley, Esq. of Essex, a Fellow of the Royal Society, began in 1719 or 1720 to execute a reflecting telescope. His scientific knowledge and his manual dexterity fitted him admirably for such a task, and, probably after many failures, he constructed two large telescopes about five feet three inches long, one of which, with a speculum six inches in diameter, was presented to the Royal Society in 1723. The celebrated Dr. Bradley and the Rev. Mr. Pound compared it with the great Huygenian refractor 123 feet long. It bore as high a magnifying power as the Huygenian telescope: it showed objects equally distinct, though not altogether so clear and bright, and it exhibited every celestial object that had been discovered by Huygens,—the five satellites of Saturn, the shadow of Jupiter's satellites on his disk, the black list in Saturn's ring, and the edge of his shadow cast on the ring. Encouraged and instructed by Mr. Hadley, Dr. Bradley began the construction of reflecting telescopes, and succeeded so well that he would have completed one of them, had he not been obliged to change his residence. Some time afterward he and the Honourable Samuel Molyneux undertook the task together at Kew, and attempted to execute specula about twenty-six inches in focal length; but notwithstanding Dr. Bradley's former experience, and Mr. Hadley's frequent instructions, it was a long time before they succeeded. The first good instrument which they finished was in May, 1724. It was twenty-six inches in focal length; but they afterward completed a very large one of eight feet, the largest that had ever been made. The first of these instruments was afterward elegantly fitted up by Mr. Molyneux, and presented to his majesty John V. King of Portugal.

The great object of these two able astronomers was to reduce the method of making specula to such a degree of certainty that they could be manufactured for public sale. Mr. Hauksbee had indeed made a good one about three and a half feet long, and had proceeded to the execution of two others, one of six feet, and another of twelve feet in focal length; but Mr. Scarlet and Mr. Hearne, having received all the information which Mr. Molyneux had acquired, constructed them for public sale; and the reflecting telescope has ever since been an article of trade with every regular optician.

As Sir Isaac Newton was at this time President of the Royal Society, he had the high satisfaction of seeing his own invention become an instrument of public use, and of great advantage to science, and he no doubt felt the full influence of this triumph of his skill. Still, however, the reflecting telescope had not achieved any new discovery in the heavens. The latest accession to astronomy had been made by the ordinary refractors of Huygens, labouring under all the imperfections of coloured light; and this long pause in astronomical discovery seemed to indicate that man had carried to its farthest limits his power of penetrating into the depths of the universe. This, however, was only one of those stationary positions from which human genius takes a new and a loftier elevation. While the English opticians were thus practising the recent art of grinding specula, Mr. James Short of Edinburgh was devoting to the subject all the energies of his youthful mind. In 1732, and in the 22d year of his age, he began his labours, and he carried to such high perfection the art of grinding and polishing specula, and of giving them the true parabolic figure, that, with a telescope fifteen inches in focal length, he read in the Philosophical Transactions at the distance of 500 feet, and frequently saw the five satellites of Saturn together,—a power which was beyond the reach even of Hadley's six-feet instrument. The celebrated Maclaurin compared the telescopes of Short with those made by the best London artists, and so great was their superiority, that his small telescopes were invariably superior to larger ones from London. In 1742, after he had settled as an optician in the metropolis, he executed for Lord Thomas Spencer a reflecting telescope, twelve feet in focal length, for 630*l.*; in 1752 he completed one for the King of Spain, at the expense of 1200*l.*; and a short time before his death, which took place in 1768, he finished the specula of the large telescope which was mounted equatorially for the observatory of Edinburgh by his brother Thomas Short, who was offered twelve hundred guineas for it by the King of Denmark.

Although the superiority of these instruments, which were all of the Gregorian form, demonstrated the value of the reflecting telescope, yet no skilful hand had yet directed it to the heavens ; and it was reserved for Dr. Herschel to employ it as an instrument of discovery, to exhibit to the eye of man new worlds and new systems, and to bring within the grasp of his reason those remote regions of space to which his imagination even had scarcely ventured to extend its power. So early as 1774 he completed a *five*-feet Newtonian reflector, and he afterward executed no fewer than *two hundred* 7 feet, *one hundred and fifty* 10 feet, and *eighty* 20 feet specula. In

1781 he began a reflector thirty feet long, and having a speculum thirty-six inches in diameter; and under the munificent patronage of George III. he completed, in 1789, his gigantic instrument forty feet long, with a speculum *forty-nine and a half* inches in diameter. The genius and perseverance which created instruments of such transcendant magnitude were not likely to terminate with their construction. In the examination of the starry heavens, the ultimate object of his labours, Dr. Herschel exhibited the same exalted qualifications, and in a few years he rose from the level of humble life to the enjoyment of a name more glorious than that of the sages and warriors of ancient times, and as immortal as the objects with which it will be for ever associated. Nor was it in the ardour of the spring of life that these triumphs of reason were achieved. Dr. Herschel had reached the middle of his course before his career of discovery began, and it was in the autumn and winter of his days that he reaped the full harvest of his glory. The discovery of a new planet at the verge of the solar system was the first trophy of his skill, and new double and multiple stars, and new nebulæ, and groups of celestial bodies were added in thousands to the system of the universe. The spring-tide of knowledge which was thus let in upon the human mind continued for a while to spread its waves over Europe; but when it sank to its ebb in England, there was no other bark left upon the strand but that of the Deucalion of Science, whose home had been so long upon its waters.

During the life of Dr. Herschel, and during the reign, and within the dominions of his royal patron, four new planets were added to the solar system, but they were detected by telescopes of ordinary power; and we venture to state, that since the reign of George III. no attempt has been made to keep up the continuity of Dr. Herschel's discoveries.

Mr. Herschel, his distinguished son, has indeed

completed more than one telescope of considerable size; Mr. Ramage, of Aberdeen, has executed reflectors rivalling almost those of Slough;—and Lord Oxmantown, an Irish nobleman of high promise, is now engaged on an instrument of great size. But what avail the enthusiasm and the efforts of individual minds in the intellectual rivalry of nations? When the proud science of England pines in obscurity, blighted by the absence of the royal favour, and of the nation's sympathy;—when its chivalry fall unwept and unhonoured;—how can it sustain the conflict against the honoured and marshalled genius of foreign lands?

CHAPTER IV.

He delivers a Course of Optical Lectures at Cambridge—Is elected Fellow of the Royal Society—He communicates to them his Discoveries on the different Refrangibility and Nature of Light—Popular Account of them—They involve him in various Controversies—His Dispute with Pardies—Linus—Lucas—Dr. Hooke and Mr. Huygens—The Influence of these Disputes on the Mind of Newton.

ALTHOUGH Newton delivered a course of lectures on optics in the University of Cambridge in the years 1669, 1670, and 1671, containing his principal discoveries relative to the different refrangibility of light, yet it is a singular circumstance, that these discoveries should not have become public through the conversation or correspondence of his pupils. The Royal Society had acquired no knowledge of them till the beginning of 1672, and his reputation in that body was founded chiefly on his reflecting telescope. On the 23d December, 1671, the celebrated Dr. Seth Ward, Lord Bishop of Sarum, who was the author of several able works on astronomy, and had filled the astronomical chair at Oxford, proposed Mr. Newton as a Fellow of the Royal

Society. The satisfaction which he derived from this circumstance appears to have been considerable; and in a letter to Mr. Oldenburg, of the 6th January, he says, " I am very sensible of the honour done me by the Bishop of Sarum in proposing me a candidate; and which, I hope, will be further conferred upon me by my election into the Society; and if so, I shall endeavour to testify my gratitude, by communicating what my poor and solitary endeavours can effect towards the promoting your philosophical designs." His election accordingly took place on the 11th January, the same day on which the Society agreed to transmit a description of his telescope to Mr. Huygens at Paris. The notice of his election, and the thanks of the Society for the communication of his telescope, were conveyed in the same letter, with an assurance that the Society " would take care that all right should be done him in the matter of this invention." In his next letter to Oldenburg, written on the 18th January, 1671–2, he announces his optical discoveries in the following remarkable manner: " I desire that in your next letter you would inform me for what time the Society continue their weekly meetings; because if they continue them for any time, I am purposing them, to be considered of and examined, an account of a philosophical discovery which induced me to the making of the said telescope; and I doubt not but will prove much more grateful than the communication of that instrument; being in my judgment the oddest, if not the most considerable detection which hath hitherto been made in the operations of nature."

This " considerable detection" was the discovery of the different refrangibility of the rays of light which we have already explained, and which led to the construction of his reflecting telescope. It was communicated to the Royal Society in a letter to Mr. Oldenburg, dated February 6th, and excited great interest among its members. The " solemn thanks" of the meeting were ordered to be transmitted to its author for his "very ingenious discourse." A desire was expressed to have it immediately printed, both for the purpose of having it well considered by philosophers, and for "securing the considerable notices thereof to the author against the arrogations of others;" and Dr. Seth Ward, Bishop of Salisbury, Mr. Boyle, and Dr. Hooke were desired to peruse and consider it, and to bring in a report upon it to the Society.

The kindness of this distinguished body, and the anxiety which they had already evinced for his reputation, excited on the part of Newton a corresponding feeling, and he gladly accepted of their proposal to publish his discourse in the monthly numbers in which the Transactions were then given to the world. "It was an esteem," says he,* "of the Royal Society for most candid and able judges in philosophical matters, encouraged me to present them with that discourse of light and colours, which since they have so favourably accepted of, I do earnestly desire you to return them my cordial thanks. I before thought it a great favour to be made a member of that honourable body; but I am now more sensible of the advantages; for believe me, sir, I do not only esteem it a duty to concur with you in the promotion of real knowledge; but a great privilege, that, instead of exposing discourses to a prejudiced and common multitude, (by which means many truths have been baffled and lost), I may with freedom apply myself to so judicious and impartial an assembly. As to the printing of that letter, I am satisfied in their judgment, or else I should have thought it too straight and narrow for public view. I designed it only to those that know how to improve upon hints of things; and, therefore, to spare tediousness, omitted many such remarks and ex-

* Letter to Oldenburg, February 10, 1671.

E

periments as might be collected by considering the
assigned laws of refractions; some of which I believe, with the generality of men, would yet be
almost as taking as any I described. But yet, since
the Royal Society have thought it fit to appear publicly, I leave it to their pleasure: and perhaps to
supply the aforesaid defects, I may send you some
more of the experiments to second it (if it be so
thought fit), in the ensuing Transactions."

Following the order which Newton himself adopted,
we have, in the preceding chapter, given an account
of the leading doctrine of the different refrangibility
of light, and of the attempts to improve the reflecting telescope which that discovery suggested. We
shall now, therefore, endeavour to make the reader
acquainted with the other discoveries respecting
colours which he at this time communicated to the
Royal Society.

Having determined, by experiments
already described, that a beam of
white light, as emitted from the sun,
consisted of seven different colours,
which possess different degrees of
refrangibility, he measured the relative extent of the coloured spaces,
and found them to have the proportions shown in *fig.* 4, which represents the *prismatic* spectrum, and
which is nothing more than an elongated image of the sun produced by
the rays being separated in different
degrees from their original direction,
the *red* being refracted *least*, and the
violet most powerfully.

Fig. 4.

Red

Orange

Yellow

Green

Blue

Indigo

Violet

If we consider light as consisting
of minute particles of matter, we may
form some notion of its decomposition by the prism from the following
popular illustration. If we take steel

filings of seven different degrees of fineness and mix them together, there are two ways in which we may conceive the mass to be decomposed, or, what is the same thing, all the seven different kinds of filings separated from each other. By means of seven sieves of different degrees of fineness, and so made that the finest will just transmit the finest powder and detain all the rest, while the next in fineness transmits the two finest powders and detains all the rest, and so on, it is obvious that all the powders may be completely separated from each other. If we again mix all the steel filings, and laying them upon a table, hold high above them a flat bar magnet, so that none of the filings are attracted, then if we bring the magnet nearer and nearer, we shall come to a point where the finest filings are drawn up to it. These being removed, and the magnet brought nearer still, the next finest powders will be attracted, and so on till we have thus drawn out of the mass all the powders in a separate state. We may conceive the bar magnet to be inclined to the surface of the steel filings, and so moved over the mass, that at the end nearest to them the heaviest or coarsest will be attracted, and all the remotest and the finest or lighter filings, while the rest are attracted to intermediate points, so that the seven different filings are not only separated, but are found adhering in separate patches to the surface of the flat magnet. The first of these methods, with the sieves, may represent the process of decomposing light, by which certain rays of white light are absorbed, or stifled, or stopped in passing through bodies, while certain other rays are transmitted. The second method may represent the process of decomposing light by refraction, or by the attraction of certain rays farther from their original direction than other rays, and the different patches of filings upon the flat magnet may represent the spaces on the spectrum.

When a beam of white light is decomposed into the seven different colours of the spectrum, any particular colour, when once separated from the rest, is not susceptible of any change, or farther decomposition, whether it is refracted through prisms or reflected from mirrors. It may become fainter or brighter, but Newton never could, by any process, alter its colour or its refrangibility.

Among the various bodies which act upon light, it is conceivable that there might have been some which acted least upon the violet rays and most upon the red rays. Newton, however, found that this never took place; but that the same degree of refrangibility always belonged to the same colour, and the same colour to the same degree of refrangibility.

Having thus determined that the seven different colours of the spectrum were original or simple, he was led to the conclusion that *whiteness* or white light is a compound of all the seven colours of the spectrum, in the proportions in which they are represented in *fig.* 4. In order to prove this, or what is called the recomposition of white light out of the seven colours, he employed three different methods.

When the beam RR was separated into its ele-

Fig. 5.

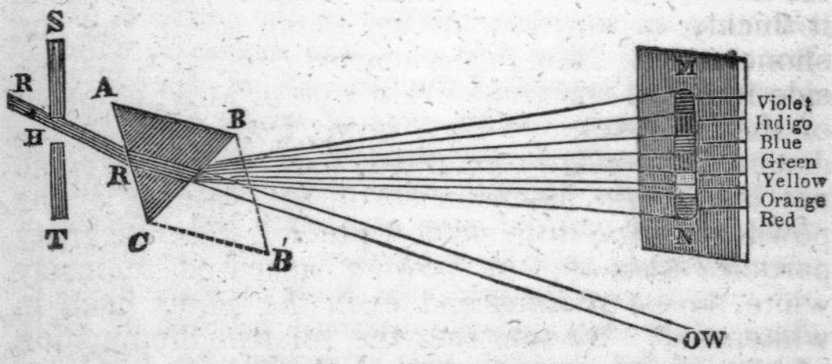

mentary colours by the prism ABC, he received the

colours on another prism BCB′, held either close to
the first or a little behind it, and by the opposite refraction of this prism they were all refracted back
into a beam of white light BW, which formed a
white circular image on the wall at W, similar to
what took place before any of the prisms were
placed in its way.

The other method of recomposing white light
consisted in making the spectrum fall upon a lens at
some distance from it. When a sheet of white
paper was held behind the lens, and removed to a
proper distance, the colours were all refracted into
a circular spot, and so blended as to reproduce light
so perfectly white as not to differ sensibly from the
direct light of the sun.

The last method of recomposing white light was
one more suited to vulgar apprehension. It consisted in attempting to compound a white by mix-
ing the coloured powders used by painters. He
was aware that such colours, from their very nature,
could not compose a pure white; but even this im-
perfection in the experiment he removed by an ingenious device. He accordingly mixed one part of
red lead, four parts of *blue bice*, and a proper proportion of *orpiment* and *verdigris*. This mixture was
dun, like wood newly cut, or like the human skin.
He now took one-third of the mixture and rubbed
it thickly on the floor of his room, where the sun
shone upon it through the opened casement, and beside it, in the shadow, he laid a piece of white paper
of the same size. " Then going from them to the
distance of twelve or eighteen feet, so that he could
not discern the unevenness of the surface of the
powder nor the little shadows let fall from the gritty
particles thereof; the powder appeared intensely
white, so as to transcend even the paper itself in
whiteness." By adjusting the relative illumination
of the powders and the paper, he was able to
make them both appear of the very same degree of.

whiteness. "For," says he, "when I was trying this, a friend coming to visit me, I stopped him at the door, and before I told him what the colours were, or what I was doing, I asked him which of the two whites were the best, and wherein they differed? And after he had at that distance viewed them well, he answered, that they were both good whites, and that he could not say which was best, nor wherein their colours differed." Hence Newton inferred that perfect whiteness may be compounded of different colours.

As all the various shades of colour which appear in the material world can be imitated by intercepting certain rays in the spectrum, and uniting all the rest, and as bodies always appear of the same colour as the light in which they are placed, he concluded, that the colours of natural bodies are not qualities inherent in the bodies themselves, but arise from the disposition of the particles of each body to stop or absorb certain rays, and thus to reflect more copiously the rays which are not thus absorbed.

No sooner were these discoveries given to the world than they were opposed with a degree of virulence and ignorance which have seldom been combined in scientific controversy. Unfortunately for Newton, the Royal Society contained few individuals of pre-eminent talent capable of appreciating the truth of his discoveries, and of protecting him against the shafts of his envious and ignorant assailants. This eminent body, while they held his labours in the highest esteem, were still of opinion that his discoveries were fair subjects of discussion, and their secretary accordingly communicated to him all the papers which were written in opposition to his views. The first of these was by a Jesuit named Ignatius Pardies, Professor of Mathematics at Clermont, who pretended that the elongation of the sun's image arose from the inequal incidence of the different rays on the first face of the prism, although

Newton had demonstrated in his own discourse that this was not the case. In April, 1672, Newton transmitted to Oldenburg a decisive reply to the animadversions of Pardies; but, unwilling to be vanquished, this disciple of Descartes took up a fresh position, and maintained that the elongation of the spectrum might be explained by the diffusion of light on the hypothesis of Grimaldi, or by the diffusion of undulations on the hypothesis of Hook. Newton again replied to these feeble reasonings; but he contented himself with reiterating his original experiments, and confirming them by more popular arguments, and the vanquished Jesuit wisely quitted the field.

Another combatant soon sprung up in the person of one Francis Linus, a physician in Liege,* who, on the 6th October, 1674, addressed a letter to a friend in London, containing animadversions on Newton's doctrine of colours. He boldly affirms, that in a perfectly clear sky the image of the sun made by a prism is never elongated, and that the spectrum observed by Newton was not formed by the true sunbeams, but by rays proceeding from some bright cloud. In support of these assertions, he appeals to frequently repeated experiments on the refractions and reflections of light which he had exhibited thirty years before to Sir Kenelm Digby, "who took notes upon them;" and he unblushingly states, that, if Newton had used the same industry as he did, he would never have "taken so impossible a task in hand, as to explain the difference between the length and breadth of the spectrum by the received laws of refraction." When this letter was shown to Newton, he refused

* This gentleman was the author of a paper in the Philosophical Transactions, entitled "Optical Assertions concerning the Rainbow." How such a paper could be published by so learned a body seems in the present day utterly incomprehensible. The dials which Linus erected at Liege, and which were the originals of those formerly in the Priory Gardens in London, are noticed in the Philosophical Transactions for 1703. In one of them the hours were distinguished by touch.

to answer it; but a letter was sent to Linus referring
him to the answer to Pardies, and assuring him that
the experiments on the spectrum were made when
there was no bright cloud in the heavens. This
reply, however, did not satisfy the Dutch experi-
mentalist. On the 25th February, 1675, he addressed
another letter to his friend, in which he gravely
attempts to prove that the experiment of Newton
was not made in a clear day;—that the prism was
not close to the hole,—and that the length of the
spectrum was not perpendicular, or parallel to the
length of the prism. Such assertions could not but
irritate even the patient mind of Newton. He more
than once declined the earnest request of Oldenburg
to answer these observations; he stated, that, as
the dispute referred to matters of fact, it could only
be decided before competent witnesses, and he
referred to the testimony of those who had seen
his experiments. The entreaties of Oldenburg, however, prevailed over his own better judgment, and,
"lest Mr. Linus should make the more stir," this
great man was compelled to draw up a long and
explanatory reply to reasonings utterly contemptible, and to assertions altogether unfounded. This
answer, dated November 13th, 1675, could scarcely
have been perused by Linus, who was dead on the
15th December, when his pupil Mr. Gascoigne, took
up the gauntlet, and declared that Linus had shown
to various persons in Liege the experiment which
proved the spectrum to be circular, and that Sir
Isaac could not be more confident on his side
than they were on the other. He admitted, however, that the different results might arise from different ways of placing the prism. Pleased with the
" handsome genius of Mr. Gascoigne's letter," Newton replied even to it, and suggested that the spectrum seen by Linus may have been the circular one,
formed by one reflexion, or, what he thought more
probable, the circular one formed by two refractions,

and one intervening reflection from the base of the prism, which would be coloured if the prism was not an isosceles one. This suggestion seems to have enlightened the Dutch philosophers. Mr. Gascoigne, having no conveniences for making the experiments pointed out by Newton, requested Mr. Lucas of Liege to perform them in his own house. This ingenious individual, whose paper gave great satisfaction to Newton, and deserves the highest praise, confirmed the leading results of the English philosopher; but though the refracting angle of his prism was 60° and the refractions equal, he never could obtain a spectrum whose length was more than from *three* to *three and a half* times its breadth, while Newton found the length to be *five* times its breadth. In our author's reply, he directs his attention principally to this point of difference. He repeated his measures with each of the three angles of *three* different prisms, and he affirmed that Mr. Lucas might *make sure to find the image as long or longer than he had yet done*, by taking a prism with plain surfaces, and with an angle of 66° or 67°. He admitted that the smallness of the angle in Mr. Lucas's prism, viz. 60°, did not account for the shortness of the spectrum which he obtained with it; and he observed in one of his own prisms that the length of the image was greater in proportion to the refracting angle than it should have been; an effect which he ascribes to its having a greater refractive power. There is every reason to believe that the prism of Lucas had actually a less dispersive power than that of Newton; and had the Dutch philosopher measured its refractive power instead of guessing it, or had Newton been less confident than he was* that all other prisms must give a

* Newton speaks with singular positiveness on this subject. "For *I know*," says he, "that Mr. Lucas's observations *cannot hold* where the refracting angle of the prism is full 60°, and the day is clear, and the full length of the colours is measured, and the breadth of the image answers to the sun's diameter: and seeing I am well assured of the

spectrum of the same length as his in relation to its refracting angle and its index of refraction, the invention of the achromatic telescope would have been the necessary result. The objections of Lucas drove our author to experiments which he had never before made,—to measure accurately the lengths of the spectra with different prisms of different angles and different refractive powers; and had the Dutch philosopher maintained his position with more obstinacy, he would have conferred a distinguished favour upon science, and would have rewarded Newton for all the vexation which had sprung from the minute discussion of his optical experiments.

Such was the termination of his disputes with the Dutch philosophers, and it can scarcely be doubted that it cost him more trouble to detect the origin of his adversaries' blunders, than to establish the great truths which they had attempted to overturn.

Harassing as such a controversy must have been to a philosopher like Newton, yet it did not touch those deep-seated feelings which characterize the noble and generous mind. No rival jealousy yet pointed the arguments of his opponents;—no charges of plagiarism were yet directed against his personal character. These aggravations of scientific controversy, however, he was destined to endure; and in the dispute which he was called to maintain both against Hooke and Huygens, the agreeable consciousness of grappling with men of kindred powers was painfully imbittered by the personality and jealousy with which it was conducted.

Dr. Robert Hooke was about seven years older than Newton, and was one of the ninety-eight original or unelected members of the Royal Society.

truth and exactness of my own observations, I shall be unwilling to be diverted by any other experiments from having a fair end made of this in the first place." On the supposition that his prism was one of very low dispersive power, Mr. Lucas might, with perfect truth, have used the very same language towards Newton.

He possessed great versatility of talent, yet, though his genius was of the most original cast, and his acquirements extensive, he had not devoted himself with fixed purpose to any particular branch of knowledge. His numerous and ingenious inventions, of which it is impossible to speak too highly, gave to his studies a practical turn which unfitted him for that continuous labour which physical researches so imperiously demand. The subjects of light, however, and of gravitation seem to have deeply occupied his thoughts before Newton appeared in the same field, and there can be no doubt that he had made considerable progress in both of these inquiries. With a mind less divergent in its pursuits, and more endowed with patience of thought, he might have unveiled the mysteries in which both these subjects were enveloped, and preoccupied the intellectual throne which was destined for his rival; but the infirm state of his health, the peevishness of temper which this occasioned, the number of unfinished inventions from which he looked both for fortune and fame, and, above all, his inordinate love of reputation, distracted and broke down the energies of his powerful intellect. In the more matured inquiries of his rivals he recognised, and often truly, his own incompleted speculations; and when he saw others reaping the harvest for which he had prepared the ground, and of which he had sown the seeds, it was not easy to suppress the mortification which their success inspired. In the history of science, it has always been a difficult task to adjust the rival claims of competitors, when the one was allowed to have completed what the other was acknowledged to have begun. He who commences an inquiry, and publishes his results, often goes much farther than he has announced to the world, and, pushing his speculations into the very heart of the subject, frequently submits them to the ear of friendship. From the pedestal of his pub-

lished labours his rival begins his researches, and
brings them to a successful issue; while he has in
reality done nothing more than complete and demonstrate the imperfect speculations of his prede-
cessor. To the world, and to himself, he is no
doubt in the position of the principal discoverer:
but there is still some apology for his rival when
he brings forward his unpublished labours; and some
excuse for the exercise of personal feeling, when he
measures the speed of his rival by his own proximity
to the goal.

The conduct of Dr. Hooke would have been
viewed with some such feeling, had not his arro-
gance on other occasions checked the natural current of our sympathy. When Newton presented
his reflecting telescope to the Royal Society, Dr.
Hooke not only criticised the instrument with undue
severity, but announced that he possessed an infallible method of perfecting all kinds of optical instruments, so that "whatever almost hath been in
notion and imagination, or desired in optics, may
be performed with great facility and truth."

Hooke had been strongly impressed with the
belief, that light consisted in the undulations of a
highly elastic medium pervading all bodies; and,
guided by his experimental investigation of the phenomena of diffraction, he had even announced the
great *principle of interference*, which has performed
such an important part in modern science. Regarding himself, therefore, as in possession of the true
theory of light, he examined the discoveries of
Newton in their relation to his own speculative
views, and, finding that their author was disposed to
consider that element as consisting of material particles, he did not scruple to reject doctrines which
he believed to be incompatible with truth. Dr.
Hooke was too accurate an observer not to admit
the general correctness of Newton's observations.
He allowed the existence of different refractions,

the unchangeableness of the simple colours, and the production of white light by the union of all the colours of the spectrum; but he maintained that the different refractions arose from the splitting and rarefying of ethereal pulses, and that there are only two colours in nature, viz. *red* and *violet*, which produce by their mixture all the rest, and which are themselves formed by the two sides of a split pulse or undulation.

In reply to these observations, Newton wrote an able letter to Oldenburg, dated June 11, 1672, in which he examined with great boldness and force of argument the various objections of his opponent, and maintained the truth of his doctrine of colours, as independent of the two hypotheses respecting the origin and production of light. He acknowledged his own partiality to the doctrine of the materiality of light; he pointed out the defects of the undulatory theory; he brought forward new experiments in confirmation of his former results; and he refuted the opinions of Hooke respecting the existence of only two simple colours. No reply was made to the powerful arguments of Newton; and Hooke contented himself with laying before the Society his curious observations on the colours of soap-bubbles, and of plates of air, and in pursuing his experiments on the diffraction of light, which, after an interval of two years, he laid before the same body.

After he had thus silenced the most powerful of his adversaries, Newton was again called upon to defend himself against a new enemy. Christian Huygens, an eminent mathematician and natural philosopher, who, like Hooke, had maintained the undulatory theory of light, transmitted to Oldenburg various animadversions on the Newtonian doctrine; but though his knowledge of optics was of the most extensive kind, yet his objections were nearly as groundless as those of his less enlightened

F

countryman. Attached to his own hypothesis respecting the nature of light, namely, to the system of undulation, he seems, like Dr. Hooke, to have regarded the discoveries of Newton as calculated to overturn it; but his principal objections related to the composition of colours, and particularly of white light, which he alleged could be obtained from the union of two colours, *yellow* and *blue*. To this and similar objections, Newton replied that the colours in question were not simple yellows and blues, but were compound colours, in which, together, all the colours of the spectrum were themselves blended; and though he evinced some strong traces of feeling at being again put upon his defence, yet his high respect for Huygens induced him to enter with patience on a fresh development of his doctrine. Huygens felt the reproof which the tone of this answer so gently conveyed, and in writing to Oldenburg, he used the expression, that Mr. Newton "maintained his doctrine with some concern." To this our author replied, "As for Mr. Huygens's expression, I confess it was a little ungrateful to me, to meet with objections which had been answered before, without having the least reason given me why those answers were insufficient." But though Huygens appears in this controversy as a rash objector to the Newtonian doctrine, it was afterward the fate of Newton to play a similar part against the Dutch philosopher. When Huygens published his beautiful law of double refraction in Iceland spar, founded on the finest experimental analysis of the phenomena, though presented as a result of the undulatory system, Newton not only rejected it, but substituted for it another law entirely inconsistent with the experiments of Huygens, which Newton himself had praised, and with those of all succeeding philosophers.

The influence of these controversies on the mind of Newton seems to have been highly exciting.

Even the satisfaction of humbling all his antago-
nists he did not feel as a sufficient compensation
for the disturbance of his tranquillity. "I intend,"
says he,* "to be no farther solicitous about matters
of philosophy. And therefore I hope you will not
take it ill if you find me never doing any thing more
in that kind; or rather that you will favour me in
my determination, by preventing, so far as you can
conveniently, any objections or other philosophical
letters that may concern me." In a subsequent letter in 1675, he says, "I had some thoughts of writing
a further discourse about colours, to be read at one
of your assemblies; but find it yet against the grain
to put pen to paper any more on that subject;" and
in a letter to Leibnitz, dated December the 9th, 1675,
he observes, "I was so persecuted with discussions
arising from the publication of my theory of light,
that I blamed my own imprudence for parting with
so substantial a blessing as my quiet to run after a
shadow."

CHAPTER V.

*Mistake of Newton in supposing that the Improvement of Refracting
Telescopes was hopeless—Mr. Hall invents the Achromatic Telescope
—Principles of the Achromatic Telescope explained—It is re-invented
by Dollond, and improved by future Artists—Dr. Blair's Aplanatic
Telescope—Mistakes in Newton's Analysis of the Spectrum—Modern
Discoveries respecting the Structure of the Spectrum.*

THE new doctrines of the composition of light,
and of the different refrangibility of the rays which
compose it, having been thus established upon an
impregnable basis, it will be interesting to take a
general view of the changes which they have under-

Letter to Oldenburg in 1672, containing his first reply to Huygens.

gone since the time of Newton, and of their influence on the progress of optical discovery.

There is no fact in the history of science more
singular than that Newton should have believed
that all bodies produced spectra of equal length, or
separated the red and violet rays to equal distances
when the refraction of the mean rays was the
same. This opinion, unsupported by experiments,
and not even sanctioned by any theoretical views,
seems to have been impressed upon his mind with
all the force of an axiom.* Even the shortness of
the spectrum observed by Lucas did not rouse him
to further inquiry; and when, under the influence
of this blind conviction he pronounced the improvement of the refracting telescope to be desperate, he
checked for a long time the progress of this branch
of science, and furnished to future philosophers a
lesson which cannot be too deeply studied.

In 1729, about two years after the death of Sir
Isaac, an individual unknown to science broke the
spell in which the subject of the spectrum had been
so singularly bound. Mr. Chester More Hall, of
More Hall in Essex, while studying the mechanism
of the human eye, was led to suppose that telescopes might be improved by a combination of
lenses of different refractive powers, and he actually
completed several object-glasses upon this principle.
The steps by which he arrived at such a construction have not been recorded; but it is obvious that
he must have discovered what escaped the sagacity
of Newton, that prisms made of different kinds of

---

* In an experiment made by Newton, he had occasion to counteract
the refraction of a prism of *glass* by another prism of *water;* and had
he completed the experiment, and studied the result of it, he could not
have failed to observe a quantity of uncorrected colour, which would
have led him to the discovery of the different dispersive powers of bodies.
But in order to increase the refractive power of the water, he mixed
with it a little sugar of lead, the high dispersive power of which seems
to have rendered the dispersive power of the water equal to that of the
glass, and thus to have corrected the uncompensated colour of the glass
prism.

glass produced different degrees of separation of the
red and *violet* rays, or gave spectra of different
lengths when the refraction of the middle ray of the
spectrum was the same.

In order to explain how such a property led him
to the construction of a *telescope without colour*, or
an *achromatic telescope*, let us take a lens LL of
crown or *plate* glass, whose focal length LY is
about twelve inches.   When the sun's rays SL,

Fig. 6.

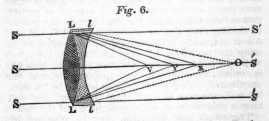

SL fall upon it, the *red* will be refracted to R, the
yellow to Y, and the *violet* to V. If we now place
behind it a concave lens *ll* of the same glass, and
of the same focus or curvature, it will be found,
both by experiment and by drawing the refracted
rays, according to the rules given in elementary
works, that the concave glass *ll* will refract the
rays LR, LR into LS′, LS′, and the rays LV, LV
into LS′, LS′ free of all colour; but as these rays
will be parallel, the two lenses will not have a
focus, and consequently cannot form an image so
as to be used as the object-glass of a telescope.
This is obvious from another consideration; for
since the curvatures of the convex and concave
lenses are the same, the two put together will be
exactly the same as if they were formed out of a
single piece of glass, having parallel surfaces like a
watch-glass, so that the parallel rays of light SL,

F 2

SL will pass on in the same direction LS', LS' affected by equal and opposite refractions as in a piece of plane glass.

Now, since the convex lens LL separated the white light SL, SL into its component coloured rays, LV, LV being the extreme violet, and LR LR the extreme red; it follows that a similar concave lens of the same glass is capable of uniting into white light LS', LS' rays, as much separated as LV, LR are. Consequently, if we take a concave lens *ll* of the same, or of a greater refractive power than the convex one, and having the power of uniting rays farther separated than LV, LR are, a less concavity in the lens *ll* will be sufficient to unite the rays LV, LR into a white ray LS'; but as the lens *ll* is now less concave than the lens LL is convex, the concavity will predominate, and the uncoloured rays LS', LS' will no longer be parallel, but will converge to some point O, where they will form a colourless or achromatic image of the sun.

The effect now described may be obtained by making the *convex* lens LL of *crown* or of *plate* glass, and the *concave* one of *flint* glass, or that of which wineglasses are made. If the concave lens *ll* has a greater refractive power than LL, which is always the case, the only effect of it will be to make the rays converge to a focus more remote than O, or to render a less curvature necessary in *ll*, if O is fixed for the focus of the combined lenses.

Such is the principle of the achromatic telescope as constructed by Mr. Hall. This ingenious individual employed working opticians to grind his lenses, and he furnished them with the radii of the surfaces, which were adjusted to correct the aberration of figure as well as of colour. His invention, therefore, was not an accidental combination of a convex and a concave lens of different kinds of glass, which might have been made merely for experiment; but it was a complete achromatic telescope, founded on a thorough knowledge of the different dispersive powers of crown and flint glass. It is a curious circumstance, however, in the history of the telescope, that this invention was actually lost. Mr. Hall never published any account of his labours, and it is probable that he kept them secret till he should be able to present his instrument to the public in a more perfect form; and it was not till John Dollond had discovered the property of light upon which the instrument depends, and had actually constructed many fine telescopes, that the previous labours of Mr. Hall were laid before the public.* From this period the achromatic telescope underwent gradual improvement, and by the successive labours of Dollond, Ramsden, Blair, Tulley, Guinand, Lerebours, and Fraunhofer, it has become one of the most valuable instruments in physical science.

Although the achromatic telescope, as constructed by Dollond, was founded on the principle that the spectra formed by crown and flint glass differed only in their relative lengths, when the refraction of the mean ray was the same, yet by a more minute examination of the best instruments, it was found that they exhibited white or luminous objects tinged on one side with a green fringe, and on the other with one of a claret colour. These colours, which did not arise from any defect of skill in the artist, were found to arise from a difference in the extent of the coloured spaces in two equal spectra formed by crown and by flint glass. This property was called the *irrationality* of the coloured spaces, and the uncorrected colours which remained when the primary spectrum of the crown glass was corrected by the primary spectrum of the flint glass were called the *secondary* or *residual spectrum.* By

* See the article OPTICS in the *Edinburgh Encyclopædia*, vol xv. p. 479, *note.*

a happy contrivance, which it would be out of place here to describe, Dr. Blair succeeded in correcting this secondary spectrum, or in removing the green and claret-coloured fringes which appeared in the best telescopes, and to this contrivance he gave the name of the *Aplanatic Telescope.*

But while Newton thus overlooked these remarkable properties of the prismatic spectrum, as formed by different bodies, he committed some considerable mistakes in his examination of the spectrum which was under his own immediate examination. It does not seem to have occurred to him that the relations of the coloured spaces must be greatly modified by the angular magnitude of the sun or the luminous body, or aperture from which the spectrum is obtained; and misled by an apparent analogy between the length of the coloured spaces and the divisions of a musical chord,* he adopted the latter, as representing the proportion of the coloured spaces in every beam of white light. Had two other observers, one situated in Mercury, and the other in Jupiter, studied the prismatic spectrum of the sun by the same instruments, and with the same sagacity as Newton, it is demonstrable that they would have obtained very different results. On account of the apparent magnitude of the sun in Mercury, the observer there would obtain a spectrum entirely without *green*, having *red, orange,* and *yellow* at one end, the *white* in the middle, and terminated at the other end with *blue* and *violet.* The observer in Jupiter would, on the contrary, have obtained a spectrum in which the colours were much more condensed. On the planet Saturn a spectrum exactly similar would have been obtained,

---

* "This result was obtained," as Newton says, "by an assistant whose eyes were more critical than mine, and who, by right lines drawn across the spectrum, noted the confines of the colours. And this operation being divers times repeated both on the same and on several papers, I found that the observations agreed well enough with one another."— OPTICS, Part II. Book III.

notwithstanding the greater diminution of the sun's apparent diameter. It may now be asked, which of all these spectra are we to consider as exhibiting the number, and arrangement, and extent of the coloured spaces proper to be adopted as the true analysis of a solar ray.

The spectrum observed by Newton has surely no claim to our notice, merely because it was observed upon the surface of the earth. The spectrum obtained in Mercury affords no analysis at all of the incident beam, the colours being almost all compound, and not homogeneous, and that of Newton is liable to the same objection. Had Newton examined his spectrum under the very same circumstances in winter and in summer, he would have found the analysis of the beam more complete in summer, on account of the diminution of the sun's diameter; and, therefore, we are entitled to say that neither the number nor the extent of the coloured spaces, as given by Newton, are those which belong to homogeneous and uncompounded light.

The spectrum obtained in Jupiter and Saturn is the only one where the analysis is complete, as it is incapable of having its character altered by any farther diminution of the sun's diameter. Hence we are forced to conclude, not only that the number and extent of the primitive homogeneous colours, as given by Newton, are incorrect; but that if he had attempted to analyze some of the primitive tints in the spectrum, he would have found them decidedly composed of heterogeneous rays. There is one consequence of these observations which is somewhat interesting. A rainbow formed in summer, when the sun's diameter is least, must have its colours more condensed and homogeneous than in winter, when the size of its disk is a maximum, and when the upper or the under limb of the sun is eclipsed, a rainbow formed at that time will lose entirely the yellow rays, and have the green and the red in perfect contact. For the same reason, a rainbow formed in Venus and Mercury will be destitute of green rays, and have a brilliant bow of white light separating two coloured arches; while in Mars, Jupiter, Saturn, and the Georgian planet, the bow will exhibit only four homogeneous colours.

From his analysis of the solar spectrum, Newton concluded, "that to the same degree of refrangibility ever belonged the same colour, and to the same colour ever belonged the same degree of refrangibility;" and hence he inferred, that *red, orange, yellow, green, blue, indigo,* and *violet* were primary and simple colours. He admitted, indeed, that "the same colours in specie with these primary ones may be also produced by composition. For a mixture of *yellow* and *blue* makes *green*, and of *red* and *yellow* makes orange;" but such compound colours were easily distinguished from the simple colours of the spectrum by the circumstance, that they are always capable of being resolved by the action of the prism into the two colours which compose them.

This view of the composition of the spectrum might have long remained unchallenged, had we not been able to apply to it a new mode of analysis. Though we cannot separate the *green* rays of the spectrum into *yellow* and *blue* by the refraction of prisms, yet if we possessed any substance which had a specific attraction for *blue* rays, and which stopped them in their course, and allowed the *yellow* rays to pass, we should thus analyze the *green* as effectually as if they were separated by refraction. The substance which possesses this property is a purplish blue glass, similar to that of which fingerglasses are made. When we view through a piece of this glass, about the twentieth of an inch thick, a brilliant prismatic spectrum, we find that it has exercised a most extraordinary absorptive action on the different colours which compose it. The *red* part of the spectrum is divided into *two red* spaces.

separated by an interval entirely devoid of light. Next to the inner red space comes a space of bright *yellow*, separated from the red by a visible interval. After the yellow comes the *green*, with an obscure space between them, then follows the *blue* and the *violet*, the last of which has suffered little or no diminution. Now it is very obvious, that in this experiment, the blue glass has actually absorbed the *red* rays, which, when mixed with the *yellow* on one side, constituted *orange*, and the *blue* rays, which, when mixed with the *yellow* on the other side, constituted *green*, so that the insulation of the *yellow* rays thus effected, and the disappearance of the *orange*, and of the greater part of the *green* light, proves beyond a doubt that the *orange* and *green* colours in the spectrum are compound colours, the former consisting of *red* and *yellow* rays, and the latter of *yellow* and *blue* rays *of the very same refrangibility.* If we compare the two red spaces of the spectrum seen through the blue glass with the red space seen without the blue glass, it will be obvious that the red has experienced such an alteration in its tint by the action of the blue glass, as would be effected by the absorption of a small portion of yellow rays; and hence we conclude, that the red of the spectrum contains a slight tinge of yellow, and that the yellow space extends over more than one-half of the spectrum, including the *red, orange, yellow, green,* and *blue* spaces.

I have found also that red light exists in the yellow space, and it is certain that in the violet space red light exists in a state of combination with the blue rays. From these and other facts which it would be out of place here to explain, I conclude that the prismatic spectrum consists of three different spectra, viz. red, yellow, and blue, all having the same length, and all overlapping each other. Hence red, yellow, and blue rays of the very same refrangibility coexist at every point of the spectrum; but the colour at any one point will be that of the predominant ray, and will depend upon the relative distance of the point from the maximum ordinate of the curve which represents the intensity of the light of each of the three spectra.

This structure of the spectrum, which harmonizes with the old hypothesis of three simple colours, will be understood from the annexed diagram, where MN is the spectrum of seven colours, all compounded of the three simple ones, *red*, *yellow*,

Fig. 7.

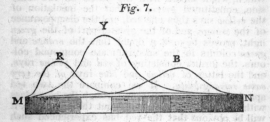

and *blue*. The ordinates of the curves R, Y, and B will express the intensities of each colour at different points of the spectrum. At the red extremity M of the spectrum, the pure *red* is scarcely altered by the very slight intermixture of yellow and blue. Farther on in the red space, the *yellow* begins to make the red incline to scarlet. It then exists in sufficient quantity to form orange, and, as the red declines, the yellow predominates over the feeble portion of red and blue which are mixed with it. As the yellow decreases in intensity, the increasing blue forms with it a good green, and the blue rising to its maximum speedily overpowers the small portion of yellow and red. When the blue becomes very faint, the red exhibits its influence in converting it into violet, and the yellow ceases to exercise a marked influence on the tint. The influence of the red over the blue space is scarcely perceptible, on account of the great intensity of the blue light; but we may easily conceive it to reappear and form the violet light, not only from the rapid decline of the blue light, but from the greater influence of the red rays upon the retina.

These views may, perhaps, be more clearly understood by supposing that a certain portion of white light is actually formed at every point of the spectrum by the union of the requisite number of the three coloured rays that exist at any point. The white light thus formed will add to the brilliancy without affecting the tint of the predominant colour.

In the violet space we may conceive the small portion of yellow which exists there to form white light with a part of the blue and a part of the red, so that the resulting tint will be violet, composed of the blue and the small remaining portion of red, mixed with the white light. This white light will possess the remarkable property of not being susceptible of decomposition by the analysis of the prism, as it is composed of red, yellow, and blue rays of the very same refrangibility. The insulation of this white light by the absorption of the predominant colours I have effected in the green, yellow, and red spaces, and by the use of new absorbing media we may yet hope to exhibit it in some of the other colours, particularly in the brightest part of the blue space, where an obvious approximation to it takes place.

Among the most important modern discoveries respecting the spectrum we must enumerate that of fixed dark and coloured lines, which we owe to the sagacity of Dr. Wollaston and M. Fraunhofer. Two or three of these lines were discovered by Dr. Wollaston, but nearly 600 have been detected by means of the fine prisms and the magnificent apparatus of the Bavarian optician. These lines are

G

parallel to one another, and perpendicular to the length of the spectrum. The largest occupy a space from 5″ to 10″ in breadth. Sometimes they occur in well-defined lines, and at other times in groups; and in all spectra formed from solar light, they preserve the same order and intensity, and the same relative position to the coloured spaces, whatever be the nature of the prism by which they are produced. Hence these lines are fixed points, by which the relative dispersive powers of different media may be ascertained with a degree of accuracy hitherto unknown in this branch of science. In the light of the fixed stars, and in that of artificial flames, a different system of lines is produced, and this system remains unaltered, whatever be the nature of the prism by which the spectrum is formed.

The most important fixed lines in the spectrum formed by light emitted from the sun, whether it is reflected from the sky, the clouds, or the moon, may be easily seen by looking at a narrow slit in the window-shutter of a dark room, through a hollow prism formed of plates of parallel glass, and filled with any fluid of a considerable dispersive power. The slit should not greatly exceed the twentieth of an inch, and the eye should look through the thinnest edge of the prism where there is the least thickness of fluid. These lines I have found to be the boundaries of spaces within which the rays have particular affinities for particular bodies.

CHAPTER VI.

Colours of thin Plates first studied by Boyle and Hooke—Newton determines the Law of their Production—His Theory of Fits of Easy Reflection and Transmission—Colours of thick Plates.

IN examining the nature and origin of colours as the component parts of white light, the attention of Newton was directed to the curious subject of the colours of thin plates, and to its application to explain the colours of natural bodies. His earliest researches on this subject were communicated, in his Discourse on Light and Colours, to the Royal Society, on the 9th December, 1675, and were read at subsequent meetings of that body. This discourse contained fuller details respecting the composition and decomposition of light than he had given in his letter to Oldenburg, and was concluded with nine propositions, showing how the colours of thin transparent plates stand related to those of all natural bodies.

The colours of thin plates seem to have been first observed by Mr. Boyle. Dr. Hooke afterward studied them with some care, and gave a correct account of the leading phenomena, as exhibited in the coloured rings upon soap-bubbles, and between plates of glass pressed together. He recognised that the colour depended upon some certain thickness of the transparent plate, but he acknowledges that he had attempted in vain to discover the relation between the thickness of the plate and the colour which it produced.

Dr. Hooke succeeded in splitting a mineral substance, called mica, into films of such extreme thinness as to give brilliant colours. One plate, for example, gave a yellow colour, another a blue colour, and the two together a deep purple; but, as plates which produced those colours were always less than the 12,000th part of an inch thick, it was quite impracticable, by any contrivance yet discovered, to measure their thickness, and determine the law according to which the colour varied with the thickness of the film. Newton surmounted this difficulty by laying a double convex lens, the radius of curvature of each side of which was fifty feet, upon the flat surface of a plano-convex object-glass, and in this way he obtained a plate of air or of space varying from the thinnest possible edge at the centre of the object-glass where it touched the plane surface, to a considerable thickness at the circumference of the lens. When light was allowed to fall upon the object-glass, every different thickness of the plate of air between the object-glass gave different colours, so that the point where the two object-glasses touched one another was the centre of a number of concentric coloured rings. Now, as the curvature of the object-glass was known, it was easy to calculate the thickness of the plate of air at which any particular colour appeared, and thus to determine the law of the phenomena.

In order to understand how he proceeded, let CED be the convex surface of the one object-glass, and AEB the flat surface of the other. Let them touch at the point E, and let homogeneous *red* rays fall upon them, as shown in the figure. At the point of contact E, where the plate of air is inconceivably thin, not a single ray of the pencil RE is reflected. The light is wholly transmitted, and, consequently, to an eye above E, there will appear at E a black spot. At *a*, where the plate of air is thicker, the red light *ra* is reflected in the direction *aa′*, and as the air has the same thickness in a circle round the point E, the eye above E, at *a*, will see next the black spot E a ring of red light. At *m*,

Fig. 8.

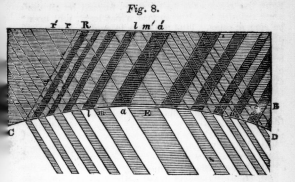

where the thickness of the air is a little greater than at *a*, the light *r′m* is all transmitted as at E, and not a single ray suffers reflection, so that to an eye above E at *m′* there will be seen without the red ring *a* a dark ring *m*. In like manner, at greater thicknesses of the plate of air, there is a succession of *red* and dark rings, diminishing in breadth as shown in the diagram.

When the same experiment was repeated in *orange*, *yellow*, *green*, *blue*, *indigo*, and *violet* light, the very same phenomenon was observed; with this difference only, that the rings were *largest* in *red* light, and *smallest* in *violet* light, and had intermediate magnitudes in the intermediate colours.

If the observer now places his eye below E, so as to see the transmitted rays, he will observe a set of rings as before, but they will have a bright spot in their centre at E, and the luminous rings will now correspond with those which were dark when seen by reflection, as will be readily understood from inspecting the preceding diagram.

When the object-glasses are illuminated by *white*

G 2

light, the *seven* systems of rings, formed by all the *seven* colours which compose white light, will now be seen at once. Had the rings in each colour been all of the same diameter they would all have formed brilliant white rings, separated by dark intervals; but, as they have all different diameters, they will overlap one another, producing rings of various colours by their mixture. These colours, reckoning from the centre E, are as follows :—

1st Order. Black, blue, white, yellow, orange, red.

2d Order. Violet, blue, green, yellow, orange, red.

3d Order. Purple, blue, green, yellow, red, bluish-red.

4th Order. Bluish-green, green, yellowish-green, red.

5th Order. Greenish-blue, red.

6th Order. Greenish-blue, red.

By accurate measurements, Sir Isaac found that the thicknesses of *air* at which the most luminous parts of the first rings were produced, were in parts of an inch $\frac{1}{178000}$, $\frac{3}{178000}$, $\frac{5}{178000}$, $\frac{7}{178000}$, $\frac{9}{178000}$, $\frac{11}{178000}$. If the medium or the substance of the thin plate is water, as in the case of the soap-bubble, which produces beautiful colours according to its different degrees of thinness, the thicknesses at which the most luminous parts of the rings appear are produced at $\frac{1}{1.336}$ of the thickness at which they are produced in air, and in the case of glass or mica at $\frac{1}{1.525}$ of that thickness; the numbers 1.336, 1.525 expressing the ratio of the sines of the angles of incidence and refraction in the substances which produce the colours.

From the phenomena thus briefly described, Sir Isaac Newton deduces that ingenious, though hypothetical, property of light, called its *fits of easy reflection and transmission*. This property consists in supposing that every particle of light from its first discharge from a luminous body possesses, at equally distant intervals, dispositions to be reflected from, and transmitted through, the surfaces of bodies upon which it is incident. Hence, if a particle of light reaches a reflecting surface of glass when it is in its *fit of reflection*, or in its disposition to be reflected, it will yield more readily to the reflecting force of the surface; and, on the contrary, if it reaches the same surface while in a *fit of easy transmission*, or in a disposition to be transmitted, it will yield with more difficulty to the reflecting force. Sir Isaac has not ventured to inquire into the cause of this property; but we may form a very intelligible idea of it by supposing, that the particles of light have two attractive and two repulsive poles at the extremities of two axes at right angles to each other, and that the particles revolve round their axes, and at equidistant intervals bring one or other of these axes into the line of the direction in which the particle is moving. If the attractive axis is in the line of the direction in which the particle moves when it reaches the refracting surface, the particle will yield to the attractive force of the medium, and be refracted and transmitted; but if the repulsive axis is in the direction of the particle's motion when it reaches the surface, it will yield to the repulsive force of the medium, and be reflected from it.

The application of the theory of alternate fits of reflection and transmission to explain the colours of thin plates is very simple. When the light falls upon the first surface AB, Fig. 8 of the plate of air between AB and CED, the rays that are in a fit of reflection are reflected, and those that are in a fit of transmission are transmitted. Let us call F the length of a fit, or the distance through which the particle of light moves while it passes from the state of being in a fit of reflection to the state of being in a fit of transmission. Now, as all the particles of light transmitted through AB were in a state of easy transmission when they entered AB, it is obvious, that, if the plate of air at E is so thin as to be less than one-half of F, the particles of light will still be in their disposition to be transmitted, and consequently the light will be all transmitted, and none reflected at the curve surface at E. When the plate becomes thicker towards *a*, so that its thickness exceeds half of F, the light will not reach the surface CE till it has come under its fit of reflection, and consequently at *a* the light will be all reflected, and none transmitted. As the thickness increases towards *m*, the light will have come under its fit of transmission, and so on, the light being reflected at *a*, *l*, and transmitted at E, *m*. This will perhaps be still more easily understood from *fig.* 9, where we

Fig. 9.

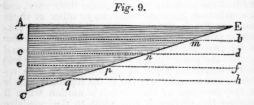

may suppose AEC to be a thin wedge of glass or any other transparent body. When light is incident on the first surface AE, all the particles of it that are in a fit of easy reflection will be reflected, and all those in a fit of easy transmission will be transmitted. As the fits of transmission all commence at AE, let the first fit of transmission end when the particles of light have reached *ab*, and the second when they have reached *ef*; and let the fits of reflection commence at *cd* and *gh*. Then, as the fit of transmission continues from AE to *ab*, all the light that falls upon the portion *m*E of the second surface will be transmitted and none reflected, so that to an eye above E the space *m*E will appear black. As the fit of reflection commences at *ab*, and continues to *cd*, all the light which falls upon the portion *nm* will be reflected, and none transmitted; and so on, the light being transmitted at *m*E and *pn*, and reflected at *nm* and *qp*. Hence to an eye above E the wedge-shaped film of which AEC is a section will be covered with parallel bands or fringes of light separated by dark fringes of the same breadth, and they will be all parallel to the thin edge of the plate, a dark fringe corresponding to the thinnest edge. To an eye placed below CE, similar fringes will be seen, but the one corresponding to the thinnest edge *m*E will be luminous.

If the thickness of the plate does not vary according to a regular law as in *fig.* 9, but if, like a film of blown glass, it has numerous inequalities, then the alternate fringes of light and darkness will vary with the thickness of the film, and throughout the whole length of each fringe the thickness of the film will be the same.

We have supposed in the preceding illustration that the light employed is homogeneous. If it is white, then the differently coloured fringes will form by their superposition a system of fringes analogous to those seen between two object-glasses, as already explained.

The same periodical colours which we have now described as exhibited by thin plates were discovered by Newton in thick plates, and he has explained them by means of the theory of fits; but it would lead us beyond the limits of a popular work like this to enter into any details of his observations, or to give an account of the numerous and important additions which this branch of optics has received from the discoveries of succeeding authors.

CHAPTER VII.

Newton's Theory of the Colours of Natural Bodies explained—Objections to it stated—New Classification of Colours—Outline of a New Theory proposed.

IF the objects of the material world had been illuminated with white light, all the particles of which possessed the same degree of refrangibility, and were equally acted upon by the bodies on which they fall, all nature would have shone with a leaden hue, and all the combinations of external objects, and all the features of the human countenance, would have exhibited no other variety but that which they possess in a pencil sketch or a China-ink drawing. The rainbow itself would have dwindled into a narrow arch of white light,—the stars would have shone through a gray sky,—and the mantle of a wintry twilight would have replaced the golden vesture of the rising and the setting sun.   But He who has exhibited such matchless skill in the organization of material bodies, and such exquisite taste in the forms upon which they are modelled, has superadded that ethereal beauty which enhances their more permanent qualities, and presents them to us in the ever-varying colours of the spectrum.   Without this the foliage of vegetable life might have filled the eye and fostered the fruit which it veils,—but the youthful green of its spring would have been blended with the dying yellow of its autumn.   Without this the diamond might have displayed to science the beauty of its forms, and yielded to the arts its adamantine virtues ;—but it would have ceased to shine in the chaplet of beauty, and to sparkle in the diadem of princes.   Without this the human countenance might have expressed all the sympathies of the heart, but the " purple light of love" would not have risen on the cheek, nor the hectic flush been the herald of its decay.

The gay colouring with which the Almighty has decked the pale marble of nature is not the result of any quality inherent in the coloured body, or in the particles by which it may be tinged, but is merely a property of the light in which they happen to be placed. Newton was the first person who placed this great truth in the clearest evidence. He found that all bodies, whatever were their peculiar colours, exhibited these colours only in white light. When they were illuminated by homogeneous *red* light they appeared *red*, by homogeneous *yellow* light, *yellow*, and so on, " their colours being most brisk and vivid under the influence of their own daylight colours." The leaf of a plant, for example, appeared *green* in the white light of day, because it had the property of reflecting that light in greater abundance than any other. When it was placed in homogeneous *red* light, it could no longer appear *green*, because there was no green light to reflect; but it reflected a portion of red light, because there was some red in the compound green which it had the property of reflecting. Had the leaf originally reflected a pure homogeneous green, unmixed with red, and reflected no white light from its outer surface, it would have appeared quite black in pure homogeneous red light, as this light does not contain a single ray which the leaf was capable of reflecting. Hence the colours of material bodies are owing to the property which they possess of stopping certain rays of white light, while they reflect or transmit to the eye the rest of the rays of which white light is composed.

So far the Newtonian doctrine of colours is capable of rigid demonstration; but its author was not content with carrying it thus far : he sought to determine the manner in which particular rays are stopped, while others are reflected or transmitted; and the result of this profound inquiry was his theory of the colours of natural bodies, which was communicated to the Royal Society on the 10th February, 1675. This theory is perhaps the loftiest of all his speculations; and though, as a physical generalization, it stands on a perishable basis, and must soon be swept away in the progress of science, it yet bears the deepest impress of the grasp of his powerful intellect.

The principles upon which this theory is founded are the following :—

1. Bodies that have the greatest refractive powers reflect the greatest quantity of light; and at the confines of equally refracting media there is no reflection.

2. The least particles of almost all natural bodies are in some measure transparent.

3. Between the particles of bodies are many pores or spaces, either empty or filled with media of less density than the particles.

4. The particles of bodies and their pores, or the spaces between the particles, have some definite size.

Upon these principles Newton explains the origin of *transparency*, *opacity*, and *colour*.

Transparency he considers as arising from the particles and their intervals or pores being too small to cause reflection at their common surfaces,* so that all the light which enters transparent bodies passes through them without any portion of it being turned from its path by reflection. If we could obtain, for example, a film of mica whose thickness does not exceed two-thirds of the millionth part of an inch, all the light which fell upon it would pass through it, and none would be reflected. If this film was then

* Optics, Book ii. Prop. iv.

cut into fragments, a number of such fragments would constitute a bundle, which would also transmit all the light which fell upon it, and be perfectly transparent.

Opacity in bodies arises, he thinks, from an opposite cause, viz. when the parts of bodies are of such a size as to be capable of reflecting the light which falls upon them, in which case the light is "stopped or stifled" by the multitude of reflections.

The *colours* of natural bodies have, in the Newtonian hypothesis, the same origin as the colours of thin plates, their transparent particles, according to their several sizes, reflecting rays of one colour, and transmitting those of another. "For if a thinned or plated body which, being of an uneven thickness, appears all over of one uniform colour, should be slit into threads, or broken into fragments of the same thickness with the plate or film, every thread or fragment should keep its colour, and consequently, a heap of such threads or fragments should constitute a mass or powder of the same colour which the plate exhibited before it was broken: and the parts of all natural bodies being like so many fragments of a plate, must, on the same grounds, exhibit the same colour."

Such is the theory of the colours of natural bodies, stated as clearly and briefly as we can. It has been very generally admitted by philosophers, both of our own and of other countries, and has been recently illustrated and defended by a French philosopher of distingushed eminence. That this theory affords the true explanation of certain colours, or, to speak more correctly, that certain colours in natural bodies are the colours of thin plates, cannot be doubted; but it will not be difficult to show that it is quite inapplicable to that great class of phenomena which may be considered as representing the colours of natural bodies.

The first objection to the Newtonian theory is the

H

total absence of all reflected light from the particles
of transparent coloured media, such as coloured
gems, coloured glasses, and coloured fluids. This
objection was urged long ago by Mr. Delaval, who
placed coloured fluids on black grounds, and never
could perceive the least trace of the reflected tints.
I have repeated the experiment with every precau-
tion, and with every variation that I could think of,
and I consider it as an established fact, that in such
coloured bodies the complementary reflected colour
cannot be rendered visible. If the fluid, for example,
be *red*, the *green* light from which the red has been
separated ought to appear either directly by looking
into the coloured mass, or ought to be recognised
by its influence in modifying the light really reflected; but as it cannot be seen, we must conclude
that it has not been reflected, but has been destroyed by some other property of the coloured
body.

A similar objection may be drawn from the disappearance of the transmitted complementary colour
in the leaves of plants and petals of flowers. I have
ascertained from numerous experiments, that the
transmitted colour is almost invariably the same
with the reflected colour, and that the same holds
true with the coloured juices expressed from them.
The complementary tints are never seen, and wherever there has been any thing like an approximation
to two tints, I have invariably found that it arose
from there being two different coloured juices existing in different sides of the leaf.

In the phenomena of the light transmitted by
coloured glasses, there are some peculiarities which,
we think, demonstrate that their colours are not
those of thin plates. The light, for example, transmitted through a particular kind of blue glass, has a
blue colour of such a peculiar composition that there
is no blue in any of the orders of colours in thin
plates which has any resemblance to it. It is entirely

destitute of the red rays which form the middle of
the red space in the spectrum; so that the particles
on which the colour depends must reflect the middle
red rays, and transmit those on each side of it,—a
property which cannot be deduced from the Newtonian doctrine.

The explanation of *opacity*, as arising from a
multitude of reflections, is liable to the same objection which we have urged against the explanation of colour. In order to appreciate its weight,
we must distinguish opacity into two kinds, namely,
the *opacity of whiteness* and the *opacity of blackness*.
Those bodies which possess the power of reflection
in the highest degree, such as white metals, chalk,
and plaster of Paris, never reflect more than one-
half of the light which falls upon them. The other
half of the incident light is, according to Newton,
lost by a multitude of reflections. But how is it
lost? Reflection merely changes the direction of the
particles of light, so that they must again emerge
from the body, unless they are reflected into fixed
returning orbits, which detain them for ever in a
state of motion within the body. In the case of
black opacity, such as that of coal, which reflects
from its first surface only $\frac{1}{25}$th of the white light,
the difficulty is still greater, and we cannot conceive
how any system of interior reflections could so
completely stifle $\frac{24}{25}$ths of the whole incident light,
without some of it returning to the eye in a visible
form.

In determining the constitution of bodies that produce *transparency* and *blackness*, the Newtonian
theory encounters a difficulty which its author has
by no means surmounted. Transparency, as we
have already seen, arises from the "particles and
their interstices being too small to cause reflections
in their common surfaces," that is, they must be
"less than any of those which exhibit colours," or
"less than is requisite to reflect the *white* and very

faint *blue* of the first order. But *this is the very same constitution which produces blackness* by reflection, and in order to explain the cause of blackness by transmission, or black opacity, Newton is obliged to introduce a new principle.

"For the production of *black*," says he, "the corpuscles must be less than any of those which exhibit colours. For at all greater sizes there is too much light reflected to constitute this colour. But if they be supposed a little less than is requisite to reflect the white and very faint blue of the first order, they will reflect so very little light as to appear intensely black, *and yet may perhaps variously refract* it to and fro within themselves so long, until it happens to be stifled and lost, by which means they will appear black in all positions of the eye, without any transparency."

This very remarkable passage exhibits, in a striking manner, the perplexity in which our author was involved by the difficulties of his subject. As the particles which produce blackness by reflection are necessarily so small as to exclude the existence of any reflective forces, he cannot ascribe the loss of the intromitted light, as he does in the case of white opacity, to "a multitude of reflections;" and therefore he is compelled to have recourse to *refracting forces* to perform the same office. The reluctance with which he avails himself of this expedient is well marked in the mode of expression which he adopts; and I am persuaded that when he wrote the above passage, he felt the full force of the objections to this hypothesis, which cannot fail to present themselves. As the size of the particles which produce blackness are intermediate between those

---

* In the same paragraph, when speaking of black bodies becoming hot, and burning sooner than others, he says that their "effect may proceed partly from the *multitude of refractions* in a little room, and partly from the easy commotion of so very small corpuscles."—*Optics*, Part iii. Prop. vii. p. 235.

which produce transparency and those which produce colour, approaching closely to the latter, it is
difficult to conceive why *they* should refract the intromitted light, while the greater and smaller particles, and even those almost of the same size, should
be destitute of that property. It is, besides, not easy
to understand how a refraction can take place within
bodies which shall stifle all the light, and prevent it
from emerging. Nay, we may admit the existence
of such refractions, and yet understand how, by a
compensation in their direction, the refracted rays
may all emerge from the opaque body.

The force of these objections is tacitly recognised
in Pemberton's View of Sir Isaac Newton's Philosophy;* and as Newton not only read and approved of
that work, but even perused a great part of it along
with its author, we may fairly consider the opinion
there stated to be his own.

"For producing *black*, the particles ought to be
smaller than for exhibiting any of the colours, viz.
of a size answering to the thickness of the bubble,
whereby reflecting little or no light, it appears colourless; *but yet they must not be too small*, for that will
make them transparent *through deficiency of reflections* in the inward parts of the body, sufficient to
stop the light from going through it; but they must
be of a size *bordering upon that* disposed to reflect
the faint blue of the first order, which affords an
evident reason why blacks usually partake a little
of that colour." In this passage all idea of refraction is abandoned, and that precise degree of size is
assumed for the particles which leaves a small power
of reflection, which is deemed sufficient to prevent
the body from becoming transparent; that is, sufficient to render it opaque or black.

The last objection which we shall state to this
theory is one to which we attach great weight, and,

* See page 354.

H 2

as it is founded on discoveries and views which have been published since the time of Newton, we venture to believe, that, had he been aware of them, he would never have proposed the theory which we are considering.

When light falls upon a thin film such as AEC, *fig.* 9, p. 80, so as to produce the colours of thin plates, it follows, from Sir Isaac Newton's theory of fits, that a portion of the light is, as usual, reflected at the first surface AE,* while the light which forms the coloured image is that which is reflected from the second surface EC, so that all the colours of thin plates are diluted with the white light reflected from the first surface. Now, in the modern theory, which ascribes the colours of thin plates to the interference of the light reflected from the second surface EC, with the light reflected from the first surface AE, the resulting tint arises from the combination of these two pencils, and consequently there is no white light reflected from the surface AE. In like manner, when the thickness of the film is such that the two interfering pencils completely destroy one another, and produce black, there is not a ray of light reflected from the first surface. Here, then, we have a criterion for deciding between the theory of fits and the theory of interference; for if there is no white light reflected from the first surface AE, the theory of fits must be rejected. In a remarkable phenomenon of blackness arising from minute fibres, which I have had occasion to describe, there was no perceptible reflection from the surface of the fibres;† and M. Fresnel describes an experiment made to determine the same point, and states the result of it to

* When Newton speaks of bodies losing their reflecting power from their thinness, he means the reflecting power of their second surfaces, as is evident from the reason he assigns.—See Optics, Part iii. Prop. xiii. p. 257.

† *Edinburgh Journal of Science*, No. I. p. 108.

have been unequivocally in favour of the doctrine of interference.

In order to apply this important fact, let us take a piece of coal, one of the blackest and most opaque of all substances, and which does not reflect to the eye a single ray out of those which enter its substance. The size of its particles is so small, that they are incapable of reflecting light. When a number of these particles are placed together, so as to form a surface, and other particles behind them, so as to form a solid, they will not acquire by this process the power of reflection; and consequently, a piece of coal so composed should be destitute of the property of reflecting light from its first surface. But this is not the case,—light is abundantly reflected from the first surface of the coal, and consequently, its elementary particles must possess the same power. Hence the blackness of coal must be ascribed to some other cause than to the minuteness of its transparent atoms.

To transparent bodies this argument has a similar application. As their atoms are still less than those of black bodies, their inability to reflect light is still greater, and hence arises their transparency. But the particles forming the surface of such bodies do reflect light, and, therefore, their transparency must have another origin.

In the case of coloured bodies, too, the particles forming their surfaces reflect white light like those of all other bodies, so that these particles cannot produce colour on the same principles as those of thin plates. In many of those cases of colour which seem to depend upon the minuteness of the particles of the body, the reflection of white light may nevertheless be observed, but this will be found to arise from a thin transparent film, behind which the colorific particles are placed.

Whatever answer may be given to these objections, we think it will be admitted by those who

have studied the subject most profoundly, that a
satisfactory theory of the colours of natural bodies
is still a *desideratum* in science. How far we may
be able to approach to it in the present state of
optics the reader will judge from the following
views.

Colours may be arranged into seven classes, each
of which depends upon different principles.

1. Transparent coloured fluids—transparent coloured gems—transparent coloured glasses—coloured
powders—and the colours of the leaves and flowers
of plants.

2. Oxidations on metals—colours of Labrador
feldspar—colours of precious and hydrophanous
opal, and other opalescences—the colours of the
feathers of birds, of the wings of insects, and of the
scales of fishes.

3. Superficial colours, as those of mother-of-pearl
and striated surfaces.

4. Opalescences and colours in composite crystals
having double refraction.

5. Colours from the absorption of common and
polarized light by doubly refracting crystals.

6. Colours at the surfaces of media of different
dispersive powers.

7. Colours at the surface of media in which the
reflecting forces extend to different distances, or follow different laws.

The first two of these classes are the most important. The Newtonian theory appears to be
strictly applicable to the phenomena of the *second*
class ; but those of the first class cannot, we conceive, be referred to the same cause.

The rays of solar light possess several remarkable
physical properties : They heat—they illuminate
—they promote chymical combination—they effect
chymical decompositions—they impart magnetism
to steel—they alter the colours of bodies—they

communicate to plants and flowers their peculiar colours, and are in many cases necessary to the development of their characteristic qualities. It is impossible to admit for a moment that these varied effects are produced by a mere mechanical action, or that they arise from the agitation of the particles of bodies by the vibration of the ether which is considered to be the cause of light. Whatever be the difficulties which attach to the theory which supposes light to consist of material particles, we are compelled, by its properties, to admit that light acts as if it were material, and that it enters into combinations with bodies, in order to produce the effects which we have enumerated.

When a beam of light falls upon a body, and the whole or a part of that which enters its substance totally disappears, we are entitled to say, that it is detained by some power exercised by the particles of the body over the particles of light. When this light is said to be lost by a multitude of reflections or refractions, the statement is not only hypothetical, but it is an hypothesis incompatible with optical principles. That the light detained within bodies has been stopped by the attractive force of the particles seems to be highly probable, and the mind will not feel any repugnance to admit that the particles of all bodies, whether solid, fluid, or aëriform, have a specific affinity for the particles of light. Considering light, therefore, as material, it is not difficult to comprehend how it should, like other elementary substances, enter into combination with bodies, and produce many chymical and physical effects, but particularly the phenomena of transparency, opacity, and colour.

In *transparent* colourless bodies, such as water and glass, the intromitted light experiences a considerable loss, because a certain number of its particles are attracted and detained by the atoms of the water or glass, and the light which emerges is colourless, because the particles exercise a proportional action over all the simple colours which compose white light.

When the transparent body has any decided *colour*, such as those enumerated in Class I., then the particles of the body have exercised a specific attraction over those rays of white light which are complementary to those which compose the colour of the transmitted light. If the transparent body, for example, is *red*, then its particles have detained the green rays which entered into the incident light, or certain other rays, which with the red are necessary to compose white light. In compound bodies, like some of the artificial glasses, the particles will attract and detain rays of light of different colours, as may be seen by analyzing the transmitted light with a prism, which will exhibit a spectrum deprived of all the rays which have been detained. In black bodies the particles exercise a powerful attraction over light, and detain all the intromitted rays.

When coloured bodies are opaque, so as to exhibit their colours principally by reflection, the light which is reflected back to the observer has received its colour from transmission through part of the thickness of the body, or, what is the same thing, the colour reflected to the eye is complementary to that which has been detained by the particles of the body while the light is passing and repassing through a thickness terminated by the reflecting surfaces; and as only a part of this light is reflected, as in the case of leaves and flowers, the transmitted light must have the same colour as the reflected light.

When coloured bodies exhibit two different colours complementary to each other, the one seen by reflection and the other by transmission, it is then highly probable that the colours are those of thin plates, though there are still other optical principles to which they may be referred. As the particles of bodies, and the medium which unites them, or, as the different atoms of a compound body may have different dispersive powers, while they exercise the same refractive force over a particular part of the spectrum, the rays for which this compensation takes place will be transmitted, while part of the complementary light is reflected.* Or in cases where the refractive and dispersive powers are the same, the reflective forces of the particles may vary according to a different law, so that at the separating surfaces either white or coloured light may be reflected.†

In those cases of colour where the reflected and the transmitted tints are not complementary, as in *leaf-gold*, where the former is *yellow* and the latter *green*;—in *leaf-silver*, where they are *white* and *blue*, and in certain pieces of fir-wood, where the reflected light is *whitish yellow*, and the transmitted light a *brilliant homogeneous red*, we may explain the separation of the colours either by the principles we have already laid down or by the doctrine of thin plates. On the first principle, the colour of the reflected light, which is supposed to be the same as that of the transmitted light, will be modified by the law according to which the particles of the body attract different rays out of the beam of white light. In pitch, for example, the blue rays are first absorbed, so that at small thicknesses the transmitted light is a fine yellow, while, by the action of a greater thickness, the yellow itself is absorbed, and the transmitted light is a bright homogeneous red. Now in leaf-gold the transmitted colour of thinner films than we can obtain may be yellow, and, consequently, the light reflected from the first strata of interrupting faces will be yellow, and will determine the predominant tint of the reflected light. On the Newtonian doctrine, Mr. Herschel has explained it

* See the *Phil. Trans.* 1829, Part I. p. 189.   † *Idem.*

by saying, "that the transmitted rays have traversed
the whole thickness of the medium, and therefore
undergo many more times the action of its atoms
than those reflected, especially those near the first
surface to which the brighter part of the reflected
colour is due."

The phenomena of the absorption of common
and polarized light, which I have described in another place,* throw much light on the subject of
coloured bodies. The relation of the absorbent action to the axes of double refraction, and, consequently, to the poles of the molecules of the crystal,
shows how the particles of light attracted by the
molecules of the body will vary, both in their nature
and number, according to the direction in which
they approach the molecules; and explains how the
colour of a body may be changed, either tempora-
rily or permanently, by heat, according as it produces a temporary or a permanent change in the
relative position of the molecules. This is not the
place to enlarge on this subject; but we may be
permitted to apply the idea to the curious experiment of Thenard on phosphorus. When this substance is rendered pure by repeated distillation, it
is transparent, and transmits yellow light; but when
it is thrown in a melted state into cold water, it
becomes jet black. When again melted, it resumes
its original colour and transparency. According to
the Newtonian theory, we must suppose that the
atoms of the phosphorus have been diminished in
size by sudden cooling,—an effect which it is not
easy to comprehend; but, according to the preceding views, we may suppose that the atoms of
the phosphorus have been forced by sudden cooling
into relative positions quite different from those
which they take when they slowly assume the solid
state, and their poles of maximum attraction, in

* *Phil. Trans.* 1819, p. 11.

place of being turned to one another, are turned in different directions, and then allowed to exercise their full action in attracting the intromitted light, and detaining it wholly within the body.*

Before concluding this chapter, there is one topic peculiarly deserving our notice, namely, the change of colour produced in bodies by continued exposure to light. The general effect of light is to diminish or dilute the colours of bodies, and in many cases to deprive them entirely of their colour. Now, it is not easy to understand how repeated undulations propagated through a body could diminish the size of its particles, or how the same effect could be produced by a multitude of reflections from particle to particle. But if light is attracted by the particles of bodies, and combines with them, it is easy to conceive that, when the molecules of a body have combined with a great number of particles of a green colour, for example, their power of combination with others will be diminished, and, consequently, the number of particles of any colour absorbed or detained must diminish with the time that the body has been exposed to light; that is, these particles must enter into the transmitted and reflected pencils, and diminish the intensity of their colour. If the body, for example, absorbs red light, and transmits and reflects green, then if the quantity of absorbed red light is diminished, it will enter into the reflected and transmitted pencils, and, forming white light by its mixture with a portion of the green rays, will actually dilute them in the same manner as if a portion of white light had been added.†

* If this view of the matter be just, we should expect that the specific gravity of the black would exceed that of the yellow phosphorus.

† Since the two preceding chapters were written, I have had occasion to confirm and extend the views which they contain by many new experiments.

I

CHAPTER VIII.

*Newton's Discoveries respecting the Inflection or Diffraction of Light
—Previous Discoveries of Grimaldi and Dr. Hooke—Labours of succeeding Philosophers—Law of Interference of Dr. Young—Fresnel's
Discoveries—New Theory of Inflection on the Hypothesis of the Materiality of Light.*

ALTHOUGH the discoveries of Newton respecting
the *Inflection of Light* were first published in his
Optics in 1704, yet there is reason to think that
they were made at a much earlier period.   Sir Isaac,
indeed, informs us, in his preface to that great work,
that the third book, which contains these discoveries, " was put together out of scattered papers ;"
and he adds at the end of his observations, that " he
designed to repeat most of them with more care and
exactness, and to make some new ones for determining the manner how the rays of light are bent in their
passage by bodies, for making the fringes of colours
with the dark lines between them.   But I was then
interrupted, and cannot now think of taking these
things into consideration."   On the 18th March, 1674,
Dr. Hooke had read a valuable memoir on the phenomena of diffraction ; and, as Sir Isaac makes no
allusion whatever to this work, it is the more probable that his " scattered papers" had been written
previous to the communication of Dr. Hooke's experiments.

The phenomena of the inflection of light were first
discovered by Francis Maria Grimaldi, a learned
Jesuit, who has described them in a posthumous
work published in 1665, two years after his death.*

Having admitted a beam of the sun's light through

* *Physico-Mathesis de Lumine coloribus et iride aliisque annexis.*
Bonon. 1665.

a small pin-hole in a piece of lead or card into a dark chamber, he found that the light diverged from this aperture in the form of a cone, and that the shadows of all bodies placed in this light were not only larger than might have been expected, but were surrounded with three coloured fringes, the nearest being the widest, and the most remote the narrowest. In strong light he discovered analogous fringes within the shadows of bodies, which increased in number with the breadth of the body, and became more distinct when the shadow was received obliquely and at a greater distance. When two small apertures or pin-holes were placed so near each other that the cones of light formed by each of them intersected one another, Grimaldi observed, that a spot common to the circumference of each, or, which is the same thing, illuminated by rays from each cone, was darker than the same spot when illuminated by either of the cones separately; and he announces this remarkable fact in the following paradoxical proposition, " *that a body actually illuminated may become more dark* by adding a *light to that which it already receives.*"

Without knowing what had been done by the Italian philosopher, our countryman, Dr. Robert Hooke, had been diligently occupied with the same subject. In 1672, he communicated his first observations to the Royal Society, and he then spoke of his paper as "containing the discovery of a new property of light not mentioned by any optical writers before him." In his paper of 1674, already mentioned, and which is no doubt the one to which he alludes, he has not only described the leading phenomena of the inflection, or the deflection of light, as he calls it, but he has distinctly announced the *doctrine of interference*, which has performed so great a part in the subsequent history of optics.*

* This doctrine is thus announced. 1. That the same rays of light falling upon the same point of an object will turn into all sorts of colours

Such was the state of the subject when Newton directed to it his powers of acute and accurate observation. His attention was turned only to the enlargement of the shadow, and to the three fringes which surrounded it; and he begins his observations by ascribing the discovery of these facts to Grimaldi. After taking exact measures of the diameter of the shadow of a human hair, and of the breadth of the fringes at different distances behind it, he discovered the remarkable fact that these diameters and breadths were not proportional to the distances from the hair at which they were measured. In order to explain these phenomena, Newton supposed that the rays which passed by the edge of the hair are deflected or turned aside from it, as if by a repulsive force, the nearest rays suffering the greatest, and those more remote a less degree of deflection.

Fig. 10.

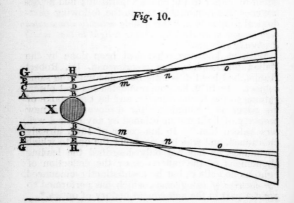

by the various inclination of the object. 2. That colours begin to appear when two pulses of light are blended so well and so near together that the sense takes them for one.

Thus, if X, fig. 10, represents a section of the hair, and AB, CD, EF, GH, &c. rays passing at different distances from X, the ray AB will be more deflected than CD, and will cross it at *m*, the ray CD will for the same reason cross EF at *n*, and EF will cross GH at *o*. Hence the curve or caustic formed by the intersections *m*, *n*, *o*, &c. will be convex outward, its curvature diminishing as it recedes from the vertex. As none of the passing light can possibly enter within this curve, it will form the boundary of the shadow of X.

The explanation given by Sir Isaac of the coloured fringes is less precise, and can be inferred only from the two following queries.

1. "Do not the rays which differ in refrangibility differ also in flexibility, and are they not, by these different inflections separated from one another, so as after separation to make the colours in the three fringes above described? And after what manner are they inflected to make those fringes?

2. "Are not the rays of light in passing by the edges and sides of bodies *bent several times backwards and forwards* with a motion like that of an eel? And do not the three fringes of light above mentioned arise from three such bendings?"

The idea thus indistinctly thrown out in the preceding queries has been ingeniously interpreted by Mr. Herschel in the manner represented in fig. 11, where SS are two rays passing by the edge of the body MN. These rays are supposed to undergo several bendings, as at *a*, *b*, *c*, and the particles of light are thrown off at one or other of the points of contrary flexure, according to the state of their fits or other circumstances. Those that are thrown outwards in the direction *a*A, *b*B, *c*C, *d*D, will produce as many caustics by their intersections as there are deflected rays; and each caustic, when received on a screen at a distance, will depict on it the brightest part or maximum of a fringe.

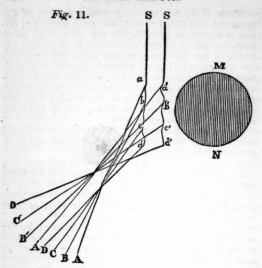

Fig. 11.

In this unsatisfactory state was the subject of the inflection of light left by Sir Isaac. His inquiries were interrupted, and never again renewed; and though he himself found that the phenomena were the same, " whether the hair was encompassed with air or with any other pellucid substance," yet this important result does not seem to have shaken his conviction, that the phenomena had their origin in the action of bodies upon light.

During two sets of experiments which I made on the inflection of light, the first in 1798, and the second in 1812 and 1813, I was desirous of examining the influence of density and refractive power over the fringes produced by inflection. I compared the fringes formed by gold-leaf with those formed by masses of gold,—and those produced by films which gave the colours of thin plates with those formed by masses of the same substance. I examined the influence of platinum, diamond, and cork in inflecting light, the effect of non-reflecting grooves and spaces in polished metals, and of cylinders of glass immersed in a mixture of oil of cassia and oil of olives of the same refractive power; and, as the fringes had the same magnitude and character under all these circumstances, I concluded that they were not produced by any force inherent in the bodies themselves, but arose from a property of the light itself, which always showed itself when light was stopped in its progress.

Dr. Thomas Young, who had supported with great ingenuity and force of argument the undulatory theory of light, as maintained by Hooke and Huygens, was the first who gave a plausible explanation of the inflection of light. By interposing a small screen at B, *fig.* 10, and intercepting the rays that passed near the hair X, he was surprised to find that all the *fringes within the shadow disappeared*. The same effect took place when the screen intercepted the rays on the other side; and hence he concluded, that the rays on each side of the hair were necessary to the production of the inner fringes, and that the fringes were produced by the *interference* of the rays that passed on one side of the hair with those that passed on the other side. In order to account for the coloured fringes without the shadow, Dr. Young conceived that the rays which pass near the edge of the hair interfere with others, which he supposes may be reflected after falling very obliquely upon its edge,—a supposition which, if correct, would certainly produce fringes very similar to those actually observed.

In pursuing these researches so successfully begun by Dr. Young, M. Fresnel had the good fortune to explain all the phenomena of inflection by means of the undulatory doctrine combined with the principle of interference. In place of transmitting the light through a small aperture, he caused it to diverge from the focus of a deep convex lens, and instead of receiving the shadow and its fringes upon a smooth white surface, as was done by Newton, he viewed them directly with his eye through a lens placed behind the shadow; and by means of a microscope he was able to measure the dimensions of the fringes with the greatest exactness. By this mode of observation he made the remarkable discovery, that the inflection of the light *depended on the distance of the inflecting body from the aperture or from the focus of divergence;** the fringes being observed to dilate as the body approached that focus, and to contract as it receded from it, their relative distances from each other, and from the margin of the shadow continuing invariable. In attempting to account for the formation of the exterior fringes, M. Fresnel found it necessary to reject the supposition of Dr. Young, that they were owing to light reflected from the edge of the body. He not only ascertained that the real place of the fringe was the $\frac{17}{100}$th of a millimetre different from what it should be on that supposition, but he found that the fringes preserved the same intensity of light, whether the inflecting body had a round or a sharp edge, and even when the edge was such as not to afford sufficient light for their production. From this difficulty the undulatory theory speedily released him, and he was led by its indications to consider the exterior fringes, as produced by an infinite number of elementary waves of light emanating from a primitive wave when partly interrupted by an opaque body.

The various phenomena of inflection, which had

---

* This effect is so great, that at the distance of *four* inches from the point of divergence, the angular inflexion of the *red* rays of the first fringe is 12' 6", while at the distance of about twenty feet, it is only 3' 55".

so long resisted every effort to generalize them, having thus received so beautiful and satisfactory an explanation from the undulatory doctrine, they must of course be regarded as affording to that doctrine the most powerful support, while the Newtonian hypothesis of the materiality of light is proportionally thrown into the shade. It is impossible, indeed, even for national partiality to consider the views of Newton as furnishing any explanation of the facts discovered by Fresnel; and, as no attempt has been made by the small though able phalanx of his disciples to stay the decision with which, on this count at least, the doctrine of emission has been threatened, we shall venture to suggest some principles by which the refractory phenomena may perhaps be yet brought within the pale of the Newtonian theory.

That the particles of light, like those of heat, are endowed with a repulsive force which prevents them from accumulating when in a state of condensation, or when they are detained by the absorptive action of opaque bodies, will be readily admitted. By this power a beam of light radiating from a luminous point has, in every azimuth, the same degree of intensity at the same distance from its centre of divergence; but if we intercept a portion of such a beam by an opaque body, the repulsive force of the light which formerly occupied its shadow is withdrawn, and consequently the rays which pass near the body will be repelled into the shadow, and will form, by their interference with those similarly repelled on the other side, the interior fringes, which are parallel to the edges of the body. The rays which pass at a greater distance will in like manner be bent towards the body, but with less force, and, interfering with those rays which retain their primitive direction, from the state of their fits or the position of their poles, they will form the exterior fringes. When the inflecting body is placed near the point of divergence, the greater proximity of the rays will produce a greater repulsive force, and consequently a greater inflection of the passing light; while the removal of the body from the point of divergence will be accompanied with an increased distance of the particles, an inferior repulsive force, and a feebler inflection. As the phenomena of inflection, considered under this aspect, arise from a property of the light itself, it follows that they will remain invariable, whatever be the nature or density of the body, or the form of the edge which acts upon the passing rays.

CHAPTER IX.

Miscellaneous Optical Researches of Newton—His Experiments on Refraction—His Conjecture respecting the Inflammability of the Diamond—His Law of Double Refraction—His Observations on the Polarization of Light—Newton's Theory of Light—His "Optics."

BEFORE concluding our account of Newton's optical discoveries, it is necessary to notice some of his minor researches, which, though of inferior importance in the science of light, have either exercised an influence over the progress of discovery, or been associated with the history of other branches of knowledge.

One of the most curious of these inquiries related to the connexion between the refractive powers and the chymical composition of bodies. Having measured the refractive powers and the densities of twenty-two substances, he found that the forces which reflect and refract light are very nearly proportional to the densities of the same bodies. In this law, however, he noticed a remarkable exception in the case of unctuous and sulphureous bodies, such as camphire, olive oil, linseed oil, spirit of turpentine, and *diamond*, which have their refractive powers two or three times greater in respect of their densities than the other substances in the table, while among themselves their refractive powers are proportional to their densities, without any considerable variation. Hence he concluded that diamond " is an unctuous substance coagulated,"—a sagacious prediction, which has been verified in the discoveries of modern chymistry. The connexion between a high degree of inflammability and a great refracting force has been still more strongly established by the high refractive power which I detected in phosphorus, and which was discovered in hydrogen by MM. Biot and Arago.

There is no part of the optical labours of Newton which is less satisfactory than that which relates to the double refraction of light. In 1690, Huygens, published his admirable treatise on light, in which he has given the law of double refraction in calcareous spar, as deduced from his theory of light, and as confirmed by direct experiment. Viewing it probably as a theoretical deduction, Newton seems to have regarded it as incorrect, and though he has given Huygens the credit of describing the phenomena more exactly than Bartholinus, yet, without assigning any reason, he rejected the law of the Dutch philosopher, and substituted another in its place. These observations of our author form the subject of the twenty-fifth and twenty-sixth queries at the end of his Optics, which was published fourteen years after the appearance of Huygens's work. The law adopted by Newton is not accompanied with any of the experiments from which it was deduced ; and though he has given it without expressing any doubt of its accuracy, it is, nevertheless, entirely incompatible with observation, and has been rejected by all succeeding philosophers.

In his speculations respecting the successive disappearance and reappearance of two of the four images which are formed when a luminous object is viewed through two rhombs of calcareous spar, one of which is made to revolve upon the other, Newton has been more successful. He concluded from these phenomena that every ray of light has two opposite sides originally endued with the property on which the unusual refraction depends, and other two opposite sides not endued with that property; and he suggested it as a subject for future inquiry, whether there are not more properties of light by which the sides of the rays differ, and are distinguished from one another. This is the first occasion on which the idea of a *polarity* in the rays of light has been suggested.*

From the various optical inquiries in which Newton was engaged, he was strongly impressed with the belief that light consists of small material particles emitted from shining substances, and that these particles could be again recombined into solid matter, so that "gross bodies and light were convertible into one another." He conceived also that the particles of solid bodies and of light exerted a mutual action upon each other, the former being agitated and heated by the latter, and the latter being attracted and repelled by the former, with forces depending on the inertia of the luminous particles. These forces he regarded as insensible at all measurable distances, and he conceived that the distances between the particles of bodies were very small when compared with the extent of their sphere of attraction and repulsion.

With the exception of Hooke, Huygens, and Euler, almost all the contemporaries and successors of Newton maintained the doctrine of the materiality of light. It was first successfully assailed by Dr. Thomas Young, and since that time it has been shaken to its foundation by those great discoveries

---

* See the twenty-ninth query at the end of his Optics, where the sides of a ray are compared with the poles of a magnet.

which have illustrated the commencement of the present century. The undulatory theory, which has thus triumphed in its turn, is still subject to grave difficulties, and we fear another century must elapse before a final decision can be pronounced on this long-agitated question.

The most important of the optical discoveries of Newton, of which we have given a general history, were communicated to the Royal Society in detached papers; but the disputes in which they had involved their author made him hesitate about the publication of his other discoveries. Although he had drawn up a connected view of his labours under the title of "Opticks, or a Treatise on the Reflexions, Refractions, Inflexions, and Colours of Light," yet he resolved not to publish this work during the life of Hooke, by whose rival jealousy his tranquillity had been so frequently interrupted. Hooke, however, died in 1702, and the Optics of Newton appeared in English in 1704. Dr. Samuel Clark proposed a Latin edition of it, which appeared in 1706, and he was generously presented by Sir Isaac with 500*l*. (or 100*l*. for each of his five children), as a token of the approbation and gratitude of the author. Both the English and the Latin editions have been frequently reprinted both in England and on the Continent,* and there perhaps never was a work of profound science so widely circulated

* The English edition was reprinted at London in 1714, 1721, and 1730, and the Latin one at London in 1706, 1719, 1721, 1728, at Lausanne in 1740, and at Padua in 1773.

K

CHAPTER X.

Astronomical Discoveries of Newton—Necessity of combined Exertion to the Completion of great Discoveries—Sketch of the History of Astronomy previous to the Time of Newton—Copernicus, 1473–1543—Tycho Brahe, 1546–1601—Kepler, 1571–1631—Galileo, 1564–1642.

From the optical labours of Newton we now proceed to the history of his astronomical discoveries —those transcendent deductions of human reason by which he has secured to himself an immortal name, and vindicated the intellectual dignity of his species. Pre-eminent as his triumphs have been, it would be unjust to affirm that they were achieved by his single arm. The torch of many a preceding age had thrown its light into the strongholds of the material universe, and the grasp of many a powerful hand had pulled down the most impregnable of its defences. An alliance, indeed, of many kindred spirits had been long struggling in this great cause, and Newton was but the leader of their mighty phalanx,—the director of their combined genius,— the general who won the victory, and therefore wears its laurels.

The history of science presents us with no example of an individual mind throwing itself far in advance of its contemporaries. It is only in the career of crime and ambition that reckless man takes the start of his species, and, uncurbed by moral and religious restraint, erects an unholy dynasty upon the ruins of ancient and venerable institutions. The achievements of intellectual power, though often begun by one mind and completed by another, have ever been the results of combined exertions. Slow in their growth, they gradually approximate to a more perfect condition :—the variety in the phenomena of nature call forth a variety of intellectual gifts ;—the powers of analysis and combination are applied to the humbler labours of observation and experiment, and in the ordeal of rival inquiry truth is finally purified from error. How different is it with those systems which the imagination rears,—those theories of wild import which are directed against the consciences and hopes of man. The fatal upas-tree distils its poison in the spring as well as the autumn of its growth, but the fruit which sustains life must have its bud prepared before the approach of winter, its blossom expanded in the spring, and its juices elaborated by the light and heat of the summer and the autumnal sun.

In the century which preceded the birth of Newton the science of astronomy advanced with the most rapid steps. Emerging from the darkness of the middle ages, the human mind seemed to rejoice in its new-born strength, and to apply itself with elastic vigour to unfold the mechanism of the heavens. The labours of Hipparchus and Ptolemy had indeed furnished many important epochs and supplied many valuable data ; but the cumbrous appendages of cycles and epicycles with which they explained the stations and retrogradations of the planets, and the vulgar prejudices which a false interpretation of Scripture had excited against a belief in the motion of the earth, rendered it difficult even for great minds to escape from the trammels of authority, and appeal to the simplicity of nature.

The sovereign of Castile, the generous and noble-minded Alphonso, had long before proscribed the rude expedients of his predecessors ; and when he declared that if the heavens were thus constituted, he could have given the Deity good advice, he must not only have felt the absurdity of the prevailing system, but must have obtained some foresight of a more simple arrangement. But neither he nor the astronomers whom he so liberally protected seem to

have established a better system, and it was left
to Copernicus to enjoy the dignity of being the
restorer of astronomy.

This great man, a native of Thorn in Prussia, following his father's profession, began his career as a
doctor of medicine, but an accidental attendance on
the mathematical lectures of Brudzevius excited a
love for astronomy, which became the leading passion of his life. Quitting a profession uncongenial
to such pursuits, he went to Bologna to study
astronomy under Dominic Maria; and after having
enjoyed the friendship and instruction of that able
philosopher, he established himself at Rome in the
humble situation of a teacher of mathematics. Here
he made numerous astronomical observations which
served him as the basis of future researches; but
an event soon occurred which, though it interrupted
for a while his important studies, placed him in a
situation for pursuing them with new zeal. The
death of one of the canons enabled his uncle, who
was Bishop of Ermeland, to appoint him to a canonry in the chapter of Frauenburg, where, in a
house situated on the brow of a mountain, he continued, in peaceful seclusion, to carry on his astronomical observations. During his residence at Rome
his talents had been so well appreciated, that the
Bishop of Fossombrona, who presided over the
council for reforming the calendar, solicited the aid
of Copernicus in this desirable undertaking. At first
he entered warmly into the views of the council,
and charged himself with the determination of the
length of the year and of the month, and of the
other motions of the sun and moon that seemed to
be required; but he found the task too irksome, and
probably felt that it would interfere with those
interesting discoveries which had already begun to
dawn upon his mind.

Copernicus is said to have commenced his inquiries by an historical examination of the opinions of

ancient authors on the system of the universe; but it is more likely that he sought for the authority of their great names to countenance his peculiar views, and that he was more desirous to present his own theory as one that he had received, rather than as one which he had invented. His mind had been long imbued with the idea that simplicity and harmony should characterize the arrangements of the planetary system, and, in the complication and disorder which reigned in the hypothesis of Ptolemy, he saw insuperable objections to its being regarded as a representation of nature. In the opinions of the Egyptian sages, in those of Pythagoras, Philolaus, Aristarchus, and Nicetas, he recognised his own earliest conviction that the earth was not the centre of the universe; but he appears to have considered it as still possible that our globe might perform some function in the system more important than that of the other planets; and his attention was much occupied with the speculation of Martianus Capella, who placed the sun between Mars and the moon, and made Mercury and Venus revolve round him as a centre; and with the system of Apollonius Pergæus, who made all the planets revolve round the sun, while the sun and moon were carried round the earth in the centre of the universe. The examination, however, of these hypotheses gradually dispelled the difficulties with which the subject was beset; and after the labours of more than thirty years, he was permitted to see the true system of the heavens. The sun he considered as immoveable in the centre of the system, while the earth revolved between the orbits of Venus and Mars, and produced by its rotation about its axis all the diurnal phenomena of the celestial sphere. The precession of the equinoxes was thus referred to a slight motion of the earth's axis, and the stations and retrogradations of the planets were the necessary consequence of their own motions combined

K 2

with that of the earth about the sun. These remarkable views were supported by numerous astronomical observations; and in 1530 Copernicus brought to a close his immortal work on the Revolutions of the Heavenly Bodies.

But while we admire the genius which triumphed over so many difficulties, we cannot fail to commend the extraordinary prudence with which he ushered his new system into the world. Aware of the prejudices, and even of the hostility with which such a system would be received, he resolved neither to startle the one nor provoke the other. He allowed his opinions to circulate in the slow current of personal communication. The points of opposition which they presented to established doctrines were gradually worn down, and they insinuated themselves into reception among the ecclesiastical circles by the very reluctance of their author to bring them into notice. In the year 1534, Cardinal Schonberg, Bishop of Capua, and Gyse, Bishop of Culm, exerted all their influence to induce Copernicus to lay his system before the world; but he resisted their solicitations; and it was not till 1539 that an accidental circumstance contributed to alter his resolution. George Rheticus, professor of mathematics at Wirtemberg, having heard of the labours of Copernicus, resigned his chair, and repaired to Frauenberg to make himself master of his discoveries. This zealous disciple prevailed upon his master to permit the publication of his system; and they seem to have arranged a plan for giving it to the world without alarming the vigilance of the church, or startling the prejudices of individuals. Under the disguise of a student of mathematics, Rheticus published in 1540 an account of the manuscript volume of Copernicus. This pamphlet was received without any disapprobation, and its author was encouraged to reprint it at Basle, in 1541, with his own name. The success of these publications, and the flattering manner in which the new astronomy was received by several able writers, induced Copernicus to place his MSS. in the hands of Rheticus. It was accordingly printed at the expense of Cardinal Schonberg, and appeared at Nuremberg in 1543. Its illustrious author, however, did not live to peruse it. A complete copy was handed to him in his last moments, and he saw and touched it a few hours before his death. This great work was dedicated to the Holy Pontiff, in order, as Copernicus himself says, that the authority of the head of the church might silence the calumnies of individuals who had attacked his views by arguments drawn from religion. Thus introduced, the Copernican system met with no ecclesiastical opposition, and gradually made its way in spite of the ignorance and prejudices of the age.

Among the astronomers who provided the materials of the Newtonian philosophy the name of Tycho Brahe merits a conspicuous place. Descended from an ancient Swedish family, he was born at Knudstorp, in Norway, in 1546, three years after the death of Copernicus. The great eclipse of the sun which happened on the 26th August, 1560, while he was at the University of Copenhagen, attracted his notice : and when he found that all its phenomena had been accurately predicted, he was seized with the most irresistible passion to acquire the knowledge of a science so infallible in its results. Destined for the profession of the law, his friends discouraged the pursuit which now engrossed his thoughts; and such were the reproaches and even persecutions to which he was exposed, that he quitted his country with the design of travelling through Germany. At the very commencement of his journey, however, an event occurred in which the impetuosity of his temper had nearly cost him his life. At a wedding-feast in Rostock, a questionable point in geometry involved him in a dispute

with a Danish nobleman of the same temperament
with himself; and the two mathematicians resolved
to settle the difference by the sword.   Tycho,
however, seems to have been second in the conflict,
for he lost the greater part of his nose, and was
obliged to supply its place by a substitute of gold
and silver, which a cement of glue attached to his
face.   During his stay at Augsburg he inspired the
burgomaster of the city, Peter Hainzell, with a love
of astronomy.   This public-spirited citizen erected
an excellent observatory at his own expense, and
here Tycho began that distinguished career which
has placed him in the first rank of practical astronomers.

Upon his return to Copenhagen in 1570, he was
received with every mark of respect.   The king invited him to court, and persons of all ranks harassed
him with their attentions.   At Herritzvold, near his
native place, the house of his maternal uncle afforded
him a retreat from the gayeties of the capital, and
he was there offered every accommodation for the
prosecution of his astronomical studies.   Here,
however, the passion of love and the pursuits of
alchymy distracted his thoughts; but though the
peasant girl of whom he was enamoured was of
easier attainment than the philosopher's stone, the
marriage produced an open quarrel with his relations,
which it required the interference of the king to allay.
In the tranquillity of domestic happiness, Tycho resumed his study of the heavens, and in 1572 he
enjoyed the singular good fortune of observing,
through all its variations, the new star in Cassiopeia,
which appeared with such extraordinary splendour
as to be visible in the daytime, and which gradually
disappeared in the following year.

Dissatisfied with his residence in Denmark, Tycho
resolved to settle in some distant country; and having gone as far as Venice in search of a suitable
residence, he at last fixed upon Basle, in Switzer-

land. The King of Denmark, however, had learned his intention from the Prince of Hesse; and when Tycho returned to Copenhagen to remove his family and his instruments, his sovereign announced to him his resolution to detain him in his kingdom. He presented him with the canonry of Roschild, with an income of 2000 crowns per annum. To this he added a pension of 1000 crowns; and he promised to give him the island of Huen, with a complete observatory erected under his own eye. This generous offer was instantly accepted. The celebrated observatory of Uraniburg was established at the expense of about 20,000*l.*; and in this magnificent retreat Tycho continued for twenty-one years to enrich astronomy with the most valuable observations. Admiring disciples crowded to this sanctuary of the sciences to acquire the knowledge of the heavens; and kings* and princes felt themselves honoured by becoming the guests of the great astronomer of the age.

One of the principal discoveries of Tycho was that of the inequality of the moon's motion, called the variation. He detected, also, the annual equation which affects the place of her apogee and nodes, and he determined the greatest and the least inclination of the lunar orbit. His observations on the planets were numerous and precise, and have formed the data of the present generalizations in astronomy.

---

* When James I. went to Copenhagen in 1590, to conclude his marriage with the Princess Anne of Denmark, he spent eight days under the roof of Tycho at Uraniburg. As a token of his gratitude, he composed a set of Latin verses in honour of the astronomer, and left him a magnificent present at his departure. He gave him also his royal license for the publication of his works in England, and accompanied it with the following complimentary letter:—

"Nor am I acquainted with these things on the relation of others, or from a mere perusal of your works, but I have seen them with my own eyes, and heard them with my own ears, in your residence at Uraniburg, during the various learned and agreeable conversations which I there held with you, which even now affect my mind to such a degree, that it is difficult to decide whether I recollect them with greater pleasure or admiration."

Though thus skilful in the observation of phenomena, his mind was but little suited to investigate their cause, and it was probably owing to this defect that he rejected the system of Copernicus. The vanity of giving his own name to another system was not likely to actuate a mind such as his, and it was more probable that he was led to adopt the immobility of the earth, and to make the sun, with all his attendant planets, circulate round it, from the great difficulty which still presented itself by comparing the apparent diameter of the stars with the annual parallax of the earth's orbit.

The death of Frederick in 1588 proved a severe calamity to Tycho, and to the science which he cultivated. During the first years of the minority of Christian IV. the regency continued the royal patronage to the observatory of Uraniburg; and in 1592 the young king paid a visit of some days to Tycho, and left him a gold chain in token of his favour. The astronomer, however, had made himself enemies at court, and the envy of his high reputation had probably added fresh malignity to the irritation of personal feelings. Under the ministry of Wolchendorf, a name for ever odious to science, Tycho's pension was stopped;—he was in 1597 deprived of the canonry of Roschild, and was thus forced, with his wife and children, to seek an asylum in a foreign land. His friend, Henry Rantzau, of Wansbeck, under whose roof he found a hospitable shelter, was fortunately acquainted with the emperor Rodolph II., who, to his love of science, added a passion for alchymy and astrology. The reputation of Tycho having already reached the imperial ear, the recommendation of Rantzau was scarcely necessary to ensure him his warmest friendship. Invited by the emperor, he repaired in 1599 to Prague, where he met with the kindest reception. A pension of three thousand crowns was immediately settled upon him, and a commodious observatory erected for his use

In the vicinity of that city. Here the exiled astronomer renewed with delight his interrupted labours, and the gratitude which he cherished for the royal favour increased the satisfaction which he felt in having so unexpectedly found a resting-place for approaching age. These prospects of better days were enhanced by the good fortune of receiving two such men as Kepler and Longomontanus for his pupils; but the fallacy of human anticipation was here, as in so many other cases, strikingly displayed. Tycho was not aware of the inroads which both his labours and his disappointments had made upon his constitution. Though surrounded with affectionate friends and admiring disciples, he was still an exile in a foreign land. Though his country had been base in its ingratitude, it was yet the land which he loved,—the scene of his earliest affection,—the theatre of his scientific glory. These feelings continually preyed upon his mind, and his unsettled spirit was ever hovering among his native mountains. In this condition he was attacked with a disease of the most painful kind, and though the paroxysms of its agonies had lengthened intermissions, yet he saw that death was approaching. He implored his pupils to persevere in their scientific labours. He conversed with Kepler on some of the profoundest points of astronomy, and with these secular occupations he mingled frequent acts of piety and devotion. In this happy condition he expired without pain at the age of fifty-five, the unquestionable victim of the councils of Christian IV.

Notwithstanding the accessions which astronomy had received from the labours of Copernicus and Tycho, no progress was yet made in developing the general laws of the system, and scarcely an idea had been formed of the power by which the planets were retained in their orbits. The labours of assiduous observers had supplied the materials for this purpose, and Kepler arose to lay the foundations of physical astronomy.

John Kepler was born at Wiel, in Wirtemberg, in 1571. He was educated for the church, and discharged even some of the clerical functions; but his devotion to science withdrew him from the study of theology. Having received mathematical instruction from the celebrated Mæstlinus, he had made such progress in the science, that he was invited in 1594 to fill the mathematical chair of Gratz in Styria. Endowed with a fertile imagination, his mind was ever intent upon subtle and ingenious speculations. In the year 1596 he published his peculiar views in a work on the Harmonies and Analogies of Nature. In this singular production, he attempts to solve what he calls the great cosmographical mystery of the admirable proportion of the planetary orbits; and by means of the six regular geometrical solids,* he endeavours to assign a reason why there are six planets, and why the dimensions of their orbits and the time of their periodical revolutions were such as Copernicus had found them. If a cube, for example, were inserted in a sphere, of which Saturn's orbit was one of the great circles, it would, he supposed, touch by its six planes the lesser sphere of Jupiter; and, in like manner, he proposes to determine, by the aid of the other geometrical solids, the magnitude of the spheres of the other planets. A copy of this work was presented by its author to Tycho Brahe, who had been too long versed in the severe realities of observation to attach any value to such wild theories. He advised his young friend "first to lay a solid foundation for his views by actual observation, and then, by ascending from these, to strive to reach the causes of things;" and there is reason to think that, by the aid of the whole Baconian philosophy, thus compressed

---

* The cube, the sphere, the tetrahedron, the octohedron, the dodecahedron, and the icosahedron.

by anticipation into a single sentence, he abandoned for a while his visionary inquiries.

In the year 1598 Kepler suffered persecution for his religious principles, and was compelled to quit Gratz; but though he was recalled by the States of Styria, he felt his situation insecure, and accepted of a pressing invitation from Tycho to settle at Prague, and assist him in his calculations. Having arrived in Bohemia in 1600, he was introduced by his friends to the Emperor Rodolph, from whom he ever afterward received the kindest attention. On the death of Tycho in 1601, he was appointed mathematician to the emperor,—a situation in which he was continued during the successive reigns of Matthias and Ferdinand; but what was of more importance to science, he was put in possession of the valuable collection of Tycho's observations. These observations were remarkably numerous; and as the orbit of Mars was more oval than that of any of the other planets, they were peculiarly suitable for determining its real form. The notions of harmony and symmetry in the construction of the solar system, which had filled the mind of Kepler, necessarily led him to believe that the planets revolved with a uniform motion in circular orbits. So firm, indeed, was this conviction, that he made numerous attempts to represent the observations of Tycho by this hypothesis. The deviations were too great to be ascribed to errors of observation; and in trying various other curves, he was led to the discovery that Mars revolved round the sun in an elliptical orbit, in one of the foci of which the sun itself was placed. The same observations enabled him to determine the dimensions of the planet's orbit, and by comparing together the times in which Mars passed over different portions of its orbit, he found that they were to one another as the areas described by the lines drawn from the centre of the planet to the centre of the sun, or, in more technical terms, that

L

the radius vector describes equal areas in equal times. These two remarkable discoveries, the first that were ever made in physical astronomy, were extended to all the other planets of the system, and were communicated to the world in 1609, in his "Commentaries on the Motions of the Planet Mars, as deduced from the observations of Tycho Brahe."

Although our author was conducted to these great laws by the patient examination of well-established facts, his imagination was ever hurrying him among the wilds of conjecture. Convinced that the mean distances of the planets from the sun bore to one another some mysterious relation, he not only compared them with the regular geometrical solids, but also with the intervals of musical tones; an idea which the ancient Pythagoreans had suggested, and which had been adopted by Archimedes himself. All these comparisons were fruitless; and Kepler was about to abandon an inquiry of about seventeen years' duration, when, on the 8th March, 1618, he conceived the idea of comparing the powers of the different members which express the planetary distances, in place of the numbers themselves. He compared the squares and the cubes of the distances with the same powers of the periodic times; nay, he tried even the squares of the times with the cubes of the distances; but his hurry and impatience led him into an error of calculation, and he rejected this law as having no existence in nature! On the 15th May, his mind again reverted to the same notion, and upon making the calculations anew, and free from error, he discovered the great law, that the squares of the periodic times of any two planets are to one another as the cubes of their distances from the sun. Enchanted with this unexpected result, he could scarcely trust his calculations; and, to use his own language, he at first believed that he was dreaming, and had taken for granted the very truth of which he was in search. This brilliant discovery was published in 1619, in his "Harmony of the World;" a work dedicated to James VI. of Scotland. Thus were established what have been called the three laws of Kepler,—the motion of the planets in elliptical orbits,—the proportionality between the areas described and their times of description,—and the relations between the squares of the periodic times and the cubes of the distances.

The relation of the movements of the planets to the sun, as the general centre of all their orbits, could not fail to suggest to Kepler that some power resided in that luminary by which these various motions were produced; and he went so far as to conjecture that this power diminishes as the square of the distance of the body on which it was exerted; but he immediately rejects this law, and prefers that of the simple distances. In his work on Mars, he speaks of gravity as a mutual and corporeal affection between similar bodies. He maintained that the tides were occasioned by the moon's attraction, and that the irregularities of the lunar motions, as detected by Tycho, were owing to the joint actions of the sun and the earth; but the relation between gravity, as exhibited on the earth's surface, and as conducting the planets in their orbits, required more patience of thought than he could command, and was accordingly left for the exercise of higher powers.

The misery in which Kepler lived forms a painful contrast with the services which he performed to science. The pension on which he subsisted was always in arrears, and though the three emperors whose reigns he adorned directed their ministers to be more punctual in its payment, the disobedience of their commands was a source of continued vexation to Kepler. When he retired to Sagan, in Silesia, to spend in retirement the remainder of his days, his pecuniary difficulties became still more harassing. Necessity at last compelled him to apply personally for the arrears which were due; and he accordingly set out in 1630 for Ratisbon; but in consequence of the great fatigue which so long a journey on horseback produced, he was seized with a fever, which carried him off on the 30th November, 1630, in the 59th year of his age.

While Kepler was thus laying the foundation of physical astronomy, Galileo was busily employed in extending the boundaries of the solar system. This distinguished philosopher was born at Pisa in 1564. He was the son of a Florentine nobleman, and was educated for the medical profession; but a passion for geometry took possession of his mind, and called forth all his powers. Without the aid of a master, he studied the writings of Euclid and of Archimedes; and such were his acquirements, that he was appointed by the Grand-duke of Tuscany to the mathematical chair of Pisa in the twenty-fifth year of his age. His opposition to the Aristotelian philosophy gained him many enemies, and at the end of three years he quitted Pisa, and accepted of an invitation to the professorship of mathematics at Padua. Here he continued for eighteen years adorning the university by his name, and diffusing around him a taste for the physical sciences. With the exception of some contrivances of inferior importance, Galileo had distinguished himself by no discovery till he had reached the forty-fifth year of his age. In the year 1609, the same year in which Kepler published his celebrated commentary on Mars, Galileo paid a visit to Venice, where he heard, in the course of conversation, that a Dutchman of the name of Jansens had constructed and presented to Prince Maurice an instrument through which he saw distant objects magnified and rendered more distinct, as if they had been brought nearer to the observer. This report was credited by some and disbelieved by others; but, in the course of a few days, Galileo received a letter from James Badovere at Paris, which placed beyond a doubt the existence of such an instrument. The idea instantly filled his mind as one of the utmost importance to science; and so thoroughly was he acquainted with the properties of lenses, that he not only discovered the principle of its construction, but was able to complete a telescope for his own use. Into one end of a leaden tube he fitted a spectacle-glass plane on one side and convex on the other, and in the other end he placed another spectacle-glass concave on one side and plane on the other. He then applied his eye to the concave glass, and saw objects "pretty large and pretty near him." They appeared three times nearer, and nine times larger in surface, than to the naked eye. He soon after made another, which represented objects above sixty times larger; and, sparing neither labour nor expense, he finally constructed an instrument so excellent, as "to show things almost a thousand times larger, and above thirty times nearer to the naked eye."

There is, perhaps, no invention that science has presented to man so extraordinary in its nature, and so boundless in its influence, as that of the telescope. To the uninstructed mind, the power of seeing an object a thousand miles distant, as large and nearly as distinct as if it were brought within a mile of the observer, must seem almost miraculous; and to the philosopher, even, who thoroughly comprehends the principles upon which it acts, it must ever appear one of the most elegant applications of science. To have been the first astronomer in whose hands such a gift was placed was a preference to which Galileo owed much of his future reputation.

No sooner had he completed his telescope than he applied it to the heavens, and on the 7th January, 1618, the first day of its use, he saw round Jupiter three bright little stars lying in a line parallel to the ecliptic, two to the east, and one to the west of the planet. Regarding them as ordinary stars, he never thought of estimating their distances. On the following day, when he accidentally directed his telescope to Jupiter, he was surprised to see the three stars to the west of the planet. To produce this effect it was requisite that the motion of Jupiter should be direct, though, according to calculation, it was actually retrograde. In this dilemma he waited with impatience for the evening of the 9th, but unfortunately the sky was covered with clouds. On the 10th he saw only two stars to the east—a circumstance which he was no longer able to explain by the motion of Jupiter. He was therefore compelled to ascribe the change to the stars themselves; and upon repeating his observations on the 11th, he no longer doubted that he had discovered three planets revolving round Jupiter. On the 13th January he for the first time saw the fourth satellite.*

This discovery, though of the utmost importance in itself, derived an additional value from the light which it threw on the true system of the universe. While the earth was the only planet enlightened by a moon, it might naturally be supposed that it alone was habitable, and was therefore entitled to the pre-eminence of occupying the centre of the system; but the discovery of four moons round a much larger planet deprived this argument of its force, and created a new analogy between the earth and the other planets. When Kepler received the "Sidereal Messenger," the work in which Galileo announced his discovery in 1610, he perused it with the deepest interest; and while it confirmed and extended his substantial discoveries, it dispelled at the same time some of those harmonic dreams which still hovered among his thoughts. In the "Dis-

---

* Simon Marius, mathematician to the Marquis of Brandenburg, assures us that he discovered the satellites of Jupiter in November, 1609.

sertation" which he published on the discovery of Galileo, he expresses his hope that satellites will be discovered round Saturn and Mars,—he conjectures that Jupiter has a motion of rotation about his axis,—and states his surprise, that, after what had been written on the subject of telescopes by Baptista Porta, they had not been earlier introduced into observatories.

In continuing his observations, Galileo applied his telescope to Venus, and in 1610 he discovered the phases of that planet, which exhibited to him the various forms of the waxing and the waning moon. This fact established beyond a doubt that the planet revolved round the sun, and thus gave an additional blow to the Ptolemaic system. In his observations on the sun, Galileo discovered his spots, and deduced from them the rotation of the central luminary. He observed that the body of Saturn had handles attached to it; but he was unable to detect the form of its ring, or render visible its minute satellites. On the surface of the moon he discovered her mountains and valleys, and determined the curious fact of her libration, in virtue of which parts of the margin of her disk occasionally appear and disappear. In the Milky Way he descried numerous minute stars which the unassisted eye was unable to perceive; and as the largest fixed stars, in place of being magnified by the telescope, became actually minute brilliant points, he inferred their immense distance as rendered necessary by the Copernican hypothesis. All his discoveries, indeed, furnished fresh arguments in favour of the new system; and the order of the planets and their relation to a central sun may now be considered as established by incontrovertible evidence.

While Galileo was occupied with these noble pursuits at Pisa, to which he had been recalled in 1611, his generous patron, Cosmo II. Grand-duke of Tuscany, invited him to Florence, that he might pursue with uninterrupted leisure his astronomical observations, and carry on his correspondence with the German astronomers. His fame had now resounded through all Europe;—the strongholds of prejudice and ignorance were unbarred;—and the most obstinate adherents of ancient systems acknowledged the meridian power of the day-star of science. Galileo was ambitious of propagating the great truths which he contributed so powerfully to establish. He never doubted that they would be received with gratitude by all,—by the philosopher as the consummation of the greatest efforts of human genius,—and by the Christian as the most transcendent displays of Almighty power. But he had mistaken the disposition of his species, and the character of the age. That same system of the heavens which had been discovered by the humble ecclesiastic of Frauenberg, which had been patronised by the kindness of a bishop, and published at the expense of a cardinal, and which the pope himself had sanctioned by the warmest reception, was, after the lapse of a hundred years, doomed to the most violent opposition, as subversive of the doctrines of the Christian faith. On no former occasion has the human mind exhibited such a fatal relapse into intolerance. The age itself had improved in liberality;—the persecuted doctrines themselves had become more deserving of reception;—the light of the Reformed faith had driven the Catholics from some of their most obnoxious positions;—and yet, under all these circumstances, the church of Rome unfurled her banner of persecution against the pride of Italy, against the ornament of his species, and against truths immutable and eternal.

In consequence of complaints laid before the Holy Inquisition, Galileo was summoned to appear at Rome in 1615, to answer for the heretical opinions which he had promulgated. He was charged with " maintaining as true the false doctrine held by many, that the sun was immoveable in the centre of the world, and that the earth revolved with a diurnal motion ;—with having certain disciples to whom he taught the same doctrine ;—with keeping up a correspondence on the subject with several German mathematicians ;—with having published letters on the solar spots, in which he explained the same doctrine as true ;—and with having glossed over with a false interpretation the passages of Scripture which were urged against it." The consideration of these charges came before a meeting of the Inquisition, which assembled on the 25th February, 1616 ; and the court, declaring their disposition to deal gently with the prisoner, pronounced the following decree :—" That Cardinal Bellarmine should enjoin Galileo to renounce entirely the above-recited false opinions; that, on his refusal to do so, he should be commanded by the commissary of the Inquisition to abandon the said doctrine, and to cease to teach and defend it; and that, if he did not obey this command, he should be thrown into prison." On the 26th of February Galileo appeared before Cardinal Bellarmine, and, after receiving from him a gentle admonition, he was commanded by the commissary, in the presence of a notary and witnesses, to desist altogether from his erroneous opinions ; and it was declared to be unlawful for him in future to teach them in any way whatever, either orally or in his writings. To these commands Galileo promised obedience, and was dismissed from the Inquisition.

The mildness of this sentence was no doubt partly owing to the influence of the Grand-duke of Tuscany, and other persons of rank and influence at the papal court, who took a deep interest in the issue of the trial. Dreading, however, that so slight a punishment might not have the effect of putting down the obnoxious doctrines, the Inquisition issued a decree denouncing the new opinions as false and contrary to the sacred writings, and prohibiting the sale of every book in which they should be maintained.

Thus liberated from his persecutors, Galileo returned to Florence, where he pursued his studies with his wonted diligence and ardour. The recantation of his astronomical opinions was so formal and unreserved, that ordinary prudence, if not a sense of personal honour, should have restrained him from unnecessarily bringing them before the world. No anathema was pronounced against his scientific discoveries; no interdict was laid upon the free exercise of his genius. He was prohibited merely from teaching a doctrine which the church of Rome considered to be injurious to its faith. We might have expected, therefore, that a philosopher so conspicuous in the eyes of the world would have respected the prejudices, however base, of an institution whose decrees formed part of the law of the land, and which possessed the power of life and death within the limits of its jurisdiction. Galileo, however, thought otherwise. A sense of degradation* seems to have urged him to retaliate, and before six years had elapsed, he began to compose his "Cosmical System, or Dialogues on the two greatest Systems of the World, the Ptolemean and the Copernican," the concealed object of which is to establish the opinions which he had promised to abandon. In this work the subject is discussed by three speakers, Sagredo, Salviatus, and Simplicius, a peripatetic philosopher, who defends the system of

* It is distinctly stated in the sentence of the Inquisition, that Galileo's enemies had charged him with having abjured his opinions in 1616, and affirmed that he had been punished by the Inquisition. In order to refute these calumnies, Galileo applied to Cardinal Bellarmine for a certificate to prove that he neither abjured his opinions nor suffered any punishment for them; but that the doctrine of the motion of the earth and the stability of the sun was only denounced to him as contrary to Scripture, and as one which could not be defended or maintained. Cardinal Bellarmine drew up such a certificate in his own handwriting.

Ptolemy with much skill against the overwhelming arguments of the rival disputants. Galileo hoped to escape notice by this indirect mode of propagating the new system, and he obtained permission to publish his work, which appeared at Florence in 1632.

The Inquisition did not, as might have been expected, immediately summon Galileo to their presence. Nearly a year elapsed before they gave any indication of their design; and, according to their own statement, they did not even take the subject under consideration till they saw that the obnoxious tenets were every day gaining ground, in consequence of the publication of the Dialogues. They then submitted the work to a careful examination, and having found it to be a direct violation of the injunction which had been formerly intimated to its author, they again cited him before their tribunal in 1633. The venerable sage, now in his seventieth year, was thus compelled to repair to Rome, and when he arrived he was committed to the apartments of the Fiscal of the Inquisition. The unchangeable friendship, however, of the Grand-duke of Tuscany obtained a remission of this severity, and Galileo was allowed to reside at the house of the Tuscan ambassador during the two months which the trial occupied. When brought before the Inquisition, and examined upon oath, he acknowledged that the Dialogues were written by himself, and that he obtained permission to publish them without notifying to the person who gave it that he had been prohibited from holding, defending, or teaching the heretical opinions. He confessed also that the Dialogues were composed in such a manner, that the arguments in favour of the Copernican system, though given as partly false, were yet managed in such a manner that they were more likely to confirm than overturn its doctrines; but that this error, which was not intentional, arose from the natural desire of making an ingenious defence of false propositions, and of opinions that had the semblance of probability.

After receiving these confessions and excuses, the Inquisition allowed Galileo a proper time for giving in his defence; but this seems to have consisted solely in bringing forward the certificate of Cardinal Bellarmine already mentioned, which made no allusion to the promise under which Galileo had come never to defend, nor teach in any way whatever, the Copernican doctrines. The court held this defence to be an aggravation of the crime rather than an excuse for it, and proceeded to pronounce a sentence which will be ever memorable in the history of the human mind.

Invoking the name of our Saviour, they declare, that Galileo had made himself liable to the suspicion of heresy, by believing the doctrine, contrary to Scripture, that the sun was the centre of the earth's orbit, and did not move from east to west; and by defending as probable the opinion that the earth moved, and was not the centre of the world; and that he had thus incurred all the censures and penalties which were enacted by the church against such offences;—but that he should be absolved from these penalties, provided he sincerely abjured and cursed all the errors and heresies contained in the formula of the church, which should be submitted to him. That so grave and pernicious a crime should not pass altogether unpunished, that he might become more cautious in future, and might be an example to others to abstain from such offences, they decreed that his Dialogues should be prohibited by a formal edict,—that he should be condemned to the prison of the Inquisition during pleasure,—and that, during the three following years, he should recite once a week the seven penitential psalms.

This sentence was subscribed by seven cardinals; and on the 22d June, 1633, Galileo signed an abjuration humiliating to himself and degrading to philosophy. At the age of seventy, on his bended knees, and with his right hand resting on the Holy Evangelists, did this patriarch of science avow his present and his past belief in all the dogmas of the Romish Church, abandon as false and heretical the doctrine of the earth's motion and of the sun's immobility, and pledge himself to denounce to the Inquisition any other person who was even suspected of heresy. He abjured, cursed, and detested those eternal and immutable truths which the Almighty had permitted him to be the first to establish. What a mortifying picture of moral depravity and intellectual weakness! If the unholy zeal of the assembly of cardinals has been branded with infamy, what must we think of the venerable sage whose gray hairs were entwined with the chaplet of immortality, quailing under the fear of man, and sacrificing the convictions of his conscience and the deductions of his reason at the altar of a base superstition? Had Galileo but added the courage of the martyr to the wisdom of the sage,—had he carried the glance of his indignant eye round the circle of his judges,—had he lifted his hands to heaven, and called the living God to witness the truth and immutability of his opinions, the bigotry of his enemies would have been disarmed, and science would have enjoyed a memorable triumph.

The great truths of the Copernican system, instead of being considered as heretical, had been actually adopted by many pious members of the Catholic church, and even some of its dignitaries did not scruple to defend it openly. Previous to the first persecution of Galileo in 1615, a Neapolitan nobleman, Vincenzio Caraffa, a person equally distinguished by his piety and birth, had solicited Paul Anthony Foscarinus, a learned Carmelite monk, to illustrate and defend the new system of the universe. With this request the ecclesiastic speedily complied; and in the pamphlet which he completed on the 6th

M

January, 1615, he defends the Copernican system
with much boldness and ingenuity; he reconciles
the various passages of Scripture with the new doctrine, and he expresses the hope that such an attempt,
now made for the first time, will prove agreeable to
philosophers, but particularly to those very learned
men, Galileo Galilei, John Kepler, and all the members of the Lyncean Academy, who, he believes,
entertain the same opinion. This remarkable production, written from the convent of the Carmelites
at Naples, is dedicated to the very Reverend Sebas-
tian Fantoni, general of the order of Carmelites, and
was published at Florence, with the sanction of the
ecclesiastical authorities, in 1630; three years before
the second persecution of Galileo.

It would be interesting to know the state of public
feeling in Italy when Galileo was doomed to the
prisons of the Inquisition. No appeal seems to have
been made against so cruel a sentence; and neither
in remonstrance nor in derision does an individual
voice seem to have been raised. The master spirits
of the age looked with sullen indifference on the
persecution of exalted genius; and Galileo lay in
chains, deserted and unpitied. This unrebuked triumph of his enemies was perhaps favourable to the
object of their vengeance. Resistance might have
heightened the rigour of a sentence, which submission seems to have alleviated. The interference
of some eminent individuals of Rome, among whom
we have no doubt that the Grand-duke of Tuscany
was the most influential, induced Pope Urban VIII.,
not only to shorten the period, but to soften the
rigour of Galileo's imprisonment. From the dun-
geon of the Inquisition, where he had remained only
four days, he was transported to the ambassador's
palace in the Garden de Medici at Rome; and when
his health had begun to suffer, he was permitted to
leave the metropolis; and would have been allowed
to return to Florence, but as the plague raged in

that city, he was sent, in July, 1633, to the archiepiscopal palace of Sienna, the residence of the Archbishop Piccolimini, where he carried on and completed his valuable investigations respecting the resistance of solids. Here he continued five months, when, in consequence of the disappearance of the plague at Florence, he was allowed to retire to his villa at Bellosguardo, and afterward to that of Arcetri in the vicinity of Florence.

Though Galileo was now, to a certain degree, liberated from the power of man, yet the afflicting dispensations of Providence began to fall thickly around him. No sooner had he returned to Arcetri, than his favourite daughter, Maria, was seized with a dangerous illness, which soon terminated in her death. He was himself attacked with hernia, palpitation of the heart, loss of appetite, and the most oppressive melancholy; and though he solicited permission to repair to Florence for medical assistance, yet this deed of mercy was denied him. In 1638, however, the pope permitted him to pay a visit to Florence, and his friend, Father Castelli, was allowed to visit him in the company of an officer of the Inquisition. But this indulgence was soon withdrawn, and at the end of a few months he was remanded to Arcetri. The sight of his right eye had begun to fail in 1636, from an opacity of the cornea. In 1637 his left eye was attacked with the same complaint; so that in a few months he was affected with total and incurable blindness. Before this calamity had supervened, he had noticed the curious phenomenon of the moon's libration, in consequence of which, parts of her visible disk that are exposed to view at one time are withdrawn at another. He succeeded in explaining two of the causes of this curious phenomenon, viz. the different distances of the observer from the line joining the centre of the earth and the moon, which produces the diurnal libration, and the unequal motion of the moon in her orbit, which produces the libration in longitude. It was left, however, to Hevelius to discover the libration in latitude, which arises from the inclination of her axis being a little less than a right angle to the ecliptic; and to Lagrange to discover the spheroidal libration, or that which arises from the action of the earth upon the lunar spheroid.

The sorrows with which Galileo was now beset, seemed to have disarmed the severity of the Inquisition. He was freely permitted to enjoy the society of his friends, who now thronged around him to express their respect and their sympathy. The Grand-duke of Tuscany was his frequent visiter, and Gassendi, Deodati, and our countryman Milton went to Italy for the purpose of visiting him. He entertained his friends with the warmest hospitality, and though simple and abstemious in his diet, yet he was fond of good wine, and seems even in his last days to have paid particular attention to the excellence of his cellar.

Although Galileo had nearly lost his hearing as well as his sight, yet his intellectual faculties were unimpaired; and while his mind was occupied in considering the force of percussion, he was seized with fever and palpitation of the heart, which, after two months' illness, terminated his life on the 8th of January, 1642.

Among the predecessors of Newton in astronomical research we must not omit the names of Bouillaud (Bulliardus), Borelli, and Dr. Hooke. Ismael Bouillaud, a native of Laon in France, and the author of several valuable astronomical works, has derived more reputation from a single sentence in his *Astronomica Philolaica*, published in 1645, than from all the rest of his labours. He was not a believer in the doctrine of attraction, which, as we have already seen, had been broached by Copernicus, and discovered by Kepler; but in speaking of that power as the cause of the planetary motions, he remarks, "that if attraction existed, it would decrease as the square of the distance." The influence of gravity was still more distinctly developed by Borelli, a Neapolitan philosopher, who published in 1666 a work on Jupiter's satellites.* In this work he maintains, that all the planets perform their motions round the sun according to a general law; that the satellites of Jupiter and of Saturn move round their primary planets in the same manner as the moon does round the earth, and that they all revolve round the sun, which is the only source of any virtue, and that this virtue attaches them, and unites them so that they cannot recede from their centre of action.†

Our countryman Dr. Robert Hooke seems to have devoted much of his attention to the cause of the planetary motions. On the 21st March, 1666, he read to the Royal Society an account of a series of experiments for determining if bodies experience any variation in their weight at different distances from the centre of the earth. His experiments, as Hooke himself saw, were by no means satisfactory, and hence he was led to the ingenious idea of measuring the force of gravity by observing, at different altitudes, the rate of a pendulum clock. About two months afterward, he exhibited to the Society an approximate representation of the forces which retain the planets in their orbits, in the paths described by a circular pendulum impelled with dif-

---

* *Theoricæ Medicearum planetarum ex causis physicis deductæ.* Flor 1666, 4to.

† M. Delambre maintains that these views of Borelli are only those of Kepler slightly modified. Newton and Huygens have attached to them a greater value. The last of these philosophers remarks, "Refert Plutarchus, fuisse jam olim qui putaret ideo manere lunam in orbe suo, quod vis recedendi a terra, ob motum circularem, inhiberetur pari vi gravitatis, qua ad terram accedere conaretur. Idemque ævo nostro, non de luna tantum sed et planetis ceteris statuit Alphonsus Borellus, ut nempe primariis eorum gravitas esset solem versus; lunis vero ad terram, Jovem ac Saturnum quos comitantur."—Huygen, *Cosmotheor*, lib. ii.; *Opera*, t. ii. p. 720.

ferent degrees of force ; but though this experiment illustrated the production of a curvilineal motion, by combining a tangential force with a central power of attraction, yet it was only an illustration, and could not lead to the true cause of the planetary motions. At a later period, however, viz. in 1674, Hooke resumed the subject in a dissertation entitled "An Attempt to prove the Motion of the Earth from Observation," which contains the following remarkable observations upon gravity:—

"I shall hereafter explain a system of the world differing in many particulars from any yet known, answering in all things to the common rules of mechanical motions. This depends upon three suppositions:—first, that all celestial bodies whatsoever have an attraction or gravitating power towards their own centres, whereby they attract, not only their own parts, and keep them from flying from them, as we may observe the earth to do, but that they also do attract all the other celestial bodies that are within the sphere of their activity, and consequently, that not only the sun and moon have an influence upon the body and motion of the earth, and the earth upon them, but that Mercury, Venus, Mars, Jupiter, and Saturn, also, by their attractive powers, have a considerable influence upon its motion, as in the same manner the corresponding attractive power of the earth hath a considerable influence upon every one of their motions also. The second supposition is this, that all bodies whatsoever that are put into a direct and simple motion will so continue to move forward in a straight line, till they are, by some other effectual powers, deflected, and sent into a motion describing a circle, ellipsis, or some other more compounded curve line. The third supposition is, that those attractive powers are so much the more powerful in operating by how much the nearer the body wrought upon is to their own centres. *Now, what these several degrees are I have not yet experimentally verified;* but it is a notion which, if fully prosecuted, as it ought to be, will mightily assist the astronomers to reduce all the celestial motions to a certain rule, which I doubt will never be done without it. He that understands the nature of the circular pendulum and circular motion will easily understand the whole of this principle, and will know where to find directions in nature for the true stating thereof. This I only hint at present to such as have ability and opportunity of prosecuting this inquiry, and are not wanting of industry for observing and calculating, wishing heartily such may be found, having myself many other things in hand, which I would first complete, and therefore cannot so well attend it. But this I do not promise the undertaker, that he will find all the great motions of the world to be influenced by this principle, and that the true understanding thereof will be the true perfection of astronomy."

This passage, which has been considered as a remarkable one by the philosophers of every country, has, we think, been misapprehended by M. Delambre, when he asserts that every thing which it contains "is to be found expressly in Kepler."*

* *Hist. de l'Astronomie aux Dix-huitieme Siècle,* p. 9.

CHAPTER XI.

*The first Idea of Gravity occurs to Newton in 1666—His first Specu-
lations upon it—Interrupted by his Optical Experiments—He resumes the Subject in consequence of a Discussion with Dr. Hooke—
He discovers the true Law of Gravity and the Cause of the Planetary
Motions—Dr. Halley urges him to publish his Principia—His Principles of Natural Philosophy—Proceedings of the Royal Society on
this Subject—The Principia appears in 1687—General Account of it,
and of the Discoveries it contains—They meet with great Opposition,
owing to the Prevalence of the Cartesian System—Account of the Reception and Progress of the Newtonian Philosophy in foreign Countries—Account of its Progress and Establishment in England.*

SUCH is a brief sketch of the labours and lives of
those illustrious men who prepared the science of
astronomy for the application of Newton's genius.
Copernicus had determined the arrangement and
general movements of the planetary bodies: Kepler
had proved that they moved in elliptical orbits;
that their *radii vectores* described arcs proportional
to the times; and that their periodic times were
related to their distances. Galileo had added to the
universe a whole system of secondary planets; and
several astronomers had distinctly referred the motion of the heavenly bodies to the power of attraction.

In the year 1666, when the plague had driven
Newton from Cambridge, he was sitting alone in
the garden at Woolsthorpe, and reflecting on the
nature of gravity,—that remarkable power which
causes all bodies to descend towards the centre of
the earth. As this power is not found to suffer any
sensible diminution at the greatest distance from
the earth's centre to which we can reach, being as
powerful at the tops of the highest mountains as at
the bottom of the deepest mines, he conceived it
highly probable, that it must extend much farther
than was usually supposed. No sooner had this

happy conjecture occurred to his mind, than he considered what would be the effect of its extending as far as the moon. That her motion must be influenced by such a power he did not for a moment doubt; and a little reflection convinced him that it might be sufficient for retaining that luminary in her orbit round the earth. Though the force of gravity suffers no sensible diminution at those small distances from the earth's centre at which we can place ourselves, yet he thought it very possible, that, at the distance of the moon, it might differ much in strength from what it is on the earth. In order to form some estimate of the degree of its diminution, he considered that, if the moon be retained in her orbit by the force of gravity, the primary planets must also be carried round the sun by the same power; and by comparing the periods of the different planets with their distances from the sun, he found, that if they were retained in their orbits by any power like gravity, its force must decrease in the duplicate proportion,* or as the squares of their distances from the sun. In drawing this conclusion, he supposed the planets to move in orbits perfectly circular, and having the sun in their centre. Having thus obtained the law of the force by which the planets were drawn to the sun, his next object was to ascertain if such a force, emanating from the earth and directed to the moon, was sufficient, when diminished in the duplicate ratio of the distance, to retain her in her orbit. In performing this calculation, it was necessary to compare the space through which heavy bodies fall in a second at a given distance from the centre of the earth, viz. at its surface, with the space through which the moon, as it were, falls to the earth in a second of time while revolving in a circular orbit. Being at

---

* "But for the duplicate proportion, I gathered it from Kepler's theorem about twenty years ago."—Newton's *Letter to Halley*, July 14, 1686.

a distance from books when he made this computation, he adopted the common estimate of the earth's diameter then in use among geographers and navigators, and supposed that each degree of latitude contained sixty English miles. In this way he found that the force which retains the moon in her orbit, as deduced from the force which occasions the fall of heavy bodies to the earth's surface, was *one-sixth* greater than that which is actually observed in her circular orbit. This difference threw a doubt upon all his speculations; but, unwilling to abandon what seemed to be otherwise so plausible, he endeavoured to account for the difference of the two forces, by supposing that some other cause* must have been united with the force of gravity in producing so great a velocity of the moon in her circular orbit. As this new cause, however, was beyond the reach of observation, he discontinued all further inquiries into the subject, and concealed from his friends the speculations in which he had been employed.

After his return to Cambridge in 1666, his attention was occupied with those optical discoveries of which we have given an account in a preceding chapter; but he had no sooner brought them to a close than his mind reverted to the great subject of the planetary motions. Upon the death of Oldenburg in August, 1678, Dr. Hooke was appointed secretary to the Royal Society; and as this learned body had requested the opinion of Newton about a system of physical astronomy, he addressed a letter to Dr. Hooke on the 28th November, 1679. In this letter he proposed a direct experiment for verifying the motion of the earth, viz. by observing whether or not bodies that fall from a considerable height descend in a vertical direction, for if the earth were at rest the body would describe exactly a vertical

* Whiston asserts that this cause was supposed by Newton to be something analogous to the vortices of Descartes.—See Whiston's *Memoirs of himself*, p. 231.

line, whereas if it revolved round its axis, the falling body must deviate from the vertical line towards the east. The Royal Society attached great value to the idea thus casually suggested, and Dr. Hooke was appointed to put it to the test of experiment. Being thus led to consider the subject more attentively, he wrote to Newton, that wherever the direction of gravity was oblique to the axis on which the earth revolved, that is, in every part of the earth except the equator, falling bodies should approach to the equator, and the deviation from the vertical, in place of being exactly to the east, as Newton maintained, should be to the south-east of the point from which the body began to move. Newton acknowledged that this conclusion was correct in theory, and Dr. Hooke is said to have given an experimental demonstration of it before the Royal Society in December, 1679.* Newton had erroneously concluded that the path of the falling body would be a spiral; but Dr. Hooke, on the same occasion on which he made the preceding experiment, read a paper to the Society, in which he proved that the path of the body would be an eccentric ellipse in vacuo, and an ellipti-spiral, if the body moved in a resisting medium.†

This correction of Newton's error, and the discovery that a projectile would move in an elliptical orbit when under the influence of a force varying in the inverse ratio of the square of the distance, led Newton, as he himself informs us in his letter to Halley,‡ to discover "the theorem by which he afterward examined the ellipsis," and to demonstrate the celebrated proposition, that a planet acted upon by an attractive force varying inversely as the squares of the distances will describe an elliptical orbit, in one of whose foci the attractive force resides.

* Waller's *Life of Hooke*, p. 22. † Ibid.
‡ July 27, 1686, *Biog. Brit.* p. 2662.

But though Newton had thus discovered the true cause of all the celestial motions, he did not yet possess any evidence that such a force actually resided in the sun and planets. The failure of his former attempt to identify the law of falling bodies at the earth's surface with that which guided the moon in her orbit threw a doubt over all his speculations, and prevented him from giving any account of them to the public.

An accident, however, of a very interesting nature induced him to resume his former inquiries, and enabled him to bring them to a close. In June, 1682, when he was attending a meeting of the Royal Society of London, the measurement of a degree of the meridian, executed by M. Picard in 1679, became the subject of conversation. Newton took a memorandum of the result obtained by the French astronomer, and having deduced from it the diameter of the earth, he immediately resumed his calculation of 1665, and began to repeat it with these new data. In the progress of the calculation he saw that the result which he had formerly expected was likely to be produced, and he was thrown into such a state of nervous irritability that he was unable to carry on the calculation. In this state of mind he intrusted it to one of his friends, and he had the high satisfaction of finding his former views amply realized. The force of gravity which regulated the fall of bodies at the earth's surface, when diminished as the square of the moon's distance from the earth, was found to be almost exactly equal to the centrifugal force of the moon as deduced from her observed distance and velocity.

The influence of such a result upon such a mind may be more easily conceived than described. The whole material universe was spread out before him; —the sun with all his attending planets;—the planets with all their satellites;—the comets wheeling in every direction in their eccentric orbits;—and the systems of the fixed stars stretching to the remotest limits of space. All the varied and complicated movements of the heavens, in short, must have been at once presented to his mind, as the necessary result of that law which he had established in reference to the earth and the moon.

After extending this law to the other bodies of the system, he composed a series of propositions on the motion of the primary planets about the sun, which were sent to London about the end of 1683, and were soon afterward communicated to the Royal Society.*

About this period other philosophers had been occupied with the same subject. Sir Christopher Wren had many years before endeavoured to explain the planetary motions "by the composition of a descent towards the sun, and an impressed motion; but he at length gave it over, not finding the means of doing it." In January, 1683–4, Dr. Halley had concluded, from Kepler's Law of the Periods and Distances, that the centripetal force decreased in the reciprocal proportion of the squares of the distances, and having one day met Sir Christopher Wren and Dr. Hooke, the latter affirmed that he had demonstrated upon that principle all the laws of the celestial motions. Dr. Halley confessed that his attempts were unsuccessful, and Sir Christopher, in order to encourage the inquiry, offered to present a book of forty shillings' value to either of the two philosophers who should, in the space of two months, bring him a convincing demonstration of it. Hooke persisted in the declaration that he possessed the method, but avowed it to be his intention to conceal it for some time. He promised, however, to show it to Sir Christopher; but there is every reason to believe that this promise was never fulfilled.

In August, 1684, Dr. Halley went to Cambridge

* *Commercium Epistolicum*, No. 7

N

for the express purpose of consulting Newton on this interesting subject. Newton assured him that he had brought this demonstration to perfection, and promised him a copy of it. This copy was received in November by the doctor, who made a second visit to Cambridge, in order to induce its author to have it inserted in the register book of the society. On the 10th of December, Dr. Halley announced to the society, that he had seen at Cambridge Mr. Newton's treatise *De Motu Corporum*, which he had promised to send to the society to be entered upon their register; and Dr. Halley was desired to unite with Mr. Paget, master of the mathematical school in Christ's Hospital, in reminding Mr. Newton of his promise "for securing the invention to himself till such time as he can be at leisure to publish it." On the 25th February Mr. Aston, the secretary, communicated a letter from Mr. Newton, in which he expressed his willingness " to enter in the register his notions about motion, and his intentions to fit them suddenly for the press." The progress of his work was, however, interrupted by a visit of five or six weeks which he made in Lincolnshire; but he proceeded with such diligence on his return, that he was able to transmit the manuscript to London before the end of April. This manuscript, entitled *Philosophiæ Naturalis Principia Mathematica*, and dedicated to the society, was presented by Dr. Vincent on the 28th April, 1686, when Sir John Hoskins, the vice-president, and the particular friend of Dr. Hooke, was in the chair. Dr. Vincent passed a just encomium on the novelty and dignity of the subject; and another member added, that " Mr. Newton had carried the thing so far, that there was no more to be added." To these remarks the vice-president replied, that the method " was so much the more to be prized as it was both invented and perfected at the same time." Dr. Hooke took offence at these remarks, and blamed Sir John for not having mentioned " what he had discovered to him ;" but the vice-president did not seem to recollect any such communication, and the consequence of this discussion was, that " these two, who till then were the most inseparable cronies, have since scarcely seen one another, and are utterly fallen out." After the breaking up of the meeting, the society adjourned to the coffee-house, where Dr. Hooke stated that he not only had made the same discovery, but had given the first hint of it to Newton.

An account of these proceedings was communicated to Newton through two different channels. In a letter dated May 22d, Dr. Halley wrote to him " that Mr. Hooke has some pretensions upon the invention of the rule of the decrease of gravity being reciprocally as the squares of the distances from the centre. He says you had the notion from him, though he owns the demonstration of the curves generated thereby to be wholly your own. How much of this is so you know best, as likewise what you have to do in this matter. Only Mr. Hooke seems to expect you would make some mention of him in the preface, which it is possible you may see reason to prefix."

This communication from Dr. Halley induced our author, on the 20th June, to address a long letter to him, in which he gives a minute and able refutation of Hooke's claims; but before this letter was despatched, another correspondent, who had received his information from one of the members that were present, informed Newton " that Hooke made a great stir, pretending that he had all from him, and desiring they would see that he had justice done him." This fresh charge seems to have ruffled the tranquillity of Newton ; and he accordingly added an angry and satirical postscript, in which he treats Hooke with little ceremony, and goes so far as to conjecture that Hooke might have acquired his knowledge of the law from a letter of his own to Huygens, directed to Oldenburg, and dated January 14th, 1672–3. "My letter to Hugenius was directed to Mr. Oldenburg, who used to keep the originals. His papers came into Mr. Hooke's possession. Mr. Hooke, knowing my hand, might have the curiosity to look into that letter, and there take the notion of comparing the forces of the planets arising from their circular motion; and so what he wrote to me afterward about the rate of gravity might be nothing but the fruit of my own garden."

In replying to this letter, Dr. Halley assured him that Hooke's "manner of claiming the discovery had been represented to him in worse colours than it ought, and that he neither made public application to the society for justice, nor pretended that you had all from him." The effect of this assurance was to make Newton regret that he had written the angry postscript to his letter; and in replying to Halley on the 14th July, 1686, he not only expresses his regret, but recounts the different new ideas which he had acquired from Hooke's correspondence, and suggests it as the best method " of compromising the present dispute," to add a scholium, in which Wren, Hooke, and Halley are acknowledged to have independently deduced the law of gravity from the second law of Kepler.*

At the meeting of the 28th April, at which the manuscript of the *Principia* was presented to the Royal Society, it was agreed that the printing of it should be referred to the council; that a letter of thanks should be written to its author; and at a meeting of the council on the 19th May, it was resolved that the MSS. should be printed at the society's expense, and that Dr. Halley should superintend it while going through the press. These resolutions were communicated by Dr. Halley in a letter dated the 22d May; and in Newton's reply on the 20th June already mentioned, he makes the fol-

* This Scholium is added to Prop. iv. lib. i, coroll. 6.

lowing observations: "The proof you sent me I like very well. I designed the whole to consist of three books; the second was finished last summer, being short, and only wants transcribing, and drawing the cuts fairly. Some new propositions I have since thought on, which I can as well let alone. The third wants the theory of comets. In autumn last I spent two months in calculation to no purpose for want of a good method, which made me afterward return to the first book, and enlarge it with diverse propositions, some relating to comets, others to other things found out last winter. The third I now design to suppress. Philosophy is such an impertinently litigious lady, that a man had as good be engaged in lawsuits as have to do with her. I found it so formerly, and now I can no sooner come near her again but she gives me warning. The first two books without the third will not so well bear the title of *Philosophiæ Naturalis Principia Mathematica*; and therefore I had altered it to this, *De Motu Corporum Libri duo.* But after second thoughts I retain the former title. It will help the sale of the book, which I ought not to diminish now 'tis yours."

In replying to this letter on the 29th June, Dr. Halley regrets that our author's tranquillity should have been thus disturbed by envious rivals; and implores him in the name of the society not to suppress the third book. "I must again beg you," says he, "not to let your resentments run so high as to deprive us of your third book, wherein your applications of your mathematical doctrine to the theory of comets, and several curious experiments, which, as I guess by what you write ought to compose it, will undoubtedly render it acceptable to those who will call themselves philosophers without mathematics, which are much the greater number."

To these solicitations Newton seems to have readily yielded. His second book was sent to the society, and presented on the 2d March, 1686–7.

The third book was also transmitted, and presented on the 6th April, and the whole work was completed and published in the month of May, 1687.

Such is a brief account of the publication of a work which is memorable, not only in the annals of one science or of one country, but which will form an epoch in the history of the world, and will ever be regarded as the brightest page in the records of human reason. We shall endeavour to convey to the reader some idea of its contents, and of the brilliant discoveries which it disseminated over Europe.

The *Principia* consists of three books. The first and second, which occupy three-fourths of the work, are entitled, *On the Motion of Bodies*; and the third bears the title, *On the System of the World*. The first two books contain the mathematical principles of philosophy, namely, the laws and conditions of motions and forces; and they are illustrated with several philosophical scholia, which treat of some of the most general and best established points in philosophy, such as the density and resistance of bodies, spaces void of matter, and the motion of sound and light. The object of the third book is to deduce from these principles the constitution of the system of the world; and this book has been drawn up in as popular a style as possible, in order that it may be generally read.

The great discovery which characterizes the Principia is that of the principle of universal gravitation, as deduced from the motion of the moon, and from the three great facts or laws discovered by Kepler. This principle is, *that every particle of matter is attracted by, or gravitates to, every other particle of matter, with a force inversely proportional to the squares of their distances.* From the first law of Kepler, namely, the proportionality of the areas to the times of their description, Newton inferred that the force which kept the planet in its orbit was always directed to the sun; and from the second law of Kepler, that every planet moves in an ellipse with the sun in one of its foci, he drew the still more general inference, that the force by which the planet moves round that focus varies inversely as the square of its distance from the focus. As this law was true in the motion of satellites round their primary planets, Newton deduced the equality of gravity in all the heavenly bodies towards the sun, upon the supposition that they are equally distant from its centre; and in the case of terrestrial bodies, he succeeded in verifying this truth by numerous and accurate experiments.

By taking a more general view of the subject, Newton demonstrated that a conic section was the only curve in which a body could move when acted upon by a force varying inversely as the square of the distance; and he established the conditions depending on the velocity and the primitive position of the body, which were requisite to make it describe a circular, an elliptical, a parabolic, or a hyperbolic orbit.

Notwithstanding the generality and importance of these results, it still remained to be determined whether the force resided in the centres of the planets, or belonged to each individual particle of which they were composed. Newton removed this uncertainty by demonstrating, that if a spherical body acts upon a distant body with a force varying as the distance of this body from the centre of the sphere, the same effect will be produced as if each of its particles acted upon the distant body according to the same law. And hence it follows that the spheres, whether they are of uniform density, or consist of concentric layers, with densities varying according to any law whatever, will act upon each other in the same manner as if their force resided in their centres alone. But as the bodies of the solar system are very nearly spherical, they will all act upon one another, and upon bodies placed on their surface, as if they were so many centres of attraction; and therefore we obtain the law of gravity which subsists between spherical bodies, namely, that one sphere will act upon another with a force directly proportional to the quantity of matter, and inversely as the square of the distance between the centres of the spheres. From the equality of action and reaction, to which no exception can be found, Newton concluded that the sun gravitated to the planets, and the planets to their satellites; and the earth itself to the stone which falls upon its surface; and, consequently, that the two mutually gravitating bodies approached to one another with velocities inversely proportional to their quantities of matter.

Having established this universal law, Newton was enabled, not only to determine the weight which the same body would have at the surface of the sun and the planets, but even to calculate the quantity of matter in the sun, and in all the planets that had satellites, and even to determine the density or specific gravity of the matter of which they were composed. In this way he found that the weight of the same body would be twenty-three times greater at the surface of the sun than at the surface of the earth, and that the density of the earth was four times greater than that of the sun, the planets increasing in density as they receded from the centre of the system.

If the peculiar genius of Newton has been displayed in his investigation of the law of universal gravitation, it shines with no less lustre in the patience and sagacity with which he traced the consequences of this fertile principle.

The discovery of the spheroidal form of Jupiter by Cassini had probably directed the attention of Newton to the determination of its cause, and consequently to the investigation of the true figure of the earth. The spherical form of the planets have been ascribed by Copernicus to the gravity or natural appetency of their parts; but upon considering the earth as a body revolving upon its axis, Newton quickly saw that the figure arising from the mutual attraction of its parts must be modified by another force arising from its rotation. When a body revolves upon an axis, the velocity of rotation increases from the poles, where it is nothing, to the equator, where it is a maximum. In consequence of this velocity the bodies on the earth's surface have a tendency to fly off from it, and this tendency increases with the velocity. Hence arises a centrifugal force which acts in combination with a force of gravity, and which Newton found to be the 289th part of the force of gravity at the equator, and decreasing, as the cosine of the latitude, from the equator to the poles. The great predominance of gravity over the centrifugal force prevents the latter from carrying off any bodies from the earth's surface, but the weight of all bodies is diminished by the centrifugal force, so that the weight of any body is greater at the poles than it is at the equator. If we now suppose the waters at the pole to communicate with those at the equator by means of a canal, one branch of which goes from the pole to the centre of the earth, and the other from the centre of the earth to the equator, then the polar branch of the canal will be heavier than the equatorial branch, in consequence of its weight not being diminished by the centrifugal force, and, therefore, in order that the two columns may be in equilibrio, the equatorial one must be lengthened. Newton found that the length of the polar must be to that of the equatorial canal as 229 to 230, or that the earth's polar radius must be seventeen miles less than its equatorial radius; that is, that the figure of the earth is an oblate spheroid, formed by the revolution of an ellipse round its lesser axis. Hence it follows, that the intensity of gravity at any point of the earth's surface is in the inverse ratio of the distance of that point from the centre, and, consequently, that it diminishes from the equator to the poles,—a result which he confirmed by the fact, that clocks required to have their pendulums shortened in order to beat true time when carried from Europe towards the equator.

The next subject to which Newton applied the principle of gravity was the tides of the ocean. The philosophers of all ages have recognised the connexion between the phenomena of the tides and the position of the moon. The College of Jesuits at Coimbra, and subsequently Antonio de Dominis and Kepler, distinctly referred the tides to the attraction of the waters of the earth by the moon, but so imperfect was the explanation which was thus given of the phenomena, that Galileo ridiculed the idea of lunar attraction, and substituted for it a fallacious explanation of his own. That the moon is the principal cause of the tides is obvious from the well-known fact, that it is high water at any given place about the time when she is in the meridian of that place; and that the sun performs a secondary part in their production may be proved from the circumstance, that the highest tides take place when the sun, the moon, and the earth are in the same straight line, that is, when the force of the sun conspires with that of the moon, and that the lowest tides take place when the lines drawn from the sun and moon to the earth are at right angles to each other, that is, when the force of the sun acts in opposition to that of the moon. The most perplexing phenomenon in the tides of the ocean, and one which is still a stumbling-block to persons slightly acquainted with the theory of attraction, is the existence of high water on the side of the earth opposite to the moon, as well as on the side next the moon. To maintain that the attraction of the moon at the same instant draws the waters of the ocean towards herself, and also draws them from the earth in an opposite direction, seems at first sight paradoxical; but the difficulty vanishes when we consider the earth, or rather the centre of the earth, and the water on each side of it as three distinct bodies placed at different distances from the moon, and consequently attracted with forces inversely proportional to the squares of their distances. The water nearest the moon will be much more powerfully attracted than the centre of the earth, and the centre of the earth more powerfully than the water farthest from the moon. The consequence of this must be, that the waters nearest the moon will be drawn away from the centre of the earth, and will consequently rise from their level, while the centre of the earth will be drawn away from the waters opposite the moon, which will, as it were, be left behind, and consequently be in the same situation as if they were raised from the earth in a direction opposite to that in which they are attracted by the moon. Hence the effect of the moon's action upon the earth is to draw its fluid parts into the form of an oblong spheroid, the axis of which passes through the moon. As the action of the sun will produce the very same effect, though in a smaller degree, the tide at any place will depend on the relative position of these two spheroids, and will be always equal either to the sum or to the difference of the effects of the two luminaries. At the time of new and full moon the two spheroids will have their axes coincident, and the height of the tide, which will then be a *spring* one, will be equal to the sum of the elevations produced in each spheroid considered separately, while at the first and third quarters the axes of the spheroids will be at right angles to each other, and the height of the tide, which will then be a *neap* one, will be equal to the difference of the elevations produced in each separate spheroid. By comparing the spring and neap tides, Newton found that the force with which the sun acted upon the waters of the earth was to that with which the sun acted upon them as 4.48 to 1;—that the force of the moon produced a tide of 8.63 feet;—that of the sun one of 1.93 feet;—and both of them combined, one of 10½ French feet,—a result which in the open sea does not deviate much from observation. Having thus ascertained the force of the moon on the waters of our globe, he found that the quantity of matter in the moon was to that in the earth as 1 to 40, and the density of the moon to that of the earth as 11 to 9.

The motions of the moon, so much within the reach of our own observation, presented a fine field for the application of the theory of universal gravitation. The irregularities exhibited in the lunar motions had been known in the time of Hipparchus and Ptolemy. Tycho had discovered the great inequality called the *variation*, amounting to 37', and depending on the alternate acceleration and retardation of the moon in every quarter of a revolution, and he had also ascertained the existence of the annual equation. Of these two inequalities Newton gave a most satisfactory explanation. The action of the sun upon the moon may be always resolved into two, one acting in the direction of the line joining the moon and earth, and consequently tending to increase or diminish the moon's gravity to the earth, and the other in a direction at right angles to this, and consequently tending to accelerate or retard the motion in her orbit. Now, it was found by Newton that this last force was reduced to nothing, or vanished at the syzigies or quadratures, so that at these four points the moon described areas proportional to the times. The instant, however, that the moon quits these positions, the force under consideration, which we may call the tangential force, begins, and it reaches its maximum in the four octants. The force, therefore, compounded of these two elements of the solar force, or the diagonal of the parallelogram which they form, is no longer directed to the earth's centre, but deviates from it at a maximum about 30 minutes, and therefore affects the angular motion of the moon, the motion being accelerated in passing from the quadratures to the syzigies, and retarded in passing from the syzigies to the quadratures. Hence the velocity is in its mean state in the octants, a maximum in the syzigies, and a minimum in the quadratures.

Upon considering the influence of the solar force in diminishing or increasing the moon's gravity to the earth, Newton saw that her distance and her periodic time must from this cause be subject to change, and in this way he accounted for the annual equation observed by Tycho. By the application of similar principles, he explained the cause of the motion of the apsides, or of the greater axis of the moon's orbit, which has an angular progressive motion of 3° 4' nearly in the course of one lunation; and he showed that the retrogradation of the nodes, amounting to 3' 10" daily, arose from one of the elements of the solar force being exerted in the plane of the ecliptic, and not in the plane of the moon's orbit, the effect of which was to draw the moon down to the plane of the ecliptic, and thus cause the line of the nodes, or the intersection of these two planes, to move in a direction opposite to that of the moon. The lunar theory thus blocked out by Newton, required for its completion the labours of another century. The imperfections of the fluxionary calculus prevented him from explaining the other inequalities of the moon's motions, and it was reserved to Euler, D'Alembert, Clairaut, Mayer, and Laplace to bring the lunar tables to a high degree of perfection, and to enable the navigator to determine his longitude at sea with a degree of precision which the most sanguine astronomer could scarcely have anticipated.

By the consideration of the retrograde motion of

O

the moon's nodes, Newton was led to discover the
cause of the remarkable phenomenon of the precession of the equinoctial points, which moved 50″ annually, and completed the circuit of the heavens in
25,920 years. Kepler had declared himself incapable of assigning any cause for this motion, and we
do not believe that any other astronomer ever made
the attempt. From the spheroidal form of the earth,
it may be regarded as a sphere with a spheroidal
ring surrounding its equator, one-half of the ring
being above the plane of the ecliptic and the other
half below it. Considering this excess of matter
as a system of satellites adhering to the earth's surface, Newton saw that the combined actions of the
sun and moon upon these satellites tended to produce a retrogradation in the nodes of the circles
which they described in their diurnal rotation, and
that the sum of all the tendencies being communicated to the whole mass of the planet, ought to produce a slow retrogradation of the equinoctial points.
The effect produced by the motion of the sun he
found to be 40″, and that produced by the action of
the moon 10″.

Although there could be little doubt that the
comets were retained in their orbits by the same
laws which regulated the motions of the planets,
yet it was difficult to put this opinion to the test of
observation. The visibility of comets only in a
small part of their orbits rendered it difficult to ascertain their distance and periodic times, and as their
periods were probably of great length, it was impossible to correct approximate results by repeated observation. Newton, however, removed this difficulty, by showing how to determine the orbit of a
comet, namely, the form and position of the orbit
and the periodic time, by three observations. By
applying this method to the comet of 1680, he calculated the elements of its orbit, and from the agree-
ment of the computed places with those which

were observed, he justly inferred that the motions of comets were regulated by the same laws as those of the planetary bodies. This result was one of great importance; for as the comets enter our system in every possible direction, and at all angles with the ecliptic, and as a great part of their orbits extend far beyond the limits of the solar system, it demonstrated the existence of gravity in spaces far removed beyond the planet, and proved that the law of the inverse ratio of the squares of the distance was true in every possible direction, and at very remote distances from the centre of our system.*

Such is a brief view of the leading discoveries which the *Principia* first announced to the world. The grandeur of the subjects of which it treats, the beautiful simplicity of the system which it unfolds, the clear and concise reasoning by which that system is explained, and the irresistible evidence by which it is supported might have ensured it the warmest admiration of contemporary mathematicians, and the most welcome reception in all the schools of philosophy throughout Europe. This, however, is not the way in which great truths are generally received. Though the astronomical discoveries of Newton were not assailed by the class of ignorant pretenders who attacked his optical writings, yet they were every where resisted by the errors and prejudices which had taken a deep hold even of the strongest minds. The philosophy of Descartes was predominant throughout Europe. Appealing to the imagination, and not to the reason of mankind, it was quickly received into popular favour, and the same causes which facilitated its introduction extended its influence, and completed its dominion over the human mind. In explaining all the movements of the heavenly bodies by a system

* In writing to Flamstead, Newton requests from him the long diameters of the orbits of Jupiter and Saturn, that he "*may see how the sesquialteral proportion fills the heavens.*"

of vortices in a fluid medium diffused through the universe, Descartes had seized upon an analogy of the most alluring and deceitful kind. Those who had seen heavy bodies revolving in the eddies of a whirlpool, or in the gyrations of a vessel of water thrown into a circular motion, had no difficulty in conceiving how the planets might revolve round the sun by analogous movements. The mind instantly grasped at an explanation of so palpable a character, and which required for its development neither the exercise of patient thought nor the aid of mathematical skill. The talent and perspicuity with which the Cartesian system was expounded, and the show of experiments with which it was sustained, contributed powerfully to its adoption, while it derived a still higher sanction from the excellent character and the unaffected piety of its author.

Thus intrenched, as the Cartesian system was, in the strongholds of the human mind, and fortified by its most obstinate prejudices, it was not to be wondered at that the pure and sublime doctrines of the Principia were distrustfully received and perseveringly resisted. The uninstructed mind could not readily admit the idea, that the great masses of the planets were suspended in empty space, and retained in their orbits by an invisible influence residing in the sun; and even those philosophers who had been accustomed to the rigour of true scientific research, and who possessed sufficient mathematical skill for the examination of the Newtonian doctrines, viewed them at first as reviving the occult qualities of the ancient physics, and resisted their introduction with a pertinacity which it is not easy to explain. Prejudiced, no doubt, in favour of his own metaphysical views, Leibnitz himself misapprehended the principles of the Newtonian philosophy, and endeavoured to demonstrate the truths in the Principia by the application of different principles. Huygens, who above all other men was qualified to appreciate the new philosophy, rejected the doctrine of gravitation as existing between the individual particles of matter, and received it only as an attribute of the planetary masses. John Bernouilli, one of the first mathematicians of his age, opposed the philosophy of Newton. Mairan, in the early part of his life, was a strenuous defender of the system of vortices. Cassini and Maraldi were quite ignorant of the Principia, and occupied themselves with the most absurd methods of calculating the orbits of comets long after the Newtonian method had been established on the most impregnable foundation; and even Fontenelle, a man of liberal views and extensive information, continued, throughout the whole of his life, to maintain the doctrines of Descartes.

The Chevalier Louville of Paris had adopted the Newtonian philosophy before 1720. S'Gravesande had introduced it into the Dutch universities at a somewhat earlier period, and Maupertuis, in consequence of a visit which he paid to England in 1728, became a zealous defender of it; but notwithstanding these and some other examples that might be quoted, we must admit the truth of the remark of Voltaire, that though Newton survived the publication of the Principia more than forty years, yet at the time of his death he had not above *twenty* followers out of England.

With regard to the progress of the Newtonian philosophy in England, some difference of opinion has been entertained. Professor Playfair gives the following account of it. "In the universities of England, though the Aristotelian physics had made an obstinate resistance, they had been supplanted by the Cartesian, which became firmly established about the time when their foundation began to be sapped by the general progress of science, and particularly by the discoveries of Newton. For more than thirty years after the publication of these discoveries, the system of vortices kept its ground; and

O 2

a translation from the French into Latin of the *Physics* of Rohault, a work entirely Cartesian, continued at Cambridge to be the text for philosophical instruction. About the year 1718, a new and more elegant translation of the same book was published by Dr. Samuel Clarke, with the addition of notes, in which that profound and ingenious writer explained the views of Newton on the principal objects of discussion, so that the notes contained virtually a refutation of the text; they did so, however, only virtually, all appearance of argument and controversy being carefully avoided. Whether this escaped the notice of the learned doctor or not is uncertain, but the new translation, from its better Latinity, and the name of the editor, was readily admitted to all the academical honours which the old one had enjoyed. Thus the stratagem of Dr. Clarke completely succeeded; the tutor might prelect from the text, but the pupil would sometimes look into the notes; and error is never so sure of being exposed as when the truth is placed close to it, side by side, without any thing to alarm prejudice, or awaken from its lethargy the dread of innovation. Thus, therefore, the Newtonian philosophy first entered the university of Cambridge under the protection of the Cartesian." To this passage Professor Playfair adds the following as a note :—

"The universities of St. Andrew's and Edinburgh were, I believe, the first in Britain where the Newtonian philosophy was made the subject of the academical prelections. For this distinction they are indebted to James and David Gregory, the first in some respects the rival, but both the friends of Newton. Whiston bewails, in the anguish of his heart, the difference, in this respect, between those universities and his own. David Gregory taught in Edinburgh for several years prior to 1690, when he removed to Oxford; and Whiston says, 'He had already caused several of his scholars to keep acts, as we call them, upon several branches of the Newtonian philosophy, while we at Cambridge, poor wretches, were ignominiously studying the fictitious hypotheses of the Cartesians."* I do not, however, mean to say, that from this date the Cartesian philosophy was expelled from those universities; the *Physics* of Rohault were still in use as a text-book,—at least occasionally, to a much later period than this, and a great deal, no doubt, depended on the character of the individual. Professor Keill introduced the Newtonian philosophy in his lectures at Oxford in 1697; but the instructions of the tutors, which constitute the real and efficient system of the university, were not cast in that mould till long afterward." Adopting the same view of the subject, Mr. Dugald Stewart has stated, "that the philosophy of Newton was publicly taught by David Gregory at Edinburgh, and by his brother, James Gregory, at St. Andrew's,† before it was able to supplant the vortices of Descartes in that very university of which Newton was a member. It was in the Scottish universities that the philosophy of Locke, as well as that of Newton, was first adopted as a branch of academical education."

Anxious as we should have been to have awarded to Scotland the honour of having first adopted the Newtonian philosophy, yet a regard for historical truth compels us to take a different view of the subject. It is well known that Sir Isaac Newton delivered lectures on his own philosophy from the Lucasian chair before the publication of the Principia; and in the very page of Whiston's life quoted by Professor Playfair, he informs us that he had heard him read such lectures in the public schools,

---

* Whiston's *Memoirs of his own Life.*

† "Dr. Reid states, that James Gregory, Professor of Philosophy at St. Andrew's, printed a thesis at Edinburgh in 1690, containing twenty-five positions, of which twenty-two were a compend of Newton's Principia."

though at that time he did not at all understand
them. Newton continued to lecture till 1699, and
occasionally, we presume, till 1703, when Whiston
became his successor, having been appointed his
deputy in 1699. In both of these capacities Whiston delivered in the public schools a course of lectures on astronomy, and a course of physico-mathe-
matical lectures, in which the mathematical philosophy of Newton was explained and demonstrated,
and both these courses were published, the one in
1707, and the other in 1710, " for the use of the
young men in the university." In 1707, the celebrated blind mathematician Nicholas Saunderson
took up his residence in Christ's College without
being admitted a member of that body. The society
not only allotted to him apartments, but gave him
the free use of their library. With the concurrence
of Whiston he delivered a course of lectures " on
the Principia, Optics, and Universal Arithmetic of
Newton," and the popularity of these lectures was
so great, that Sir Isaac corresponded on the subject
of them with their author; and on the ejection of
Whiston from the Lucasian chair in 1711, Saunderson
was appointed his successor. In this important office
he continued to teach the Newtonian philosophy till
the time of his death, which took place in 1739.

But while the Newtonian philosophy was thus
regularly taught in Cambridge, after the publication
of the Principia, there were not wanting other exertions for accelerating its progress. About 1694, the
celebrated Dr. Samuel Clarke, while an under-grad-
uate, defended, in the public schools, a question taken
from the Newtonian philosophy; and his translation
of Rohault's Physics, which contains references in
the notes to the Principia, and which was published
in 1697 (and not in 1718, as stated by Professor
Playfair), shows how early the Cartesian system
was attacked by the disciples of Newton. The
author of the Life of Saunderson informs us, that

public exercises or acts founded on every part of the Newtonian system were very common about 1707, and so general were such studies in the university, that the Principia rose to four times its original price.* One of the most ardent votaries of the Newtonian. philosophy was Dr. Laughton, who had been tutor in Clare Hall from 1694, and it is probable that during the whole, or at least a greater part, of his tutorship he had inculcated the same doctrines. In 1709–10, when he was proctor of that college, instead of appointing a moderator, he discharged the office himself, and devoted his most active exertions to the promotion of mathematical knowledge. Previous to this, he had even published a paper of questions on the Newtonian philosophy, which appear to have been used as theses for disputations; and such was his ardour and learning that they powerfully contributed to the popularity of his college. Between 1706 and 1716, the year of his death, the celebrated Roger Cotes, the friend and disciple of Newton, filled the Plumian chair of astronomy and experimental philosophy at Cambridge. During this period he edited the second edition of the Principia, which he enriched with an admirable preface, and thus contributed, by his writings as well as by his lectures, to advance the philosophy of his master. About the same time, the learned Dr. Bentley, who first made known the philosophy of his friend to the readers of general literature, filled the high office of master of Trinity College, and could not fail to have exerted his utmost influence in propagating doctrines which he so greatly admired. Had any opposition been offered to the introduction of the true system of the universe, the talents and influence of these individuals would have immediately suppressed it; but no such opposition seems to have been made;

* Nichols's Literary Anecdotes, vol. iii. p. 322. Cotes states in his preface to the second edition of the Principia, that copies of the first edition could only be obtained at an immense price.

and though there may have been individuals at Cambridge ignorant of mathematical science, who adhered to the system of Descartes, and patronised the study of the Physics of Rohault, yet it is probable that similar persons existed in the universities of Edinburgh and St. Andrew's; and we cannot regard their adherence to error as disproving the general fact, that the philosophy of Newton was quickly introduced into all the universities of Great Britain.

But while the mathematical principles of the Newtonian system were ably expounded in our seats of learning, its physical truths were generally studied, and were explained and communicated to the public by various lecturers on experimental philosophy. The celebrated Locke, who was incapable of understanding the Principia from his want of mathematical knowledge, inquired of Huygens if all the mathematical propositions in that work were true. When he was assured that he might depend upon their certainty, he took them for granted, and carefully examined the reasonings and corollaries deduced from them. In this manner he acquired a knowledge of the physical truths in the Principia, and became a firm believer in the discoveries which it contained. In the same manner he studied the treatise on Optics, and made himself master of every part of it which was not mathematical.* From a manuscript of Sir Isaac Newton's, entitled "A demonstration that the planets, by their gravity towards the sun, may move in ellipses,† found among the papers of Mr. Locke, and published by Lord King," it would appear that he himself had been at considerable trouble in explaining to his friend that interesting doctrine. This manuscript is endorsed, "Mr. Newton, March, 1689." It begins with three hypotheses

---

* Preface to Desaguliers's *Experimental Philosophy*. Dr. Desaguliers states that he was told this anecdote several times by Sir Isaac Newton himself.

† *The Life of John Locke*, p. 209-215, Lond. 1829.

(the first two being the two laws of motion, and the third the parallelogram of motion), which introduce the proposition of the proportionality of the areas to the times in motions round an immoveable centre of attraction.* Three lemmas, containing properties of the ellipse, then prepare the reader for the celebrated proposition, that when a body moves in an ellipse,† the attraction is reciprocally as the square of the distance of the body from the focus to which it is attracted. These propositions are demonstrated in a more popular manner than in the Principia, but there can be no doubt that, even in their present modified form, they were beyond the capacity of Mr. Locke.

Dr. John Keill was the first person who publicly taught natural philosophy by experiments. Desaguliers informs us that this author " laid down very simple propositions, which he proved by experiments, and from these he deduced others more compound, which he still confirmed by experiments, till he had instructed his auditors in the laws of motion, the principles of hydrostatics and optics, and some of the chief propositions of Sir Isaac Newton concerning light and colours. He began these courses in Oxford about the year 1704 or 1705, and in that way introduced the love of the Newtonian philosophy." When Dr. Keill left the university, Desaguliers began to teach the Newtonian philosophy by experiments. He commenced his lectures at Harthall in Oxford, in 1710, and delivered more than a hundred and twenty courses ; and when he went to settle in London in 1713, he informs us that he found " the Newtonian philosophy generally received among persons of all ranks and professions, and even among the ladies by the help of experiments." Such were the steps by which the Newtonian philosophy was established in Great Britain. From

---

* *Principia*, lib. i. prop. i.   † *Ib.* lib. i. prop. xi.

the time of the publication of the Principia, its
mathematical doctrines formed a regular part of academical education; and before twenty years had
elapsed, its physical truths were communicated to
the public in popular lectures illustrated by experiments, and accommodated to the capacities of those
who were not versed in mathematical knowledge.
The Cartesian system, though it may have lingered
for a while in the recesses of our universities, was
soon overturned; and long before his death, Newton
enjoyed the high satisfaction of seeing his philosophy triumphant in his native land.

CHAPTER XII.

*Doctrine of Infinite Quantities—Labours of Pappus—Kepler—Cavaleri
—Roberval—Fermat—Wallis—Newton discovers the Binomial Theorem—and the Doctrine of Fluxions in 1666—His Manuscript Work
containing this Doctrine communicated to his Friends—His Treatise
on Fluxions—His Mathematical Tracts—His Universal Arithmetic—
His Methodus Differentialis—His Geometria Analytica—His Solution of the Problems proposed by Bernouilli aud Leibnitz—Account
of the celebrated Dispute respecting the Invention of Fluxions—Commercium Epistolicum—Report of the Royal Society—General View
of the Controversy.*

PREVIOUS to the time of Newton, the doctrine of
infinite quantities had been the subject of profound
study. The ancients made the first step in this
curious inquiry by a rude though ingenious attempt
to determine the area of curves. The method of
exhaustions which was used for this purpose consisted in finding a given rectilineal area to which the
inscribed and circumscribed polygonal figures continually approached by increasing the number of
their sides. This area was obviously the area
of the curve, and in the case of the parabola it was
found by Archimedes to be two-thirds of the area

formed by multiplying the ordinate by the abscissa. Although the synthetical demonstration of the results was perfectly conclusive, yet the method itself was limited and imperfect.

The celebrated Pappus of Alexandria followed Archimedes in the same inquiries; and in his demonstration of the property of the centre of gravity of a plane figure, by which we may determine the solid formed by its revolution, he has shadowed forth the discoveries of later times.

In his curious tract on Stereometry, published in 1615, Kepler made some advances in the doctrine of infinitesimals. Prompted to the task by a dispute with the seller of some casks of wine, he studied the measurement of solids formed by the revolution of a curve round any line whatever. In solving some of the simplest of these problems, he conceived a circle to be formed of an infinite number of triangles having all their vertices in the centre, and their infinitely small bases in the circumference of the circle, and by thus rendering familiar the idea of quantities infinitely great and infinitely small, he gave an impulse to this branch of mathematics. The failure of Kepler, too, in solving some of the more difficult of the problems which he himself proposed roused the attention of geometers, and seems particularly to have attracted the notice of Cavaleri.

This ingenious mathematician was born at Milan in 1598, and was Professor of Geometry at Bologna. In his method of Indivisibles, which was published in 1635, he considered a line as composed of an infinite number of points, a surface of an infinite number of lines, and a solid of an infinite number of surfaces; and he lays it down as an axiom that the infinite sums of such lines and surfaces have the same ratio when compared with the linear or superficial unit, as the surfaces and solids which are to be determined. As it is not true that an infinite

P

number of infinitely small points can make a line, or an infinite number of infinitely small lines a surface, Pascal removed this verbal difficulty by considering a line as composed of an infinite number of infinitely short lines, a surface as composed of an infinite number of infinitely narrow parallelograms, and a solid of an infinite number of infinitely thin solids. But, independent of this correction, the conclusions deduced by Cavaleri are rigorously true, and his method of ascertaining the ratios of areas and solids to one another, and the theorems which he deduced from it may be considered as forming an era in mathematics.

By the application of this method, Roberval and Toricelli showed that the area of the cycloid is three times that of its generating circle, and the former extended the method of Cavaleri to the case where the powers of the terms of the arithmetical progression to be summed were fractional.

In applying the doctrine of infinitely small quantities to determine the tangents of curves, and the maxima and minima of their ordinates, both Roberval and Fermat made a near approach to the invention of fluxions—so near indeed that both Lagrange and Laplace* have pronounced the latter to be the true inventer of the differential calculus. Roberval supposed the point which describes a curve to be actuated by two motions, by the composition of which it moves in the direction of a tangent; and had he possessed the method of fluxions, he could, in every case, have determined the relative velocities of these motions, which depend on the nature of the curve, and consequently the direction of the tangent which he assumed to be in the diagonal of a parallelogram whose sides had the

* " On peut regarder Fermat," says Lagrange, " comme le premier inventeur des nouveaux calculs ;" and Laplace observes, " Il paraitque Fermat, le veritable inventeur du calcul differentiel, l'ait envisagé comme un cas particulier de celui des differences," &c.

same ratio as the velocities. But as he was able to determine these velocities only in the conic sections, &c. his ingenious method had but few applications.

The labours of Peter Fermat, a counsellor of the parliament of Toulouse, approached still nearer to the fluxionary calculus. In his method of determining the maxima and minima of the ordinates of curves, he substitutes $x + e$ for the independent variable x in the function which is to become a maximum, and as these two expressions should be equal when e becomes infinitely small or 0, he frees this equation from surds and radicals, and after dividing the whole by e, e is made $= 0$, and the equation for the maximum is thus obtained. Upon a similar principle he founded his method of drawing tangents to curves. But though the methods thus used by Fermat are in principle the same with those which connect the theory of tangents and of maxima and minima with the analytical method of exhibiting the differential calculus, yet it is a singular example of national partiality to consider the inventer of these methods as the inventer of the method of fluxions.

"One might be led," says Mr. Herschel, "to suppose by Laplace's expression that the calculus of finite differences had then already assumed a systematic form, and that Fermat had actually observed the relation between the two calculi, and derived the one from the other. The latter conclusion would scarcely be less correct than the former. No method can justly be regarded as bearing any analogy to the differential calculus which does not lay down a system of rules (no matter on what considerations founded, by what names called, or by what extraneous matter enveloped) by means of which the second term of the development of any function of $x + e$ in powers of e, can be correctly calculated, 'quæ extendet se,' to use Newton's expression,

'*citra* ullum molestum calculum in terminis surdis
æque ac in integris procedens.' It would be strange
to suppose Fermat or any other in possession of
such a method before any single surd quantity had
ever been developed in a series. But, in point of
fact, his writings present no trace of the kind; and
this, though fatal to his claim, is allowed by both the
geometers cited. Hear Lagrange's candid avowal.
'Il fait disparaitre dans cette equation,' that of the
maximum between x and e, 'les radicaux et les frac-
tions s'il y en à.' Laplace, too, declares that 'il sa-
voit etendre son calcul aux fonctions irrationelles
en se debarrassant des irrationalités par l'elevation
des radicaux aux puissances." This is at once giving up the point in question. It is allowing unequivocally that Fermat in these processes only took
a circuitous route to avoid a difficulty which it is
one of the most express objects of the differential
calculus to face and surmount. The whole claim
of the French geometer arises from a confusion (too
often made) of the calculus and its applications, the
means and the end, under the sweeping head of
'nouveaux calculs' on the one hand, and an assertion somewhat too unqualified, advanced in the
warmth and generality of a preface, on the other."*

The discoveries of Fermat were improved and
simplified by Hudde, Huygens, and Barrow; and by
the publication of the *Arithmetic of Infinites* by Dr.
Wallis, Savilian professor of geometry at Oxford,
mathematicians were conducted to the very entrance
of a new and untrodden field of discovery. This
distinguished author had effected the quadrature of
all curves whose ordinates can be expressed by any
direct integral powers; and though he had extended
his conclusions to the cases where the ordinates are
xpressed by the inverse or fractional powers, yet

---

* Art. *Mathematics*, in the *Edinburgh Encyclopædia*, volume xiii.
p. 365.

he failed in its application. Nicolas Mercator (Kauff-man) surmounted the difficulty by which Wallis had been baffled, by the continued division of the numerator by the denominator to infinity, and then applying Wallis's method to the resulting positive powers. In this way he obtained, in 1667, the first general quadrature of the hyperbola, and, at the same time, gave the regular development of a function in series.

In order to obtain the quadrature of the circle, Dr. Wallis considered that if the equations of the curves of which he had given the quadrature were arranged in a series, beginning with the most simple, these areas would form another series. He saw also that the equation of the circle was intermediate between the first and second terms of the first series, or between the equation of a straight line and that of a parabola, and hence he concluded, that by interpolating a term between the first and second term of the second series, he would obtain the area of the circle. In pursuing this singularly beautiful thought, Dr. Wallis did not succeed in obtaining the indefinite quadrature of the circle, because he did not employ general exponents; but he was led to express the entire area of the circle by a fraction, the numerator and denominator of which are each obtained by the continued multiplication of a certain series of numbers.

Such was the state of this branch of mathematical science, when Newton, at an early age, directed to it the vigour of his mind. At the very beginning of his mathematical studies, when the works of Dr. Wallis fell into his hands, he was led to consider how he could interpolate the general values of the areas in the second series of that mathematician. With this view he investigated the arithmetical law of the coefficients of the series, and obtained a general method of interpolating, not only the series above referred to, but also other series. These

were the first steps taken by Newton, and, as he
himself informs us, they would have entirely escaped
from his memory if he had not, a few weeks
before,* found the notes which he made upon the
subject. When he had obtained this method, it occurred to him that the very same process was applicable to the ordinates, and, by following out this
idea, he discovered the general method of reducing
radical quantities composed of several terms into
infinite series, and was thus led to the discovery of
the celebrated *Binomial Theorem*. He now neglected
entirely his methods of interpolation, and employed
that theorem alone as the easiest and most direct
method for the quadratures of curves, and in the solution of many questions which had not even been
attempted by the most skilful mathematicians.

After having applied the Binomial theorem to the
rectification of curves, and to the determination of
the surfaces and contents of solids, and the position
of their centres of gravity, he discovered the general
principle of deducing the areas of curves from the
ordinate, by considering the area as a nascent quantity, increasing by continual fluxion in the proportion of the length of the ordinate, and supposing
the abscissa to increase uniformly in proportion to
the time. In imitation of Cavalerius, he called the
momentary increment of a line a point, though it is
not a geometrical point, but an infinitely short line;
and the momentary increment of an area or surface
he called a line, though it is not a geometrical line,
but an infinitely narrow surface. By thus regarding
lines as generated by the motion of points, surfaces
by the motions of lines, and solids by the motion of
surfaces, and by considering that the ordinates, ab-
scissæ, &c. of curves thus formed, vary according
to a regular law depending on the equation of the

---

* These facts are mentioned in Newton's letter to Oldenburgh, October 24, 1676.

curve, he deduces from this equation the velocities with which these quantities are generated; and by the rules of infinite series he obtains the ultimate value of the quantity required. To the velocities with which every line or quantity is generated, Newton gave the name of *Fluxions*, and to the lines or quantities themselves that of *Fluents*. This method constitutes the doctrine of fluxions which Newton had invented previous to 1666, when the breaking out of the plague at Cambridge drove him from that city, and turned his attention to other subjects.

But though Newton had not communicated this great invention to any of his friends, he composed his treatise, entitled *Analysis per equationes numero terminorum infinitas*, in which the principle of fluxions and its numerous applications are clearly pointed out. In the month of June, 1669, he communicated this work to Dr. Barrow, who mentions it in a letter to Mr. Collins, dated the 20th June, 1669, as the production of a friend of his residing at Cambridge, who possesses a fine genius for such inquiries. On the 31st July, he transmitted the work to Collins; and having received his approbation of it, he informs him that the name of the author of it was Newton, a fellow of his own college, and a young man who had only two years before taken his degree of M.A. Collins took a copy of this treatise, and returned the original to Dr. Barrow; and this copy having been found among Collins's papers by his friend Mr. William Jones, and compared with the original manuscript borrowed from Newton, it was published with the consent of Newton in 1711, nearly fifty years after it was written.

Though the discoveries contained in this treatise were not at first given to the world, yet they were made generally known to mathematicians by the correspondence of Collins, who communicated them to James Gregory; to MM. Bertet and Vernon in

France; to Slusius in Holland; to Borelli in Italy; and to Strode, Townsend, and Oldenburg, in letters dated between 1669 and 1672.

Hitherto the method of fluxions was known only to the friends of Newton and their correspondents; but, in the first edition of the Principia, which appeared in 1687, he published, for the first time, the fundamental principle of the fluxionary calculus, in the second lemma of the second book. No information, however, is here given respecting the algorithm or notation of the calculus; and it was not till 1693–5[?] that it was communicated to the mathematical world in the second volume of Dr. Wallis's works, which were published in that year. This information was extracted from two letters of Newton written in 1692.

About the year 1672, Newton had undertaken to publish an edition of Kinckhuysen's Algebra, with notes and additions. He therefore drew up a treatise, entitled, *A Method of Fluxions*, which he proposed as an introduction to that work; but the fear of being involved in disputes about this new discovery, or perhaps the wish to render it more complete, or to have the sole advantage of employing it in his physical researches, induced him to abandon this design. At a later period of his life he again resolved to give it to the world; but it did not appear till after his death, when it was translated into English, and published in 1736, with a commentary by Mr. John Colson, Professor of Mathematics in Cambridge.*

To the first edition of Newton's Optics, which appeared in 1704, there were added two mathematical

* Dr. Pemberton informs us that he had prevailed upon Sir Isaac to publish this treatise during his lifetime, and that he had for this purpose examined all the calculations and prepared part of the figures. But as the latter part of the treatise had never been finished, Sir Isaac was about to let him have other papers to supply what was wanting, when his death put a stop to the plan.—Preface to Pemberton's *View of Sir Isaac Newton's Philosophy*.

treatises, entitled, *Tractatus duo de speciebus et mag-nitudine figurarum curvilinearum*, the one bearing the title of *Tractatus de Quadratura Curvarum*, and the other *Enumeratio linearum tertii ordinis*. The first contains an explanation of the doctrine of fluxions, and of its application to the quadrature of curves; and the second a classification of seventy-two curves of the third order, with an account of their proper-ties. The reason for publishing these two tracts in his Optics (in the subsequent editions of which they are omitted) is thus stated in the advertisement:—
"In a letter written to M. Leibnitz in the year 1679, and published by Dr. Wallis, I mentioned a method by which I had found some general theorems about squaring curvilinear figures on comparing them with the conic sections, or other the simplest figures with which they might be compared. And some years ago I lent out a manuscript containing such theo-rems; and having since met with some things copied out of it, I have on this occasion had it public, pre-fixing to it an introduction, and joining a scholium concerning that method. And I have joined with it another small tract concerning the curvilineal figures of the second kind, which was also written many years ago, and made known to some friends, who have solicited the making it public."

In the year 1707, Mr. Whiston published the alge-braical lectures which Newton had, during nine years, delivered at Cambridge, under the title of *Arithmetica Universalis, sive de Compositione et Resolutione Arith-metica Liber*. We are not accurately informed how Mr. Whiston obtained possession of this work; but it is stated by one of the editors of the English edition, that "Mr. Whiston thinking it a pity that so noble and useful a work should be doomed to a col-lege confinement, obtained leave to make it public." It was soon afterward translated into English by Mr. Ralphson; and a second edition of it, with im-provements by the author, was published at London in 1712, by Dr. Machin, secretary to the Royal Society. With the view of stimulating mathematicians to write annotations on this admirable work, the celebrated S'Gravesande published a tract, entitled, *Specimen Commentarii in Arithmeticam Universalem;* and Maclaurin's Algebra seems to have been drawn up in consequence of this appeal.

Among the mathematical works of Newton we must not omit to enumerate a small tract entitled, *Methodus Differentialis,* which was published with his consent in 1711. It consists of six propositions, which contain a method of drawing a parabolic curve through any given number of points, and which are useful for constructing tables by the interpolation of series, and for solving problems depending on the quadrature of curves.

Another mathematical treatise of Newton's was published for the first time in 1779, in Dr. Horsley's edition of his works.* It is entitled, *Artis Analyticæ Specimina, vel Geometria Analytica.* In editing this work, which occupies about 130 quarto pages, Dr. Horsley used three manuscripts, one of which was in the handwriting of the author; another, written in an unknown hand, was given by Mr. William Jones to the Honourable Charles Cavendish; and a third, copied from this by Mr. James Wilson, the editor of Robins's works, was given to Dr. Horsley by Mr. John Nourse, bookseller to the king. Dr. Horsley has divided it into twelve chapters, which treat of infinite series; of the reduction of affected equations; of the specious resolution of equations; of the doctrine of fluxions; of maxima and minima; of drawing tangents to curves; of the radius of curvature; of the quadrature of curves; of the area of curves which are comparable with the conic sections; of the construction of mechanical problems, and on finding the lengths of curves.

* Isaci Newtoni Opera quæ extant omnia, vol. i p. 388–519.

In enumerating the mathematical works of our author, we must not overlook his solutions of the celebrated problems proposed by Bernouilli and Leibnitz. On the Kalends of January, 1697, John Bernouilli addressed a letter to the most distinguished mathematicians in Europe,† challenging them to solve the two following problems:

1. To determine the curve line connecting two given points which are at different distances from the horizon, and not in the same vertical line, along which a body passing by its own gravity, and beginning to move at the upper point, shall descend to the lower point in the shortest time possible.

2. To find a curve line of this property that the two segments of a right line drawn from a given point through the curve, being raised to any given power, and taken together, may make every where the same sum.

On the day after he received these problems, Newton addressed to Mr. Charles Montague, the President of the Royal Society, a solution of them both. He announced that the curve required in the first problem must be a cycloid, and he gave a method of determining it. He solved also the second problem, and he showed that by the same method other curves might be found which shall cut off three or more segments having the like properties. Leibnitz, who was struck with the beauty of the problem, requested Bernouilli, who had allowed six months for its solution, to extend the period to twelve months. This delay was readily granted, solutions were obtained from Newton, Leibnitz, and the Marquis de L'Hopital; and although that of Newton was anonymous, yet Bernouilli recognised in it his powerful mind, " *tanquam*," says he, " *ex ungue leonem*," as the lion is known by his claw.

The last mathematical effort of our author was

* " Acutissimis qui toto orbe florent Mathematicis."

made with his usual success, in solving a problem
which Leibnitz proposed in 1716, in a letter to the
Abbé Conti, "for the purpose, as he expressed it,
of feeling the pulse of the English analysts." The
object of this problem was to determine the curve
which should cut at right angles an infinity of curves
of a given nature, but expressible by the same equation.   Newton received this problem about five
o'clock in the afternoon, as he was returning from
the Mint; and though the problem was extremely
difficult, and he himself much fatigued with business,
yet he finished the solution of it before he went
to bed.

Such is a brief account of the mathematical writings of Sir Isaac Newton, not one of which were
voluntarily communicated to the world by himself.
The publication of his Universal Arithmetic is said
to have been a breach of confidence on the part of
Whiston; and, however this may be, it was an unfinished work, never designed for the public.   The
publication of his Quadrature of Curves, and of his
Enumeration of Curve Lines, was rendered necessary, in consequence of plagiarisms from the manuscripts of them which he had lent to his friends, and
the rest of his analytical writings did not appear till
after his death.   It is not easy to penetrate into the
motives by which this great man was on these
occasions actuated.   If his object was to keep possession of his discoveries till he had brought them
to a higher degree of perfection, we may approve of
the propriety, though we cannot admire the prudence
of such a step.   If he wished to retain to himself
his own methods, in order that he alone might have
the advantage of them in prosecuting his physical
inquiries, we cannot reconcile so selfish a measure
with that openness and generosity of character
which marked the whole of his life.   If he withheld
his labours from the world in order to avoid the disputes and contentions to which they might give rise,

he adopted the very worst method of securing his tranquillity. That this was the leading motive under which he acted, there is little reason to doubt. The early delay in the publication of his method of fluxions, after the breaking out of the plague at Cambridge, was probably owing to his not having completed the algorithm of that calculus; but no apology can be made for the imprudence of withholding it any longer from the public. Had he published this noble discovery even previous to 1673, when his great rival had not even entered upon those studies which led him to the same method, he would have secured to himself the undivided honour of the invention, and Leibnitz could have aspired to no other fame but that of an improver of the doctrine of fluxions. But he unfortunately acted otherwise. He announced to his friends that he possessed a method of great generality and power; he communicated to them a general account of its principles and applications; and the information which was thus conveyed directed the attention of mathematicians to subjects to which they might not have otherwise applied their powers. In this way the discoveries which he had previously made were made subsequently by others; and Leibnitz, in place of appearing in the theatre of science as the disciple and the follower of Newton, stood forth with all the dignity of a rival; and, by the early publication of his discoveries had nearly placed himself on the throne which Newton was destined to ascend.

It would be inconsistent with the popular nature of a work like this, to enter into a detailed history of the dispute between Newton and Leibnitz respecting the invention of fluxions. A brief and general account of it, however, is indispensable.

In the beginning of 1673, Leibnitz came to London in the suite of the Duke of Hanover, and he became acquainted with the great men who then adorned the capital of England. Among these was Olden-

burg, a countryman of his own, who was then secretary to the Royal Society. About the beginning
of March, in the same year, Leibnitz went to Paris,
where, with the assistance of Huygens, he devoted
himself to the study of the higher geometry. In
the month of July he renewed his correspondence
with Oldenburg, and he communicated to him some of
the discoveries which he had made relative to series,
particularly the series for a circular arc in terms of
the tangent. Oldenburg informed him in return of
the discoveries on series which had been made by
Newton and Gregory; and in 1676 Newton communicated to him, through Oldenburg, a letter of fifteen
closely printed quarto pages, containing many of his
analytical discoveries, and stating that he possessed
a general method of drawing tangents, which he
thought it necessary to conceal in two sentences of
transposed characters. In this letter neither the
method of fluxions nor any of its principles are
communicated; but the superiority of the method
over all others is so fully described, that Leibnitz
could scarcely fail to discover that Newton possessed that secret of which geometers had so long
been in quest.

Had Leibnitz at the time of receiving this letter
been entirely ignorant of his own differential method,
the information thus conveyed to him by Newton
could not fail to stimulate his curiosity, and excite
his mightiest efforts to obtain possession of so great
a secret. That this new method was intimately
connected with the subject of series was clearly indicated by Newton; and as Leibnitz was deeply
versed in this branch of analysis, it is far from im-
probable that a mind of such strength and acuteness
might attain his object by direct investigation. That
this was the case may be inferred from his letter to
Oldenburg (to be communicated to Newton) of the
21st June, 1677, where he mentions that he had for
some time been in possession of a method of draw-

ing tangents more general than that of Slusius, namely, by the differences of ordinates. He then proceeds with the utmost frankness to explain this method, which was no other than the differential calculus. He describes the algorithm which he had adopted, the formation of differential equations, and the application of the calculus to various geometrical and analytical questions. No answer seems to have been returned to this letter either by Newton or Oldenburg, and, with the exception of a short letter from Leibnitz to Oldenburg, dated 12th July, 1677, no further correspondence seems to have taken place. This, no doubt, arose from the death of Oldenburg in the month of August, 1677,* when the two rival geometers pursued their researches with all the ardour which the greatness of the subject was so well calculated to inspire.

In the hands of Leibnitz the differential calculus made rapid progress. In the *Acta Eruditorum*, which was published at Leipsic in November, 1684, he gave the first account of it, describing its algorithm in the same manner as he had done in his letter to Oldenburg, and pointing out its application to the drawing of tangents, and the determination of maxima and minima. He makes a remote reference to the *similar* calculus of Newton, but lays no claim to the sole invention of the differential method. In the same work for June, 1686, he resumes the subject; and when Newton had not published a single word upon

* Henry Oldenburg, whose name is so intimately associated with the history of Newton's discoveries, was born at Bremen, and was consul from that town to London during the usurpation of Cromwell. Having lost his office, and being compelled to seek the means of subsistence, he became tutor to an English nobleman, whom he accompanied to Oxford in 1656. During his residence in that city he became acquainted with the philosophers who established the Royal Society, and upon the death of William Crown, the first secretary, he was appointed in 1663, joint secretary along with Mr. Wilkins. He kept up an extensive correspondence with the philosophers of all nations, and he was the author of several papers in the Philosophical Transactions, and of some works which have not acquired much celebrity. He died at Charlton, near Greenwich, in August, 1677.

fluxions, and had not even made known his notation, the differential calculus was making rapid advances on the Continent, and in the hands of James and John Bernouilli had proved the means of solving some of the most important and difficult problems.

The silence of Newton was at last broken, and in the second lemma of the second book of the Principia, he explained the fundamental principle of the fluxionary calculus. His explanation, which occupied only three pages, was terminated with the following scholium:—"In a correspondence which took place about ten years ago between that very skilful geometer, G. G. Leibnitz, and myself, I announced to him that I possessed a method of determining maxima and minima, of drawing tangents, and of performing similar operations which was equally applicable to rational and irrational quantities, and concealed the same in transposed letters involving this sentence, (*data equatione quotcunque fluentes quantitates involvente, fluxiones invenire et vice versa*). This illustrious man replied that he also had fallen on a method of the same kind, and he communicated to me his method which scarcely differed from mine except in the notation [and in the idea of the generation of quantities."]* This celebrated scholium, which is so often referred to in the present controversy, has, in our opinion, been much misapprehended. While M. Biot considers it as "eternalizing the rights of Leibnitz by recognising them in the Principia," Professor Playfair regards it as containing "a highly favourable opinion on the subject of the discoveries of Leibnitz." To us it appears to be nothing more than the simple statement of the fact, that the method communicated by Leibnitz was nearly the same as his own; and this much he might have said, whether he believed that Leibnitz had seen the fluxionary calculus among the

---

* These words in brackets are in the second edition, but not in the first.

papers of Collins, or was the independent inventor of his own. It is more than probable, indeed, that when Newton wrote this scholium he regarded Leibnitz as a second inventor; but when he found that Leibnitz and his friends had showed a willingness to believe, and had even ventured to throw out the suspicion, that he himself had borrowed the doctrine of fluxions from the differential calculus, he seems to have altered the opinion which he had formed of his rival, and to have been willing in his turn to retort the charge.

This change of opinion was brought about by a series of circumstances over which he had no control. M. Nicolas Fatio de Duillier, a Swiss mathematician, resident in London, communicated to the Royal Society, in 1699, a paper on the line of quickest descent, which contains the following observations:—" Compelled by the evidence of facts, I hold Newton to have been the first inventor of this calculus, and the earliest by several years; and whether Leibnitz, the *second inventor*, has borrowed any thing from the other, I would prefer to my own judgment that of those who have seen the letters and other copies of the same manuscripts of Newton." This imprudent remark, which by no means amounts to a charge of plagiarism, for Leibnitz is actually designated the *second inventor*, may be considered as showing that the English mathematicians had been cherishing suspicions unfavourable to Leibnitz, and there can be no doubt that a feeling had long prevailed that this mathematician either had, or might have seen, among the papers of Collins, the " *Analysis per Equationes, &c.*," which contained the principles of the fluxionary method. Leibnitz replied to the remark of Duillier with much good feeling. He appealed to the facts as exhibited in his correspondence with Oldenburg; he referred to Newton's scholium as a testimony in his favour; and, without disputing or acknowledging the priority of Newton's

Q 2

claim, he asserted his own right to the invention of
the differential calculus. Fatio transmitted a reply to
the Leipsic Acts; but the editor refused to insert it.
The dispute, therefore, terminated, and the feelings
of the contending parties continued for some time
in a state of repose, though ready to break out on
the slightest provocation.

When Newton's Optics appeared in 1704, accompanied by his Treatise on the Quadrature of Curves,
and his enumeration of lines of the third order, the
editor of the Leipsic Acts (whom Newton supposed
to be Leibnitz himself) took occasion to review the
first of these tracts. After giving an imperfect
analysis of its contents, he compared the method
of fluxions with the differential calculus, and, in a
sentence of some ambiguity, he states that Newton
employed fluxions in place of the differences of Leibnitz, and made use of them in his Principia in the
same manner as Honoratus Fabri, in his Synopsis
of Geometry, had substituted progressive motion in
place of the indivisibles of Cavaleri.* As Fabri,
therefore, was not the inventor of the method
which is here referred to, but borrowed it from Cavaleri, and only changed the mode of its expression,
there can be no doubt that the artful insinuation
contained in the above passage was intended to convey the impression that Newton had *stolen* his method of fluxions from Leibnitz. The indirect character of this attack, in place of mitigating its severity,
renders it doubly odious; and we are persuaded that
no candid reader can peruse the passage without a
strong conviction that it justifies, in the fullest man-

* As this passage is of essential importance in this controversy, we
shall give it in the original. " *Pro differentiis igitur Leibnitianis D.
Newtonus adhibet, semperque adhibuit, fluxiones,* quæ sunt quam prox-
ime ut fluentium augmenta, æqualibus temporis particulis quam mini-
mis genita; iisque tam in suis Principiis Naturæ Mathematicis, tum in
aliis postea editis, eleganter est usus; *quem admodum et Honoratus
Fabrius in sua Synopsi Geometrica, motuumque progressus Cavalle-
rianæ methodo substituit.*"

ner, the indignant feelings which it excited among the English philosophers. If Leibnitz was the author of the review, or if he was in any way a party to it, he merited the full measure of rebuke which was dealt out to him by the friends of Newton, and deserved those severe reprisals which doubtless imbittered the rest of his days. He who dared to accuse a man like Newton, or indeed any man holding a fair character in society, with the odious crime of plagiarism, placed himself without the pale of the ordinary courtesies of life, and deserved to have the same charge thrown back upon himself. The man who conceives his fellow to be capable of such intellectual felony, avows the possibility of himself committing it, and almost substantiates the weakest evidence of the worst accusers.

Dr. Keill, as the representative of Newton's friends, could not brook this base attack upon his countryman. In a letter printed in the Philosophical Transactions for 1708, he maintained that Newton was "beyond all doubt" the first inventor of fluxions. He referred for a direct proof of this to his letters published by Wallis; and he asserted "that the same calculus was afterward published by Leibnitz, the name and the mode of notation being changed." If the reader is disposed to consider this passage as retorting the charge of plagiarism upon Leibnitz, he will readily admit that the mode of its expression is neither so coarse nor so insidious as that which is used by the writer in the Leipsic Acts. In a letter to Hans Sloane, dated March, 1711, Leibnitz complained to the Royal Society of the treatment he had received. He expressed his conviction that Keill had erred more from rashness of judgment than from any improper motive, and that he did not regard the accusation as a calumny; and he requested that the society would oblige Mr. Keill to disown publicly the injurious sense which his words might bear. When this letter was read to the society, Keill justified himself to Sir Isaac Newton and the other members by showing them the obnoxious review of the Quadrature of Curves in the Leipsic Acts. They all agreed in attaching the same injurious meaning to the passage which we formerly quoted, and authorized Keill to explain and defend his statement. He accordingly addressed a letter to Sir Hans Sloane, which was read at the society on the 24th May, 1711, and a copy of which was ordered to be sent to Leibnitz. In this letter, which is one of considerable length, he declares that he never meant to state that Leibnitz knew either the name of Newton's method or the form of notation, and that the real meaning of the passage was, "that Newton was the first inventor of fluxions or of the differential calculus, and that he had given, in two letters to Oldenburg, and which he had transmitted to Leibnitz, indications of it sufficiently intelligible to an acute mind, from which Leibnitz derived, or at least might derive, the principles of his calculus."

The charge of plagiarism which Leibnitz thought was implied in the former letter of his antagonist is here greatly modified, if not altogether denied. Keill expresses only an *opinion* that the letter *seen* by Leibnitz contained intelligible indications of the fluxionary calculus. Even if this opinion were correct, it is no proof that Leibnitz either saw these indications or availed himself of them, or if he did perceive them, it might have been in consequence of his having previously been in possession of the differential calculus, or having enjoyed some distant view of it. Leibnitz should, therefore, have allowed the dispute to terminate here ; for no ingenuity on his part, and no additional facts, could affect an opinion which any other person as well as Keill was entitled to maintain.

Leibnitz, however, took a different view of the subject, and wrote a letter to Sir Hans Sloane, dated December 19, 1711, which excited new feelings, and involved him in new embarrassments. Insensible to the mitigation which had been kindly impressed upon the supposed charge against his honour, he alleges that Keill had attacked his candour and sincerity more openly than before;—that he acted without any authority from Sir Isaac Newton, who was the party interested;—and that it was in vain to justify his proceedings by referring to the provocation in the Leipsic Acts, because in that journal *no injustice had been done to any party, but every one had received what was his due.* He branded Keill with the odious appellation of an upstart, and one little acquainted with the circumstances of the case;* he called upon the society to silence his vain and unjust clamours,† which, he believed, were disapproved by Newton himself, who was well acquainted with the facts, and who, he was persuaded, would willingly give his opinion on the matter.

This unfortunate letter was doubtless the cause of all the rancour and controversy which so speedily followed, and it placed his antagonist in a new and a more favourable position. It may be correct, though few will admit it, that Keill's second letter was more injurious than the first; but it was not true that Keill acted without the authority of Newton, because Keill's letter was approved of and transmitted by the Royal Society, of which Newton was the president, and therefore became the act of that body. The obnoxious part, however, of Leibnitz's letter consisted in his appropriating to himself the opinions of the reviewer in the Leipsic Acts, by declaring that, in a review which charged Newton with plagiarism, every person had got what was his due. The whole character of the controversy was now changed: Leibnitz places himself in the

* Homine docto, sed novo, et parum perito rerum ante actarum cognitare.
† Vanæ et injustæ vociferationes.

position of the party who had first disturbed the tranquillity of science by maligning its most distinguished ornament; and the Royal Society was imperiously called upon to throw all the light they could upon a transaction which had exposed their venerable president to so false a charge.   The society, too, had become a party to the question, by their approbation and transmission of Keill's second letter, and were on that account alone bound to vindicate the step which they had taken.

When the letter of Leibnitz, therefore, was read, Keill appealed to the registers of the society for the proofs of what he had advanced; Sir Isaac also expressed his displeasure at the obnoxious passage in the Leipsic Review, and at the defence of it by Leibnitz, and he left it to the society to act as they thought proper.   A committee was therefore appointed on the 11th March, consisting of Dr. Arbuthnot, Mr. Hill, Dr. Halley, Mr. Jones, Mr. Machin, and Mr. Burnet, who were instructed to examine the ancient registers of the society, to inquire into the dispute, and to produce such documents as they should find, together with their own opinions on the subject.   On the 24th April the committee produced the following report :—

"We have consulted the letters and letter-books in the custody of the Royal Society, and those found among the papers of Mr. John Collins, dated between the years 1669 and 1677, inclusive; and showed them to such as knew and avouched the hands of Mr. Barrow, Mr. Collins, Mr. Oldenburg, and Mr. Leibnitz; and compared those of Mr. Gregory with one another, and with copies of some of them taken in the hand of Mr. Collins; and have extracted from them what relates to the matter referred to us; all which extracts herewith delivered to you we believe to be genuine and authentic.   And by these letters and papers we find,—

"I. Mr. Leibnitz was in London in the beginning

of the year 1673; and went thence, in or about March, to Paris, where he kept a correspondence with Mr. Collins by means of Mr. Oldenburg, till about September, 1676, and then returned by London and Amsterdam to Hanover: and that Mr. Collins was very free in communicating to able mathematicians what he had received from Mr. Newton and Mr. Gregory.

"II. That when Mr. Leibnitz was the first time in London, he contended for the invention of another differential method properly so called; and, notwithstanding that he was shown by Dr. Pell that it was Newton's method, persisted in maintaining it to be his own invention, by reason that he had found it by himself without knowing what Newton had done before, and had much improved it. And we find no mention of his having any other differential method than Newton's before his letter of the 21st of June, 1677, which was a year after a copy of Mr. Newton's letter of the 10th of December, 1672, had been sent to Paris to be communicated to him; and above four years after, Mr. Collins began to communicate that letter to his correspondent; in which letter the method of fluxions was sufficiently described to any intelligent person.

"III. That by Mr. Newton's letter of the 13th of June, 1676, it appears that he had the method of fluxions above five years before the writing of that letter. And by his Analysis per Æquationes numero Terminorum Infinitas, communicated by Dr. Barrow to Mr. Collins in July, 1669, we find that he had invented the method before that time.

"IV. That the differential method is one and the same with the method of fluxions, excepting the name and mode of notation; Mr. Leibnitz calling those quantities differences which Mr. Newton calls moments or fluxions; and marking them with the letter *d*—a mark not used by Mr. Newton.

" And therefore we take the proper question to be

not who invented this or that method, but who was the first inventor of the method. And we believe that those who have reputed Mr. Leibnitz the first inventor knew little or nothing of his correspondence with Mr. Collins and Mr. Oldenburg long before, nor of Mr. Newton's having that method above fifteen years before Mr. Leibnitz began to publish it in the Acta Eruditorum of Leipsic.

"For which reason we reckon Mr. Newton the first inventor; and are of opinion that Mr. Keill, in asserting the same, has been no ways injurious to Mr. Leibnitz. And we submit to the judgment of the society whether the extract and papers now presented to you, together with what is extant to the same purpose in Dr. Wallis's third volume, may not deserve to be made public."

This report being read, the society unanimously ordered the collection of letters and manuscripts to be printed, and appointed Dr. Halley, Mr. Jones, and Mr. Machin to superintend the press. Complete copies of it, under the title of *Commercium Epistolicum D. Johannis Collins et aliorum de analysi promota*, were laid before the society on the 8th January, 1713, and Sir Isaac Newton, as president, ordered a copy to be delivered to each person of the committee appointed for that purpose, to examine it before its publication.

Leibnitz received information of the appearance of the Commercium Epistolicum when he was at Vienna; and "being satisfied," as he expresses it, "that it must contain *malicious falsehoods*, I did not think proper to send for it by post, but wrote to M. Bernouilli to give me his sentiments. M. Bernouilli wrote me a letter dated at Basle, June 7th, 1713, in which he said *that it appeared probable that Sir Isaac Newton had formed his calculus after having seen mine*."* This letter was published by a friend of

---

* Letter to Count Bothman in Des Maizeaux's *Recueil de diverses pieces*, tom. ii. p. 44, 45.

Leibnitz, with reflections, in a loose sheet entitled *Charta Volans*, and dated July 29, 1713. It was widely circulated without either the name of the author, printer, or place of publication, and was communicated to the *Journal Literaire* by another friend of Leibnitz, who added remarks of his own, and stated, that when Newton published the Principia in 1687, *he did not understand the true differential method; and that he took his fluxions from Leibnitz.*

In this state of the controversy, Mr. Chamberlayne conceived the design of reconciling the two distinguished philosophers; and in a letter dated April 28, 1714,* he addressed himself to Leibnitz, who was still at Vienna. In replying to this letter, Leibnitz declared that he had given no occasion for the dispute; "that Newton procured a book to be published, which was written purposely to discredit him, and sent it to Germany, &c. as in the name of the society;" and he stated *that there was room to doubt whether Newton knew his invention before he had it of him.* Mr. Chamberlayne communicated this letter to Sir Isaac Newton, who replied that Leibnitz had attacked his reputation in 1705, by intimating that he had borrowed from him the method of fluxions; that if Mr. C. could point out to him any thing in which he had injured Mr. Leibnitz, he would give him satisfaction; that he would not retract things which he knew to be true; and that he believed that the Royal Society had done no injustice by the publication of the Commercium Epistolicum.

The Royal Society, having learned that Leibnitz complained of their having condemned him unheard, inserted a declaration in their journals on the 20th May, 1714, that they did not pretend that the report of their committee should pass for a decision of the society. Mr. Chamberlayne sent a copy of this to Leibnitz, along with Sir Isaac's letter, and Dr. Keill's

* See Des Maizeaux, tom. ii. p. 116.

R

answer to the papers inserted in the Journal Literaire. After perusing these documents, M. Leibnitz
replied, "that Sir Isaac's letter was written with
very little civility; that he was not in a humour
to put himself in a passion against such people;
that there were other letters among those of Oldenburg and Collins which should have been published;
and that on his return to Hanover, he would be able
to publish a Commercium Epistolicum which would
be of service to the history of learning." When
this letter was read to the Royal Society, Sir Isaac
remarked, that the last part of it injuriously accused
the society of having made a partial selection of
papers for the Commercium Epistolicum; that he
did not interfere in any way in the publication of
that work, and had even withheld from the committee two letters, one from Leibnitz in 1693, and
another from Wallis in 1695, which were highly
favourable to his cause. He stated that he did not
think it right for M. Leibnitz himself, but that, if
he had letters to produce in his favour, that they
might be published in the Philosophical Transactions, or in Germany.

About this time the Abbé Conti, a noble Venetian, came to England. He was a correspondent of
Leibnitz, and in a letter which he had received soon
after his arrival,* he enters upon his dispute with
Newton. He charges the English "with wishing
to pass for almost the only inventors." He declares
"that Bernouilli had judged rightly in saying that
Newton did not possess before him the infinitesimal
characteristic and algorithm." He remarks that
Newton preceded him only in series; and he confesses that during his second visit to England, "Collins showed him part of his correspondence," or, as
he afterward expresses it, he saw "some of the letters of Newton at Mr. Collins's." He then attacks

* Written in November or December, 1715.

Sir Isaac's philosophy, particularly his opinions about gravity and vacuum, the intervention of God for the preservation of his creatures; and he accuses him of reviving the occult qualities of the schools. But the most remarkable passage in this letter is the following: " I am a great friend of experimental philosophy, but Newton deviates much from it *when he pretends that all matter is heavy,* or that each particle of matter attracts every other particle."

The above letter to the Abbé Conti was generally shown in London, and came to be much talked of at court, in consequence of Leibnitz having been privy counsellor to the Elector of Hanover when that prince ascended the throne of England. Many persons of distinction, and particularly the Abbé Conti, urged Newton to reply to Leibnitz's letter, but he resisted all their solicitations. One day, however, King George I. inquired when Sir Isaac Newton's answer to Leibnitz would appear; and when Sir Isaac heard this, he addressed a long reply to the Abbé Conti, dated February 26th, O. S. 1715-16. This letter, written with dignified severity, is a triumphant refutation of the allegations of his adversary; and the following passage deserves to be quoted, as connected with that branch of the dispute which relates to Leibnitz's having seen part of Newton's letters to Mr. Collins. " He complains of the committee of the Royal Society, as if they had acted partially in omitting what made against me; but he fails in proving the accusation. For he instances in a paragraph concerning my ignorance, pretending that they omitted it, and yet you will find it in the Commercium Epistolicum, p. 547, lines 2, 3, and I am not ashamed of it. He saith that he saw this paragraph in the hands of Mr. Collins when he was in London the second time, that is in October, 1676. It is in my letter of the 24th of October, 1676, and therefore he then saw that letter. And in that and some other letters writ before that time, I described my method of fluxions; and in the same letter I described also two general methods of series, one of which is now claimed from me by Mr. Leibnitz." The letter concludes with the following paragraph: "But as he has lately attacked me with an accusation which amounts to plagiary; if he goes on to accuse me, it lies upon him by the laws of all nations to prove his accusations, on pain of being accounted guilty of calumny. He hath hitherto written letters to his correspondents full of affirmations, complaints, and reflections, without proving any thing. But he is the aggressor, and it lies upon him to prove the charge."

In transmitting this letter to Leibnitz, the Abbé Conti informed him that he himself had read with great attention, and without the least prejudice, the Commercium Epistolicum, and the little piece* that contains the extract; that he had also seen at the Royal Society the original papers of the Commercium Epistolicum, and some other original pieces relating to it. "From all this," says he, "I infer, that, if all the digressions are cut off, the only point is, whether Sir Isaac Newton had the method of fluxions or infinitesimals before you, or whether you had it before him. You published it first, it is true, but you have owned also that Sir Isaac Newton had given many hints of it in his letters to Mr. Oldenburg and others. This is proved very largely in the Commercium, and in the extract of it. What answer do you give? This is still wanting to the public, in order to form an exact judgment of the affair." The Abbé adds, that Mr. Leibnitz's own friends waited for his answer with great impatience, and that they thought he could not dispense with answering, if not Dr. Keill, at least Sir Isaac New-

* This is the *Recensio Commercii Epistolici*, or review of it, which was first published in the *Phil. Trans.* 1715.

ton himself, who had given him a defiance in express terms.

Leibnitz was not long in complying with this request. He addressed a letter to the Abbé Conti, dated April 9th, 1716, but he sent it through M. Ramond at Paris, to communicate it to others. When it was received by the Abbé Conti, Newton wrote observations upon it, which were communicated only to some of his friends, and which, while they placed his defence on the most impregnable basis, at the same time threw much light on the early history of his mathematical discoveries.

The death of Leibnitz on the 14th November, 1716, put an end to this controversy, and Newton some time afterward published the correspondence with the Abbé Conti, which had hitherto been only privately circulated among the friends of the disputants.*

In 1722, a new edition of the Commercium Epistolicum was published, and there was prefixed to it a general review of its contents, which has been falsely ascribed to Newton.† When the third edi-

* M. Biot remarks, that the animosity of Newton was not calmed by the death of Leibnitz, for he had no sooner heard of it than he caused to be printed two manuscript letters of Leibnitz, written in the preceding year, accompanying them with a very bitter refutation (en les accompagnant d'un refutation tres-amere). Who that reads this sentence does not believe that the bitter refutation was written after Leibnitz's death? The implied charge is untrue; the bitter refutation was written before Leibnitz's death, and consequently he showed no animosity over the grave of his rival; and in our opinion none even before his death.

† M. Biot states that Sir Isaac Newton *caused* this edition of the Commercium Epistolicum to be printed; that *Sir Isaac placed* at the head of it a partial abstract of the collection; and that this abstract *appeared to have been written by himself.* These groundless charges may be placed, without any refutation, beside the assertion of Montucla, that Newton wrote the notes (les notes) on the Commercium Epistolicum; and the equally incorrect statement of La Croix, that Newton added to it notes (des notes), with his own hand. We should not have noticed the charges of M. Biot, had he not adduced them as proofs of Newton's animosity to Leibnitz after his death. See Mr. Herschel's History of *Mathematics* in the *Edinburgh Encyclopædia,* vol. xiii. p. 368, *note.*

tion of the Principia was published in 1725, the
celebrated scholium which we have already quoted,
and in which Leibnitz's differential calculus was
mentioned, was struck out either by Newton or by
the editor. This step was perhaps rash and ill-
advised; but as the scholium had been adduced by
Leibnitz and others as a proof that Newton acknowledged him to be an independent inventor of the
calculus,—an interpretation which it does not bear,
and which Newton expressly states he never intended it to bear,—he was justified in withdrawing
a passage which had been so erroneously interpreted, and so greatly misapplied.

In viewing this controversy, at the distance of
more than a century, when the passions of the individual combatants have been allayed, and national
jealousies extinguished, it is not difficult to form a
correct estimate of the conduct and claims of the
two rival analysts. By the unanimous verdict of
all nations, it has been decided that Newton invented
fluxions at least ten years before Leibnitz. Some
of the letters of Newton which bore reference to
this great discovery were perused by the German
mathematician; but there is no evidence whatever
that he borrowed his differential calculus from these
letters. Newton was therefore the *first* inventor,
and Leibnitz the *second*. It was impossible that the
former could have been a plagiarist; but it was
possible for the latter. Had the letters of Newton
contained even stronger indications than they do of
the new calculus, no evidence short of proof could
have justified any allegation against Leibnitz's
honour. The talents which he displayed in the improvement of the calculus showed that he was
capable of inventing it; and his character stood
sufficiently high to repel every suspicion of his integrity. But if it would have been criminal to
charge Leibnitz with plagiarism, what must we
think of those who dared to accuse Newton of bor-

rowing his fluxions from Leibnitz? This odious
accusation was made by Leibnitz himself, and by
Bernouilli; and we have seen that the former repeated it again and again, as if his own good name
rested on the destruction of that of his rival. It was
this charge against Newton that gave rise to the attack of Keill, and the publication of the Commercium
Epistolicum; and, notwithstanding this high provocation, the committee of the Royal Society contented
themselves with asserting Newton's priority, without retorting the charge of plagiarism upon his rival.

Although an attempt has been recently made to
place the conduct of Leibnitz on the same level with
that of Newton, yet the circumstances of the case
will by no means justify such a comparison. The
conduct of Newton was at all times dignified and
just. He knew his rights, and he boldly claimed
them. Conscious of his integrity, he spurned with
indignation the charge of plagiarism with which an
ungenerous rival had so insidiously loaded him; and
if there was one step in his frank and unhesitating
procedure which posterity can blame it is his omission, in the third edition of the Principia, of the
references to the differential calculus of Leibnitz.
This omission, however, was perfectly just. The
scholium which he had left out was a mere historical
statement of the fact, that the German mathematician had sent him a method which was the same as
his own; and when he found that this simple assertion had been held by Leibnitz and others as a re-
cognition of his independent claim to the invention,
he was bound either to omit it altogether, or to
enter into explanations which might have involved
him in a new controversy.

The conduct of Leibnitz was not marked with the
same noble lineaments. That he was the aggressor
is universally allowed. That he first dared to
breathe the charge of plagiarism against Newton,
and that he often referred to it, has been sufficiently

apparent; and when arguments failed him he had recourse to threats—declaring that he would publish another Commercium Epistolicum, though he had no appropriate letters to produce. All this is now matter of history; and we may find some apology for it in his excited feelings, and in the insinuations which were occasionally thrown out against the originality of his discovery; but for other parts of his conduct we seek in vain for an excuse. When he assailed the philosophy of Newton in his letters to the Abbé Conti, he exhibited perhaps only the petty feelings of a rival; but when he dared to calumniate that great man in his correspondence with the Princess of Wales, by whom he was respected and beloved; when he ventured to represent the Newtonian philosophy as physically false, and as dangerous to religion; and when he founded these accusations on passages in the Principia and the Optics glowing with all the fervour of genuine piety, he cast a blot upon his name, which all his talents as a philosopher, and all his virtues as a man, will never be able to efface.

CHAPTER XIII.

James II. attacks the Privileges of the University of Cambridge—Newton chosen one of the Delegates to resist this Encroachment—He is elected a Member of the Convention Parliament—Burning of his Manuscripts—His supposed Derangement of Mind—View taken of this by foreign Philosophers—His Correspondence with Mr. Pepys and Mr. Locke at the time of his Illness—Mr. Millington's Letter to Mr. Pepys on the subject of Newton's Illness—Refutation of the Statement that he laboured under Mental Derangement.

FROM the year 1669, when Newton was installed in the Lucasian chair, till 1695, when he ceased to reside in Cambridge, he seems to have been seldom absent from his college more than three or four weeks in the year. In 1675, he received a dispensation from Charles II. to continue in his fellowship of Trinity College without taking orders, and we have already seen in the preceding chapter how his time was occupied till the publication of the Principia in 1687.

An event now occurred which drew Newton from the seclusion of his studies, and placed him upon the theatre of public life. Desirous of re-establishing the Catholic faith in its former supremacy, King James II. had begun to assail the rights and privileges of his Protestant subjects. Among other illegal acts, he sent his letter of mandamus to the University of Cambridge to order Father Francis, an ignorant monk of the Benedictine order, to be received as master of arts, and to enjoy all the privileges of this degree, without taking the oaths of allegiance and supremacy. The university speedily perceived the consequences which might arise from such a measure. Independent of the infringement of their rights which such an order involved, it was obvious that the highest interests of the university were endangered, and that Roman Catholics might soon become a majority in the convocation. They therefore unanimously refused to listen to the royal order, and they did this with a firmness of purpose which irritated the despotic court. The king reiterated his commands, and accompanied them with the severest threatenings in case of disobedience. The Catholics were not idle in supporting the views of the sovereign. The honorary degree of M.A. which conveys no civil rights to its possessor, having been formerly given to the secretary of the ambassador from Morocco, it was triumphantly urged that the University of Cambridge had a greater regard for a Mahometan than for a Roman Catholic, and was more obsequious to the ambassador from Morocco than to their own lawful sovereign. Though this reasoning might impose upon the ignorant, it produced little effect upon the members of the university. A few weak-minded individuals, however, were disposed to yield a reluctant consent to the royal wishes. They proposed to confer the degree, and at the same time to resolve that it should not in future be regarded as a precedent. To this it was replied, that the very act of submission in one case would be a stronger argument for continuing the practice than any such resolution would be against its repetition. The university accordingly remained firm in their original decision. The vice-chancellor was summoned before the ecclesiastical commission to answer for this act of contempt. Newton was among the number of those who resisted the wishes of the court, and he was consequently chosen one of the nine delegates who were appointed to defend the independence of the university. These delegates appeared before the High Court. They maintained that not a single precedent could be found to justify so extraordinary a measure; and they showed that Charles II. had, under similar circumstances, been pleased to withdraw his mandamus. This representation had its full weight, and the king was induced to abandon his design.*

The part which Newton had taken in this affair, and the high character which he now held in the scientific world, induced his friends to propose him as member of parliament for the university. He was accordingly elected in 1688, though by a very narrow majority,† and he sat in the Convention Parliament till its dissolution. In the year 1688 and 1689, Newton was absent from Cambridge during the greater part of the year, owing, we presume, to his attendance in parliament; but it appears from

* See Burnet's *History of his own Times*, vol. i. p. 697. Lond. 1724.

† The other candidates were Sir Robert Sawyer and Mr. Finch, and the votes stood thus.

Sir Robert Sawyer, 125
Mr. Newton,   122
Mr. Finch,   117

the books of the University that from 1690 to 1695 he was seldom absent, and must therefore have renounced his parliamentary duties.

During his stay in London he had no doubt experienced the unsuitableness of his income to the new circumstances in which he was placed, and it is probable that this was the cause of the limitation of his residence to Cambridge. His income was certainly very confined, and but little suited to the generosity of his disposition. Demands were doubtless made upon it by some of his less wealthy relatives ; and there is reason to think that he himself, as well as his influential friends, had been looking forward to some act of liberality on the part of the government.

An event however occurred which will ever form an epoch in his history ; and it is a singular circumstance, that this incident has been for more than a century unknown to his own countrymen, and has been accidentally brought to light by the examination of the manuscripts of Huygens. This event has been magnified into a temporary aberration of mind, which is said to have arisen from a cause scarcely adequate to its production.

While he was attending divine service in a winter morning, he had left in his study a favourite little dog called Diamond. Upon returning from chapel he found that it had overturned a lighted taper on his desk, which set fire to several papers on which he had recorded the results of some optical experiments. These papers are said to have contained the labours of many years, and it has been stated that when Mr. Newton perceived the magnitude of his loss, he exclaimed, "Oh, Diamond, Diamond, little do you know the mischief you have done me!" It is a curious circumstance that Newton never refers to the experiments which he is said to have lost on this occasion, and his nephew, Mr. Conduit, makes no allusion to the event itself. The distress, however

which it occasioned is said to have been so deep as
to affect even the powers of his understanding.

This extraordinary effect was first communicated
to the world in the Life of Newton by M. Biot, who
received the following account of it from the celebrated M. Van Swinden.

"There is among the manuscripts of the celebrated Huygens a small journal in folio, in which
he used to note down different occurrences. It is
side ζ, No. 8, p. 112, in the catalogue of the library
of Leyden. The following extract is written by
Huygens himself, with whose handwriting I am well
acquainted, having had occasion to peruse several
of his manuscripts and autograph letters. '*On the
29th May*, 1694, *M. Colin,** a Scotsman, informed me
that eighteen months ago the illustrious geometer, Isaac
Newton, had become insane, either in consequence of
his too intense application to his studies, or from ex-
cessive grief at having lost, by fire, his chymical laboratory and several manuscripts. When he came to the
Archbishop of Cambridge, he made some observations
which indicated an alienation of mind. He was immediately taken care of by his friends, who confined him to
his house and applied remedies, by means of which he
had now so far recovered his health that he began to understand the Principia.'*" Huygens mentioned this circumstance to Leibnitz, in a letter dated 8th June,
1694, to which Leibnitz replies in a letter dated the
23d, "I am very glad that I received information of
the cure of Mr. Newton, at the same time that I first
heard of his illness, which doubtless must have been

* This M. Colin was probably a young bachelor of arts whom Newton seems afterward to have employed in some of his calculations.
These bachelors were distinguished by the title of Dominus, and it was
usual to translate this word and to call them *Sir*. In a letter from Newton to Flamstead, dated Cambridge, June 29th, 1695, is the following
passage: "I want not your calculations, but your observations only, for
besides myself and my servant, Sir Collins (whom I can employ for a
little money, which I value not) tells me that he can calculate an eclipse
and work truly.

very alarming. 'It is to men like you and him, sir, that I wish a long life.'"

The first publication of the preceding statement produced a strong sensation among the friends and admirers of Newton. They could not easily believe in the prostration of that intellectual strength which had unbarred the strongholds of the universe. The unbroken equanimity of Newton's mind, the purity of his moral character, his temperate and abstemious life, his ardent and unaffected piety, and the weakness of his imaginative powers, all indicated a mind which was not likely to be overset by any affliction to which it could be exposed. The loss of a few experimental records could never have disturbed the equilibrium of a mind like his. If they were the records of discoveries, the discoveries themselves indestructible would have been afterward given to the world. If they were merely the details of experimental results, a little time could have easily reproduced them. Had these records contained the first fruits of early genius—of obscure talent, on which fame had not yet shed its rays, we might have supposed that the first blight of such early ambition would have unsettled the stability of an untried mind. But Newton was satiated with fame. His mightiest discoveries were completed and diffused over all Europe, and he must have felt himself placed on the loftiest pinnacle of earthly ambition. The incredulity which such views could not fail to encourage was increased by the novelty of the information. No English biographer had ever alluded to such an event. History and tradition were equally silent, and it was not easy to believe that the Lucasian Professor of Mathematics at Cambridge, a member of the English parliament, and the first philosopher in Europe could have lost his reason without the dreadful fact being known to his own countrymen.

But if the friends of Newton were surprised by the nature of the intelligence, they were distressed

S

at the view which was taken of it by foreign philosophers. While one maintained that the intellectual
exertions of Newton had terminated with the publication of the Principia, and that the derangement of
his mind was the cause of his abandoning the sciences, others indirectly questioned the sincerity of
his religious views, and ascribed to the aberration
of his mind those theological pursuits which gilded
his declining age. " But the fact," says M. Biot,
" of the derangement of his intellect, whatever may
have been the cause of it, will explain why, after the
publication of the Principia in 1687, Newton, though
only forty-five years old, never more published a
new work on any branch of science, but contented
himself with giving to the world those which he had
composed long before that epoch, confining himself
to the completion of those parts which might require
development. We may also remark, that even
these developments appear always to be derived
from experiments and observations formerly made,
such as the additions to the second edition of the
Principia, published in 1713, the experiments on
thick plates, those on diffraction, and the chymical
queries placed at the end of the Optics in 1704; for
in giving an account of these experiments Newton
distinctly says that they were taken from ancient
manuscripts which he had formerly composed; and
he adds, that though he felt the necessity of extending them, or rendering them more perfect, he was
not able to resolve to do this, these matters being no
longer in his way. Thus it appears that though he
had recovered his health sufficiently to understand
all his researches, and even in some cases to make
additions to them, and useful alterations, as appears
from the second edition of the Principia, for which
he kept up a very active mathematical correspondence with Mr. Cotes, yet he did not wish to under-
take new labours in those departments of science
where he had done so much, and where he so dis-

tinctly saw what remained to be done." Under the influence of the same opinion, M. Biot finds "it extremely probable that his dissertation on the scale of heat was written before the fire in his laboratory;" he describes Newton's conduct about the longitude bill as "almost puerile on so solemn an occasion, and one which might lead to the strangest conclusions, particularly if we refer it to the fatal accident which Newton had suffered in 1695."

The celebrated Marquis de la Place viewed the illness of Newton in a light still more painful to his friends. He maintained that he never recovered the vigour of his intellect, and he was persuaded that Newton's theological inquiries did not commence till after that afflicting epoch of his life. He even commissioned Professor Gautier of Geneva to make inquiries on this subject during his visit to England, as if it concerned the interests of truth and justice to show that Newton became a Christian and a theological writer only after the decay of his strength and the eclipse of his reason.

Such having been the consequences of the disclosure of Newton's illness by the manuscript of Huygens, I felt it to be a sacred duty to the memory of that great man, to the feelings of his countrymen, and to the interests of Christianity itself, to inquire into the nature and history of that indisposition which seems to have been so much misrepresented and misapplied. From the ignorance of so extraordinary an event which has prevailed for such a long period in England, it might have been urged with some plausibility that Huygens had mistaken the real import of the information that was conveyed to him; or that the Scotchman from whom he received it had propagated an idle and a groundless rumour. But we are, fortunately, not confined to this very reasonable mode of defence. There exists at Cambridge a manuscript journal written by Mr. Abraham de la Pryme, who was a student in the university

while Newton was a fellow of Trinity. This manuscript is entitled "*Ephemeris Vitæ*, or Diary of my
own Life, containing an account likewise of the most
observable and remarkable things that I have taken
notice of from my youth up hitherto." Mr. de la
Pryme was born in 1671, and begins the diary in
1685. This manuscript is in the possession of his
collateral descendant, George Pryme, Esq., Professor of Political Economy at Cambridge, to whom I
have been indebted for the following extract.

"1692, *February* 3d.—What I heard to-day I must
relate. There is one Mr. Newton (whom I have
very oft seen), Fellow of Trinity College, that is
mighty famous for his learning, being a most excellent mathematician, philosopher, divine, &c. He
has been Fellow of the Royal Society these many
years; and among other very learned books and
tracts, he's written one upon the mathematical principles of philosophy, which has got him a mighty
name, he having received, especially from Scotland,
abundance of congratulatory letters for the same;
but of all the books that he ever wrote, there was
one of colours and light, established upon thousands
of experiments which he had been twenty years of
making, and which had cost him many hundred of
pounds. This book, which he valued so much, and
which was so much talked of, had the ill luck to
perish and be utterly lost just when the learned
author was almost at putting a conclusion at the
same, after this manner: In a winter's morning,
leaving it among his other papers on his study table
while he went to chapel, the candle, which he had
unfortunately left burning there too, catched hold
by some means of other papers, and they fired the
aforesaid book, and utterly consumed it and several
other valuable writings; and, which is most wonder-
ful, did no further mischief. But when Mr. Newton
came from chapel, and had seen what was done,
every one thought he would have run mad, he was

so troubled thereat that he was not himself for a month after. A long account of this his system of light and colours you may find in the Transactions of the Royal Society, which he had sent up to them long before this sad mischance happened unto him."

From this extract we are enabled to fix the approximate date of the accident by which Newton lost his papers. It must have been previous to the 3d January, 1692, a month before the date of the extract; but if we fix it by the dates in Huygens's manuscript, we should place it about the 29th November, 1692, eighteen months previous to the conversation between Collins and Huygens. The manner in which Mr. Pryme refers to Newton's state of mind is that which is used every day when we speak of the loss of tranquillity which arises from the ordinary afflictions of life; and the meaning of the passage amounts to nothing more than that Newton was very much troubled by the destruction of his papers, and did not recover his serenity, and return to his usual occupations, for a month. The very phrase that "every person thought he would have run mad" is in itself a proof that no such effect was produced; and, whatever degree of indisposition may be implied in the phrase "he was not himself for a month after," we are entitled to infer that one month was the period of its duration, and that previous to the 3d February, 1692, the date of Mr. Pryme's memorandum, "Newton was himself again."

These facts and dates cannot be reconciled with those in Huygens's manuscript. It appears from that document, that, so late as May, 1694, Newton had only *so far* recovered his health as *to begin to again understand the Principia.* His supposed malady, therefore, was in force from the 3d of January, 1692, till the month of May, 1694,—a period of more than two years. Now, it is a most important circumstance, which M. Biot ought to have known, that in *the very middle of this period,*

Newton wrote his four celebrated letters to **Dr. Bentley** on the Existence of a Deity,—letters which evince a power of thought and a serenity of mind absolutely incompatible even with the slightest obscuration of his faculties. No man can peruse these letters without the conviction that their author then possessed the full vigour of his reason, and was capable of understanding the most profound parts of his writings. The first of these letters was written on the 10th December, 1692, the second on the 17th January, 1693, the third on the 25th February, and the 4th on the 11th* February, 1693. His mind was, therefore, strong and vigorous on these four occasions; and as the letters were written at the express request of Dr. Bentley, who had been appointed to deliver the lecture founded by Mr. Boyle for vindicating the fundamental principles of natural and revealed religion, we must consider such a request as showing his opinion of the strength and freshness of his friend's mental powers.

In 1692, Newton, at the request of Dr. Wallis, transmitted to him the first proposition of his book on quadratures, with examples of it in first, second, and third fluxions.† These examples were written in consequence of an application from his friend; and the author of the review of the Commercium Epistolicum, in which this fact is quoted, draws the conclusion, that he had not at that time forgotten his method of second fluxions. It appears, also, from the second book of the Optics,‡ that in the month of June, 1692, he had been occupied with the subject of haloes, and had made accurate observations both on the colours and the diameters of the rings in a halo which he had then seen around the sun.

* They are thus dated in Horsley's edition of Newton's Works, the *fourth* letter having an earlier date than the *third*.

† See *Newtoni Opera*, tom. iv. p. 480, and *Wallasii Opera*, 1693, tom. ii. p. 391–396.

‡ *Optics*, part iv. obs. 13.

But though these facts stand in direct contradiction to the statement recorded by Huygens, the reader will be naturally anxious to know the real nature and extent of the indisposition to which it refers. The following letters,* written by Newton himself, Mr. Pepys, Secretary to the Admiralty, and Mr. Millington of Magdalene College, Cambridge, will throw much light upon the subject.

Newton, as will be presently seen, had fallen into a bad state of health some time in 1692, in consequence of which both his sleep and his appetite were greatly affected. About the middle of September, 1693, he had been kept awake for five nights by this nervous disorder, and in this condition he wrote the following letter to Mr. Pepys:

"SIR,   Sept. 13, 1693.
"Some time after Mr. Millington had delivered your message, he pressed me to see you the next time I went to London. I was averse; but upon his pressing consented, before I considered what I did, for I am extremely troubled at the embroilment I am in, and have neither ate nor slept well this twelvemonth, nor have my former consistency of mind. I never designed to get any thing by your interest, nor by King James's favour, but am now sensible that I must withdraw from your acquaintance, and see neither you nor the rest of my friends any more, if I may but leave them quietly. I beg your pardon for saying I would see you again, and rest your most humble and most obedient servant,

"IS. NEWTON."

From this letter we learn, on his own authority, that his complaint had lasted for a twelvemonth, and that during that twelvemonth he neither ate nor slept well, nor enjoyed his former *consistency of*

* For these letters I have been indebted to the kindness of Lord Braybrooke.

mind. It is not easy to understand exactly what is
meant by not enjoying his former consistency of
mind ; but whatever be its import, it is obvious that
he must have been in a state of mind so sound as to
enable him to compose the four letters to Bentley,
all of which were written during the twelvemonth
here referred to.

On the receipt of this letter, his friend Mr. Pepys
seems to have written to Mr. Millington of Magdalene College to inquire after Mr. Newton's health ;
but the inquiry having been made in a vague manner, an answer equally vague was returned.   Mr.
Pepys, however, who seems to have been deeply
anxious about Newton's health, addressed the following more explicit letter to his friend Mr. Millington :—

" SIR,   *Septemb.* 26, 1693.
"After acknowledging your many old favours,
give me leave to do it a little more particularly upon
occasion of the new one conveyed to me by my
nephew Jackson.   Though, at the same time, I
must acknowledge myself not at the ease I would
be glad to be at in reference to the excellent Mr.
Newton ; concerning whom (methinks) your answer
labours under the same kind of restraint which (to
tell you the truth) my asking did.   For I was loth
at first dash to tell you that I had lately received a
letter from him so surprising to me for the incon-
sistency of every part of it, as to be put into great
disorder by it, from the concernment I have for him,
lest it should arise from that which of all mankind I
should least dread from him and most lament for,—I
mean a discomposure in head, or mind, or both.   Let
me therefore beg you, sir, having now told you the true
ground of the trouble I lately gave you, to let me
know the very truth of the matter, as far at least as
comes within your knowledge.   For I own too great
an esteem for Mr. Newton, as for a public good, to

be able to let any doubt in me of this kind concerning him lie a moment uncleared, where I can have any hopes of helping it. I am, with great truth and respect, dear sir, your most humble, and most affectionate servant,

"S. PEPYS."

To this letter Mr. Millington made the following reply:—

Coll. Magd. Camb.
"HONOR'D SIR, *Sept. the* 30, 1693.
"Coming home from a journey on the 28th instant at night, I met with your letter which you were pleased to honour me with of the 26th. I am much troubled I was not at home in time for the post, that I might as soon as possible put you out of your generous payne that you are in for the worthy Mr. Newton. I was, I must confess, very much surprised at the inquiry you were pleased to make by your nephew about the message that Mr. Newton made the ground of his letter to you, for I was very sure I never either received from you or delivered to him any such, and therefore I went immediately to wayt upon him, with a design to discourse him about the matter, but, he was out of town, and since I have not seen him, till upon the 28th I met him at Huntingdon, where, upon his own accord, and before I had time to ask him any question, he told me that he had writt to you a very odd letter, at which he was much concerned; added, that it was in a distemper that much seized his head, and that kept him awake for above five nights together, which upon occasion he desired I would represent to you, and beg your pardon, he being very much ashamed he should be so rude to a person for whom he hath so great an honour. He is now very well, and, though I fear he is under some small degree of melancholy, yet I think there is no reason to suspect it hath at

all touched his understanding, and I hope never will; and so I am sure all ought to wish that love learning or the honour of our nation, *which it is a sign how much it is looked after, when such a person as Mr. Newton lyes so neglected by those in power.* And thus, honoured sir, I have made you acquainted with all I know of the cause of such inconsistencys in the letter of so excellent a person; and I hope it will remove the doubts and fears you are, with so much compassion and publickness of spirit, pleased to entertain about Mr. Newton; but if I should have been wanting in any thing tending to the more full satisfaction, I shall, upon the least notice, endeavour to amend it with all gratitude and truth. Honored sir, your most faithfull and most obedient servant,

"JOH. MILLINGTON."

Mr. Pepys was perfectly satisfied with this answer, as appears from the following letter:—

"SIR,   *October 3d,* 1693.
"You have delivered me from a fear that indeed gave me much trouble, and from my very heart I thank you for it; an evil to Mr. Newton being what every good man must feel for his own sake as well as his. God grant it may stopp here. And for the kind reflection hee has since made upon his letter to mee, I dare not take upon mee to judge what answer I should make him to it, or whether any or no; and therefore pray that you will bee pleased either to bestow on mee what directions you see fitt for my own guidance towards him in it, or to say to him in my name, but your own pleasure, whatever you think may be most welcome to him upon it, and most expressive of my regard and affectionate esteem of him, and concernment for him.   *   *
      *   *   *   *   Dear sir, your most humble and most faithful servant,
"S. PEPYS."

It does not appear from the memoirs of Mr. Pepys whether he ever returned any answer to the letter of Mr. Newton which occasioned this correspondence; but we find that in less than two months after the date of the preceding letter, an opportunity occurred of introducing to him a Mr. Smith, who wished to have his opinion on some problem in the doctrine of chances. This letter from Pepys is dated November 22d, 1693. Sir Isaac replied to it on the 26th November, and wrote to Pepys again on the 16th December, 1693; and in both these letters he enters fully into the discussion of the mathematical question which had been submitted to his judgment.*

It is obvious, from Newton's letter to Mr. Pepys, that the subject of his receiving some favour from the government had been a matter of anxiety with himself, and of discussion among his friends.† Mr. Millington was no doubt referring to this anxiety, when he represents Newton as an honour to the nation, and expresses his surprise "that such a person should *lye so neglected by those in power.*" And we find the same subject distinctly referred to in two letters written to Mr. Locke during the preceding year. In one of these, dated January 26th, 1691–2, he says, " Being fully convinced that Mr. Montague, upon an old grudge which I thought had been worn out, is false to me, I have done with him, and intend to sit still, unless my Lord Monmouth be still my friend." Mr. Locke seems to have assured him of the continued friendship of this nobleman, and Mr. Newton, still referring to the same topic, in a letter dated February 16th, 1691–2, remarks,

---

* These three letters have been published by Lord Braybrooke in the Life and Correspondence of Mr. Pepys.

† This anxiety will be understood from the fact that, by an order of council dated January 28th, 1674-5, Mr. Newton was excused from making the usual payments of one shilling per week, "on account of his low circumstances, as he represented."

"I am very glad Lord Monmouth is still my friend, but intend not to give his lordship and you any farther trouble. My inclinations are to sit still." In a later letter to Mr. Locke, dated September, 1693, and given below, he asks his pardon for saying or thinking that there was a design to sell him an office. In these letters Mr. Newton no doubt referred to some appointment in London which he was solicitous to obtain, and which Mr. Montague and his other friends may have failed in procuring. This opinion is confirmed by the letter of Mr. Montague announcing to him his appointment to the wardenship of the mint, in which he says that he is very glad he can *at last* give him good proof of his friendship.

In the same month in which Newton wrote to Mr. Pepys, we find him in correspondence with Mr. Locke. Displeased with his opinions respecting innate ideas, he had rashly stated that they struck at the root of all morality; and that he regarded the author of such doctrines as a Hobbist. Upon reconsidering these opinions, he addressed the following remarkable letter to Locke, written three days after his letter to Mr. Pepys, and consequently during the illness under which he then laboured.

"SIR,

"Being of opinion that you endeavoured to embroil me with women, and by other means, I was so much affected with it, as that when one told me you were sickly and would not live, I answered, 'twere better if you were dead. I desire you to forgive me this uncharitableness; for I am now satisfied that what you have done is just, and I beg your pardon for my having hard thoughts of you for it, and for representing that you struck at the root of morality, in a principle you laid in your book of ideas, and designed to pursue in another book, and that I took you for a Hobbist.*   I beg your pardon also for saying or thinking that there was a design to sell me an office, or to embroil me.—I am your most humble and unfortunate servant,

" Is. NEWTON.

" *At the Bull, in Shoreditch, London,*
        Sept. 16th, 1693."

To this letter Locke returned the following answer, so nobly distinguished by philosophical magnanimity and Christian charity :—

"Sir,   *Oates, Oct. 5th, 1693.*
    " I have been, ever since I first knew you, so entirely and sincerely your 'friend, and thought you so much mine, that I could not have believed what you tell me of yourself had I had it from anybody else. And, though I cannot but be mightily troubled that you should have had so many wrong and unjust thoughts of me, yet next to the return of good offices, such as from a sincere good-will I have ever done you, I receive your acknowledgment of the contrary as the kindest thing you have done me, since it gives me hopes I have not lost a friend I so much valued.   After what your letter expresses, I shall not need to say any thing to justify myself to you.   I shall always think your own reflection on my carriage, both to you and all mankind, will sufficiently do that.   Instead of that, give me leave to assure you that I am more ready to forgive you than you can be to desire it; and I do it so freely and fully, that I wish for nothing more than the opportunity to convince you that I truly love and esteem you, and that I have the same good-will for you as if

---

* The system of Hobbes was at this time very prevalent.   According to Dr. Bentley, " the taverns and coffee-houses, nay, Westminster Hall and the very churches, were full of it ;" and he was convinced from personal observation, that " not one English infidel in a hundred was other than a Hobbist."—Monk's *Life of Bentley,* p. 31.

T

nothing of this had happened. To confirm this to you more fully, I should be glad to meet you any where, and the rather, because the conclusion of your letter makes me apprehend it would not be wholly useless to you. But whether you think it fit or not, I leave wholly to you. I shall always be ready to serve you to my utmost, in any way you shall like, and shall only need your commands or permission to do it.

"My book is going to press for a second edition; and, though I can answer for the design with which I write it, yet, since you have so opportunely given me notice of what you have said of it, I should take it as a favour if you would point out to me the places that gave occasion to that censure, that, by explaining myself better, I may avoid being mistaken by others, or unawares doing the least prejudice to truth or virtue. I am sure you are so much a friend to them both, that, were you none to me, I could expect this from you. But I cannot doubt but you would do a great deal more than this for my sake, who, after all, have all the concern of a friend for you, wish you extremely well, and am, without compliment, &c."*

To this letter Newton made the following reply:—

" SIR,

" The last winter, by sleeping too often by my fire, I got an ill habit of sleeping; and a distemper, which this summer has been epidemical, put me farther out of order, so that when I wrote to you, I had not slept an hour a night for a fortnight together, and for five days together not a wink. I remember I wrote to you, but what I said of your book I remember not. If you please to send me a transcript

---

* The draft of this letter is endorsed "J. L. to I. Newton."

of that passage, I will give you an account of it if I can.—I am your most humble servant,

"Is. NEWTON.

"*Cambridge, Oct. 5th,* 1693."

Although the first of these letters evinces the existence of a nervous irritability which could not fail to arise from want of appetite and of rest, yet it is obvious that its author was in the full possession of his mental powers. The answer of Mr. Locke, indeed, is written upon that supposition; and it deserves to be remarked, that Mr. Dugald Stewart, who first published a portion of these letters, never imagines for a moment that Newton was labouring under any mental alienation.

The opinion entertained by Laplace, that Newton devoted his attention to theology only in the latter part of his life, may be considered as deriving some countenance from the fact, that the celebrated general scholium at the end of the second edition of the Principia, published in 1713, did not appear in the first edition of that work. This argument has been ably controverted by Dr. J. C. Gregory of Edinburgh, on the authority of a manuscript of Newton, which seems to have been transmitted to his ancestor, Dr. David Gregory, between the years 1687 and 1698. This manuscript, which consists of twelve folio pages in Newton's handwriting, contains, in the form of additions and scholia to some propositions in the third book of the Principia, an account of the opinions of the ancient philosophers on gravitation and motion, and on natural theology, with various quotations from their works. Attached to this manuscript are three very curious paragraphs. The first two appear to have been the original draught of the general scholium already referred to; and the third relates to the subject of an ethereal medium, respecting which he maintains an opinion diametrically opposite to that which he afterward published at the end of his Optics.* The first paragraph expresses nearly the same ideas as some sentences in the scholium beginning " Deus summus est ens æternum, infinitum, absolute perfectum ;"† and it is remarkable that the second paragraph is found only in the third edition of the Principia, which appeared in 1726, the year before Newton's death.

In the middle of the year 1694, about the time when our author is said to be beginning to understand the Principia, we find him occupied with the difficult and profound subject of the lunar theory. In order to procure observations for verifying the equations which he had deduced from the theory of gravity, he paid a visit to Flamstead, at the Royal Observatory of Greenwich, on the 1st September, 1694, when he received from him a series of lunar observations. On the 7th of October he wrote to Flamstead that he had compared the observations with his theory, and had satisfied himself that by both together "the moon's theory may be reduced to a good degree of exactness, perhaps to the exactness of two or three minutes." He wrote him again on the 24th October, and the correspondence was continued till 1698, Newton making constant application for observations to compare with his theory

---

* Dr. Gregory concludes his account of this manuscript, which he has kindly permitted me to read, in the following words :—" I do not know whether it is true, as stated by Huygens, 'Newtonum incidisse in Phrenitim ;' but I think every gentleman who examines this manuscript will be of opinion that he must have thoroughly recovered from his phrenitis before he wrote either the Commentary on the Opinions of the Ancients, or the Sketch of his own Theological and Philosophical Opinions which it contains."

† This paragraph is as follows :—" Deum esse ens summe perfectum concedunt omnes. Entis autem summe perfecti Idea est ut sit substantia, una, simplex, indivisibilis, viva et vivifica, ubique semper necessario existens, summe intelligens omnia, libere volens bona, voluntate efficiens possibilia, effectibus nobilioribus similitudinem propriam quantum fieri potest communicans, omnia in se continens tanquam eorum principium et locus, omnia per presentiam substantialem cernens et regens, et cum rebus omnibus, secundum leges accuratas ut naturæ totius fundamentum et causa constanter co-operans, nisi ubi aliter agere bonum est,"

of the planetary motions; while Flamstead, not sufficiently aware of the importance of the inquiry, received his requests as if they were idle intrusions in which the interests of science were but slightly concerned.*

In reviewing the details which we have now given respecting the health and occupations of Newton from the beginning of 1692 till 1695, it is impossible to draw any other conclusion than that he possessed a sound mind, and was perfectly capable of carrying on his mathematical, his metaphysical, and his astronomical inquiries. His friend and admirer, Mr. Pepys, residing within fifty miles of Cambridge, had never heard of his being attacked with any illness till he inferred it from the letter to himself written in September, 1693. Mr. Millington, who lived in the same university, had been equally unacquainted with any such attack, and, after a personal interview with Newton, for the express purpose of ascertaining the state of his health, he assures Mr. Pepys "that he is very well,—that he fears he is under some small degree of melancholy, but that there is

---

* The following extract, characteristic of Flamstead's manner, is from a letter to Newton dated January 6, 1698-9.

"Upon hearing occasionally that you had sent a letter to Dr. Wallis about the parallax of the fixed stars to be printed, and that you had mentioned me therein with respect to the theory of the moon, I was concerned to be publicly brought upon the state about what, perhaps, will never be fitted for the public, and thereby the world *put into an expectation of what perhaps they are never likely to have.*' I do not love to be printed upon every occasion, much less to be dunned and teased by foreigners about mathematical things, or to be thought *by your own people to be trifling* away my time when I should be about the king's business." On the first of the above passages in italics Flamstead has the following memorandum:—"When Mr. Halley boasts 'tis done, and given to him as a secret, tells the Society so and foreigners." In the second passage in italics, Mr. Flamstead refers, in a note, to Mr. Colson's letter to him, in which he seems to have represented practical astronomy as trifling. Mr. Flamstead adds, "Was Mr. Newton a trifler when he read mathematics for a salary at Cambridge: surely, then, astronomy is of some good use, though his place be more beneficial." For these extracts from the original manuscript in the collection of Corpus Christi College, Oxford, I have been indebted to the kindness of Professor Rigaud of Oxford.

no reason to suspect that it hath at all touched his understanding."

During this period of bodily indisposition, his mind, though in a state of nervous irritability, and disturbed by want of rest, was capable of putting forth its highest powers. At the request of Dr. Wallis he drew up an example of one of his propositions on the quadrature of curves in second fluxions. He composed, at the desire of Dr. Bentley, his profound and beautiful letters on the existence of the Deity. He was requested by Locke to reconsider his opinions on the subject of innate ideas; and we find him grappling with the difficulties of the lunar theory.

But with all these proofs of a vigorous mind, a diminution of his mental powers has been rashly inferred from the cessation of his great discoveries, and from his unwillingness to enter upon new investigations. The facts, however, here assumed are as incorrect as the inference which is drawn from them. The ambition of fame is a youthful passion, which is softened, if not subdued, by age. Success diminishes its ardour, and early pre-eminence often extinguishes it. Before the middle period of life Newton was invested with all the insignia of immortality; but endowed with a native humility of mind, and animated with those hopes which teach us to form an humble estimate of human greatness, he was satisfied with the laurels which he had won, and he sought only to perfect and complete his labours. His mind was principally bent on the improvement of the Principia; but he occasionally diverged into new fields of scientific research, —he solved problems of great difficulty which had been proposed to try his strength,—and he devoted much of his time to profound inquiries in chronology and in theological literature.

The powers of his mind were therefore in full requisition; and, when we consider that he was

called to the discharge of high official functions
which forced him into public life, and compelled
him to direct his genius into new channels, we can
scarcely be surprised that he ceased to produce any
original works on abstract science. In the direction of the affairs of the mint, and of the Royal Society, to which we shall now follow him, he found
ample occupation for his time ; while the leisure of
his declining years was devoted to those exalted
studies in which philosophy yields to the supremacy
of faith, and hope administers to the aspirations of
genius.

CHAPTER XIV.

*No Mark of National Gratitude conferred upon Newton—Friendship
between him and Charles Montague, afterward Earl of Halifax—Mr
Montague appointed Chancellor of the Exchequer in 1694—He resolves
upon a Recoinage—Nominates Mr. Newton Warden of the Mint in
1695—Mr. Newton appointed Master of the Mint in 1699—Notice of
the Earl of Halifax—Mr. Newton elected Associate of the Academy
of Sciences in 1699—Member for Cambridge in 1701—and President
of the Royal Society in 1703—Queen Anne confers upon him the
Honour of Knighthood in 1705—Second Edition of the Principia,
edited by Cotes—His Conduct respecting Mr. Ditton's Method of finding the Longitude.*

HITHERTO we have viewed Newton chiefly as a
philosopher leading a life of seclusion within the
walls of a college, and either engaged in the duties
of his professorship, or ardently occupied in mathematical and scientific inquiries. He had now reached
the fifty-third year of his age, and while those of his
own standing at the university had been receiving
high appointments in the church, or lucrative offices
in the state, he still remained without any mark of
the respect or gratitude of his country. All Europe
indeed had been offering incense to his name, and

Englishmen themselves boasted of him as the pride of their country and the ornament of their species, but he was left in comparative poverty,* with no other income than the salary of his professorship, eked out with the small rental of his paternal inheritance. Such disregard of the highest genius, dignified by the highest virtue, could have taken place only in England, and we should have ascribed it to the turbulence of the age in which he lived, had we not seen, in the history of another century, that the successive governments which preside over the destinies of our country have never been able either to feel or to recognise the true nobility of genius.

Among his friends at Cambridge Newton had the honour of numbering Charles Montague, grandson of Henry Earl of Manchester, a young man of high promise, and every way worthy of his friendship. Though devoted to literary pursuits, and twenty years younger than Newton, he cherished for the philosopher all the veneration of a disciple, and his affection for him gathered new strength as he rose to the highest honours and offices of the state. In the year 1684 we find him co-operating with Newton in the establishment of a philosophical society at Cambridge; but though both of them had made personal application to different individuals to become members, yet the plan failed, from the want, as Newton expresses it, of persons willing to try experiments.

Mr. Montague sat along with Newton in the convention parliament, and such were the powers which he displayed in that assembly as a public speaker, that he was appointed a commissioner of the treasury, and soon afterward a privy counsellor. In these situations his talents and knowledge of business were highly conspicuous, and in 1694 he was ap-

* See page 215, note.

pointed chancellor of the exchequer. The current coin of the nation having been adulterated and debased, one of his earliest designs was to recoin it and restore it to its intrinsic value. This scheme, however, met with great opposition. It was characterized as a wild project, unsuitable to a period of war, as highly injurious to the interests of commerce, and as likely to sap the foundation of the government. But he had weighed the subject too deeply, and had intrenched himself behind opinions too impartial and too well-founded, to be driven from a measure which the best interests of his country seemed to require.

The persons whom Mr. Montague had consulted about the recoinage were Newton, Locke, and Halley, and in consequence of Mr. Overton, the warden of the mint, having been appointed a commissioner of customs, he embraced the opportunity which was thus offered of serving his friend and his country by recommending Newton to that important office. The notice of this appointment was conveyed in the following letter to Newton.

"SIR,   London, 19th March, 1695.
"I am very glad that, at last, I can give you a good proof of my friendship, and the esteem the king has of your merits. Mr. Overton, the warden of the mint, is made one of the commissioners of the customs, and the king has promised me to make Mr. Newton warden of the mint. The office is the most proper for you. 'Tis the chief office in the mint, 'tis worth five or six hundred pounds per annum, and has not too much business to require more attendance than you can spare. I desire that you will come up as soon as you can, and I will take care of your warrant in the mean time. Let me see you as soon as you come to town, that I may carry you to kiss the king's hand. I believe you may have a lodging near me.—I am, &c.   CHARLES MONTAGUE."

In this new situation the mathematical and chymical knowledge of our author was of great service to the nation, and he became eminently useful in carrying on the recoinage, which was completed in the short space of two years. In the year 1699, he was promoted to the mastership of the mint,—an office which was worth twelve or fifteen hundred pounds per annum, and which he held during the remainder of his life. In this situation he wrote an official report on the Coinage, which has been published; and he drew up a table of Assays of Foreign Coins, which is printed at the end of Dr. Arbuthnot's Tables of Ancient Coins, Weights, and Measures, which appeared in 1727.

While our author filled the inferior office of warden of the mint, he retained his professorship at Cambridge; but upon his promotion in 1699, he appointed Mr. Whiston to be his deputy, with all the emoluments of the office; and when he resigned the chair in 1703, he succeeded in getting him nominated his successor.

The appointment of Newton to the mastership of the mint must have been peculiarly gratifying to the Royal Society, and it was probably from a feeling of gratitude to Mr. Montague, as much as from a regard for his talents, that this able statesman was elected president of that learned body on the 30th November, 1695. This office he held for three years, and on the 30th January, 1697, Newton had the satisfaction of addressing to him his solution of the celebrated problems proposed by John Bernouilli.

This accomplished nobleman was created Earl of Halifax in 1700, and after the death of his first wife he conceived a strong attachment for Mrs. Catharine Barton, the widow of Colonel Barton, and the niece of Newton. This lady was young, gay, and beautiful, and though she did not escape the censures of her contemporaries, she was regarded by those who knew her as a woman of strict honour and virtue.

We are not acquainted with the causes which prevented her union with the Earl of Halifax, but so great was the esteem and affection which he bore her, that in the will in which he left 100l. to Mr. Newton, he bequeathed to his niece a very large portion of his fortune. This distinguished statesman died in 1715, in the fifty-fourth year of his age. Himself a poet and an elegant writer, he was the liberal patron of genius, and he numbered among his intimate friends Congreve, Halley, Prior, Tickell, Steele, and Pope. His conduct to Newton will be for ever remembered in the annals of science. The sages of every nation and of every age will pronounce with affection the name of Charles Montague, and the persecuted science of England will continue to deplore that he was the first and the last English minister who honoured genius by his friendship and rewarded it by his patronage.

The elevation of Mr. Newton to the highest offices in the mint was followed by other marks of honour. The Royal Academy of Sciences at Paris having been empowered by a new charter granted in 1699, to admit a very small number of foreign associates, Newton was elected a member of that distinguished body. In the year 1701, on the assembling of a new parliament, he was re-elected one of the members for the University of Cambridge.* In 1703 he was chosen President of the Royal Society of London, and he was annually re-elected to this office during the remaining twenty-five years of his life. On the 16th of April, 1705, when Queen Anne was living at the royal residence of Newmarket, she went with Prince George of Denmark and the rest of the court to visit the University of Cambridge. After the meeting of the Regia Consilia, her majesty held a

---

* The candidates in 1701 were as follows:

Mr. Henry Boyle, afterward Lord Carleton,	180	Both of Trinity
Mr. Newton	161	College.
Mr. Hammond	64	

court at Trinity Lodge, the residence of Dr. Bentley, then master of Trinity; where the honour of knighthood was conferred upon Mr. Newton, Mr. John Ellis, the vice-chancellor, and Mr. James Montague, the university counsel.*

On the dissolution of the parliament, which took place in 1705, Sir Isaac was again a candidate for the representation of the University, but notwithstanding the recent expression of the royal favour, he lost his election by a very great majority.† This singular result was perhaps owing to the loss of that personal influence which his residence in the university could not fail to command, though it is more probable that the ministry preferred the candidates of a more obsequious character, and that the electors looked for advantages which Sir Isaac Newton was not able to obtain for them.

Although the first edition of the Principia had been for some time sold off, and copies of it had become extremely rare, yet Sir Isaac's attention was so much occupied with his professional avocations that he could not find leisure for preparing a new edition. Dr. Bentley, who had repeatedly urged him to this task, at last succeeded, by engaging Roger Cotes, Plumian Professor of Astronomy at Cambridge, to superintend its publication at the university press. In June, 1709, Sir Isaac committed this important trust to his young friend; and about the middle of July he promised to send him in the course of a fortnight his own revised copy of the work. Business, however, seems to have intervened, and Mr. Cotes was obliged to remind Sir Isaac of his promise, which he did in the following letter:—

* The banquet which was on this occasion given in the college hall to the royal visiter seems to have cost about 1000l., and the university was obliged to borrow 500l., to defray the expense of it.—Monk's *Life of Bentley*, p. 143, 144.

† The candidates in 1705 were as follows:

The Hon. Arthur Annesley 182
Hon. Dixie Windsor . 170
Mr. Godolphin . . . 162
Sir Isaac Newton . . 117

" SIR,   *Cambridge, Aug.* 18*th*, 1709.

" The earnest desire I have to see a new edition of your *Principia* makes me somewhat impatient till we receive your copy of it, which you were pleased to promise me about the middle of last month you would send down in about a fortnight's time. I hope you will pardon me for this uneasiness, from which I cannot free myself, and for giving you this trouble to let you know it. I have been so much obliged by yourself and by your book, that (I desire you to believe me) I think myself bound in gratitude to take all the care I possibly can that it shall be correct.—Your obliged servant,

" ROGER COTES.

" *For Sir Isaac Newton, at his house in*
    Jermyn-street, near St. James's
       Church, Westminster."

This was the first letter of that celebrated correspondence, consisting of nearly three hundred letters, in which Sir Isaac and Mr. Cotes discussed the various improvements which were thought necessary in a new edition of the Principia. This valuable collection of letters is preserved in the library of Trinity College; and we cannot refrain from repeating the wish expressed by Dr. Monk, " that one of the many accomplished Newtonians who are resident in that society would favour the world by publishing the whole collection."

When the work was at last printed, Mr. Cotes expressed a wish that Dr. Bentley should write the preface to it, but it was the opinion both of Sir Isaac and Dr. Bentley that the preface should come from the pen of Mr. Cotes himself. This he accordingly undertook; but previous to its execution he addressed the following letter to Dr. Bentley, in order to learn from Sir Isaac the particular view with which it should be written.

U

"SIR, *March 10th*, 1712–13.

"I received what you wrote to me in Sir Isaac's letter. I will set about the index in a day or two. As for the preface, I should be glad to know from Sir Isaac with what view he thinks proper to have it written. You know the book has been received abroad with some disadvantage, and the cause of it may be easily guessed at. The *Commercium Epistolicum*, lately published by order of the Royal Society, gives such indubitable proofs of Mr. Leibnitz's want of candour, that I shall not scruple in the least to speak out the full truth of the matter, if it be thought convenient. There are some pieces of his looking this way which deserve a censure, as his *Tentamen de motuum cælestium causis*. If Sir Isaac is willing that something of this nature may be done, I should be glad if, while I am making the index, he would consider of it, and put down a few notes of what he thinks most material to be insisted on. This I say upon supposition that I write the preface myself. But I think it will be much more advisable that you, or he, or both of you should write it while you are in town. You may depend upon it I will own it, and defend it as well as I can, if hereafter there be occasion.—I am sir, &c."

We are not acquainted with the instructions which were given to Mr. Cotes in consequence of this application; but it appears from the preface itself, which contains a long and able summary of the Newtonian philosophy, that Sir Isaac had prohibited any personal reference to the conduct of Leibnitz.

The general preface is dated 12th May, 1713, and in a subsidiary preface of only a few lines, dated March 28th, 1713, Sir Isaac mentions the leading alterations which had been made in this edition. The determination of the forces by which bodies may revolve in given orbits was simplified and enlarged. The theory of the resistance of fluids was more accurately investigated, and confirmed by new experiments. The theory of the moon and the precession of the equinoxes were more fully deduced from their principles; and the theory of comets was confirmed by several examples of their orbits more accurately computed.

In the year 1714, several captains and owners of merchant vessels petitioned the House of Commons to consider the propriety of bringing in a bill to reward inventions for promoting the discovery of the longitude at sea. A committee was appointed to investigate the subject, and Mr. Ditton and Mr. Whiston, having thought of a new method of finding the longitude, submitted it to the committee. Four members of the Royal Society, viz. Sir Isaac Newton, Dr. Halley, Mr. Cotes, and Dr. Clarke, were examined on the subject, along with Mr. Ditton and Mr. Whiston. The last three of these philosophers stated their opinions verbally. Mr. Cotes considered the proposed scheme as correct in theory and on shore, and both he and Dr. Halley were of opinion that expensive experiments would be requisite. Newton, when called upon for his opinion, read the following memorandum, which deserves to be recorded.

"For determining the longitude at sea there have been several projects, true in theory, but difficult to execute.

"1. One is by a watch to keep time exactly; but by reason of the motion of the ship, the variation of heat and cold, wet or dry, and the difference of gravity in different latitudes, such a watch hath not yet been made.

"2. Another is by the eclipses of Jupiter's satellites; but by reason of the length of telescopes requisite to observe them, and the motion of a ship at sea, those eclipses cannot yet be there observed.

"3. A third is by the place of the moon; but her theory is not yet exact enough for that purpose; it is exact enough to determine the longitude within two or three degrees, but not within a degree.

"4. A fourth is Mr. Ditton's project, and this is rather for keeping an account of the longitude at sea than for finding it, if at any time it should be lost, as it may easily be in cloudy weather. How far this is practicable, and with what charge, they that are skilled in sea affairs are best able to judge. In sailing by this method, whenever they are to pass over very deep seas, they must sail due east or west; they must first sail into the latitude of the next place to which they are going beyond it, and then keep due east or west till they come at that place. In the first three ways there must be a watch regulated by a spring, and rectified every visible sunrise and sunset, to tell the hour of the day or night. In the fourth way such a watch is not necessary. In the first way there must be two watches, this and the other above mentioned. In any of the first three ways, it may be of some service to find the longitude within a degree, and of much more service to find it within forty minutes, or half a degree if it may, and the success may deserve rewards accordingly. In the fourth way, it is easier to enable seamen to know their distance and bearing from the shore 40, 60, or 80 miles off, than to cross the seas; and some part of the reward may be given when the first is performed on the coast of Great Britain for the safety of ships coming home; and the rest when seamen shall be enabled to sail to an assigned remote harbour without losing their longitude if it may be."

The committee brought up their report on the 11th June, and recommended that a bill should be introduced into parliament for the purpose of rewarding inventions or discoveries connected with the determination of the longitude. The bill passed the House of Commons on the 3d July, and was agreed to by the Lords on the 8th of the same month.*

* Journals of the House of Commons, vol. xvii. p. 677, 716.

In giving an account of this transaction,* Mr. Whiston states, that nobody understood Sir Isaac's paper, and that after sitting down he obstinately kept silence, though he was much pressed to explain himself more distinctly. At last, seeing that the scheme was likely to be rejected, Whiston ventured to say that Sir Isaac did not wish to explain more through fear of compromising himself, but that he really approved of the plan. Sir Isaac, he goes on to say, repeated word for word what Whiston had said. This is the part of Mr. Newton's conduct which M. Biot has described as puerile, and "tending to confirm the fact of the aberration of his intellect in 1693." Before we can admit such a censure we must be satisfied with the correctness of Whiston's statement. Newton's paper is perfectly intelligible, and we may easily understand how he might have approved of Mr. Ditton's plan as ingenious and practicable under particular circumstances, though he did not think it of that paramount importance which would have authorized the House of Commons to distinguish it by a parliamentary reward. The conflict between public duty and a disposition to promote the interests of Mr. Whiston and Mr. Ditton was no doubt the cause of that embarrassment of manner which the former of these mathematicians has so unkindly brought before the public.

* Whiston's "Longitude Discovered." Lond 1738.

U 2

CHAPTER XV.

ON the accession of George I. to the British throne
in 1714, Sir Isaac Newton became an object of interest at court. His high situation under government, his splendid reputation, his spotless character, and, above all, his unaffected piety attracted
the attention of the Princess of Wales, afterward
queen-consort to George II. This lady, who possessed a highly cultivated mind, derived the greatest
pleasure from conversing with Newton and corresponding with Leibnitz. In all her difficulties, she
received from Sir Isaac that information and assistance which she had elsewhere sought in vain, and
she was often heard to declare in public that she
thought herself fortunate in living at a time which
enabled her to enjoy the conversation of so great a
genius. But while Newton was thus esteemed by
the house of Hanover, Leibnitz, his great rival, endeavoured to weaken and undermine his influence.
In his correspondence with the princess, he represented the Newtonian philosophy, not only as physically false, but as injurious to the interests of
religion. He asserted that natural religion was
rapidly declining in England, and he supported this
position by referring to the works of Locke, and to

the beautiful and pious sentiments contained in the 28th query at the end of the Optics. He represented the principles of these great men as precisely the same with those of the materialists, and thus endeavoured to degrade the character of English philosophers.

These attacks of Leibnitz became subjects of conversation at court, and when they reached the ear of the king, his majesty expressed his expectation that Sir Isaac Newton would draw up a reply. He accordingly entered the lists on the mathematical part of the controversy, and left the philosophical part of it to Dr. Clarke, who was a full match for the German philosopher. The correspondence which thus took place was carefully perused by the princess, and from the estimation in which Sir Isaac continued to be held, we may infer that the views of the English philosopher were not very remote from her own.

When Sir Isaac was one day conversing with her royal highness on some points of ancient history, he was led to mention to her, and to explain, a new system of chronology which he composed during his residence at Cambridge, where he was in the habit, as he himself expresses it, "of refreshing himself with history and chronology when he was weary with other studies." The princess was so much pleased with his ingenious system, that she subsequently, in the year 1718, sent a message by the Abbé Conti to Sir Isaac, requesting him to speak with her, and she, on this occasion, requested a copy of the interesting work which contained his system of chronology. Sir Isaac informed her that it existed merely in separate papers, which were not only in a state of confusion, but which contained a very imperfect view of the subject, and he promised, in a few days, to draw up an abstract of it for her own private use, and on the condition that it should not be communicated to any other person. Some time after the

princess received the manuscript, she requested that
the Abbé Conti might be allowed to have a copy of
it. Sir Isaac granted this request, and the Abbé was
informed that he received a copy of the manuscript
with Sir Isaac's leave, and at the princess's request,
and that it was to be kept secret.* The manuscript
which was thus rashly put into the hands of a
foreigner was entitled " A Short Chronicle from the
First Memory of Things in Europe to the Conquest
of Persia by Alexander the Great." It consists of
about twenty-four quarto printed pages,† with an
introduction of four pages, in which Sir Isaac states
that he " does not pretend to be exact to a year, that
there may be errors of five or ten years, and sometimes twenty, but not much above."

The Abbé Conti kept his promise of secrecy during
his residence in England, but he no sooner reached
Paris than he communicated it to M. Freret, a
learned antiquarian, who not only translated it, but
drew up observations upon it for the purpose of re-
futing some of its principal results. Sir Isaac was
unacquainted with this transaction till he was informed of it by the French bookseller, M. Cavalier,
who requested his leave to publish it, and charged
one of his friends in London to procure Sir Isaac's
answer, which was as follows:—

" I remember that I wrote a Chronological index
for a particular friend, on condition that it should not
be communicated. As I have not seen the manuscript which you have under my name, I know not
whether it be the same. That which I wrote was
not at all done with design to publish it. I intend
not to meddle with that which hath been given you

* This anecdote concerning the Chronological manuscript is not correctly given in the Biographia Britannica, and in some of the other lives
of Newton. I have followed implicitly Newton's own account of it in
the *Phil. Trans.* 1725, vol. xxxiii. No. 389, p. 315.

† M. Biot has supposed that this abstract was an imperfect edition of
Newton's work on Chronology.

under my name, nor to give any consent to the publishing of it.—I am your very humble servant,

"ISAAC NEWTON.

"*London, May 27th*, 1725, O. S."

Before this letter was written, viz. on the 21st May, the bookseller had received the royal privilege for printing the work; and when it was completed, he sent a copy in a present to Sir Isaac, who received it on the 11th November, 1725. It was entitled, *Abregé de Chronologie de M. Le Chevalier Newton, fait par lui-meme, et traduit sur le manuscript Anglais*, and was accompanied with observations by M. Freret,* the object of which was to refute the leading points of the system.† An advertisement was prefixed to it, in which the bookseller defends himself for printing it without the author's leave, on the ground that he had written three letters to obtain permission, and had declared that he would take Sir Isaac's silence for consent. When Sir Isaac received this work, he drew up a paper entitled, *Remarks on the Observations made on a Chronological Index of Sir Isaac Newton, translated into French by the Observator, and published at Paris*, which was printed in the *Philosophical Transactions for* 1725.‡ In this paper Sir Isaac gives a history of the transaction,—charges the Abbé Conti with a breach of promise, and blames the publisher for having asked his leave to print the translation without sending him a copy for his perusal, without acquainting him with the name of the translator, and without announcing his intention of printing along with it a refutation of the original.

* Father Souciet was supposed by Halley and others to have been the author of these observations, but there is no doubt that they were written by M. Freret.

† It is stated in the *Biogr. Britannica*, Art. *Newton*, that the copy of the French translation was not accompanied with the refutation. Though the reverse of this is not distinctly stated by Sir Isaac himself, yet it may be inferred from his observations.

‡ Vol. xxxiii. No. 389, p. 315.

The observations made by the translator against the conclusions deduced by the author were founded on an imperfect knowledge of Sir Isaac's system; and they are so specious, that Halley himself confesses that he was at first prejudiced in favour of the observations, taking the calculations for granted, and not having seen Sir Isaac's work.

To all the observations of M. Freret Sir Isaac returned a triumphant answer. This presumptuous antiquary had ventured to state at the end of his observations, " that he believed he had stated enough concerning the epochs of the Argonauts, and the length of generations, to make people cautious about the rest; for these are the two foundations of all this new system of chronology." He founds his arguments against the epochs of the Argonauts, as fixed by our author, on the supposition that Sir Isaac places the vernal equinox at the time of the Argonautic expedition *in the middle of the sign of Aries,* whereas Sir Isaac places it *in the middle of the constellation,*—a point corresponding with the middle of the back of Aries, or 8° from the first star of Aries. This position of the colure is assigned on the authority of Eudoxus, as given by Hipparchus, who says that the colure passed over the back of Aries. Setting out with this mistake, M. Freret concludes that the Argonautic expedition took place 532 years earlier than Sir Isaac made it. His second objection to the new system relates to the length of generations, which he says is made only 18 or 20 years. Sir Isaac, on the contrary, reckons a generation at 33 years, or 3 generations at 100; and it was the lengths of the reigns of kings that he made 18 or 20 years. This deduction he founds on the reigns of 64 French kings. Now, the ancient Greeks and Egyptians reckoned the length of a reign equal to that of a generation; and it was by correcting this mistake, and adopting a measure founded on fact, that Sir Isaac placed the Argonautic expedition forty-four years after the death of Solomon, and fixed some of the other points of his system.

This answer of Sir Isaac's to the objections of Freret called into the field a fresh antagonist, Father Souciet, who published five dissertations on the new chronology. These dissertations were written in a tone highly reprehensible; and the friends of Sir Isaac, being apprehensive that the manner in which his system was attacked would affect him more than the arguments themselves, prevailed upon a friend to draw up an abstract of Souciet's objections, stripped of the "extraordinary ornaments with which they were clothed." The perusal of these objections had no other effect upon him than to convince him of the ignorance of their author; and he was induced to read the entire work, which produced no change in his opinion.

In consequence of these discussions, Sir Isaac was prevailed upon to prepare his larger work for the press. He had nearly completed it at the time of his death, and it was published in 1728, under the title of *The Chronology of Ancient Kingdoms amended, to which is prefixed a short Chronicle*, from the first memory of Things in Europe *to the Conquest of Persia by Alexander the Great*. It was dedicated to the queen by Mr. Conduit, and consists of six chapters: 1. On the Chronology of the Greeks;* 2. Of the Empire of Egypt; 3. Of the Assyrian Empire; 4. Of the two contemporary Empires of the Babylonians and Medes; 5. A Description of the Temple of Solomon; 6. Of the Empire of the Persians. The sixth chapter was not copied out with the other five, which makes it doubtful whether or not it was intended for publication; but as it was found among his papers, and appeared to be a continuation of the

* According to Whiston, Sir Isaac wrote out eighteen copies of this chapter with his own hand, differing little from one another.—*Whiston's Life*, p. 39.

same work, it was thought right to add it to the other five chapters.*

After the death of Newton, Dr. Halley, who had not yet seen the larger work, felt himself called upon, both as astronomer-royal and as the friend of the author, to reply to the first and last dissertations of Father Souciet, which were chiefly astronomical; and in two papers printed in the Philosophical Transactions for 1727,† he has done this in a most convincing and learned argument.

Among the supporters of the views of Newton, we may enumerate Dr. Reid, Nauze, and some other writers; and among its opponents, M. Freret, who left behind him a posthumous work on the subject, M. Fourmond, Mr. A. Bedford, Dr. Shuckford, Dr. Middleton, Whiston, and the late M. Delambre. The object of M. Fourmond is to show the uncertainty of the astronomical argument, arising on the one hand from the vague account of the ancient sphere as given by Hipparchus; and, on the other, from the extreme rudeness of ancient astronomical observations. Delambre has taken a similar view of the subject: he regards the observations of ancient astronomers as too incorrect to form the basis of a system of chronology; and he maintains, that if we admit the accuracy of the details in the sphere of Eudoxus, and suppose them all to belong to the same epoch, all the stars which it contains ought at that epoch to be found in the place where they are marked, and we might thence verify the accuracy, and ascertain the state of the observations. It follows, however, from such an examination, that the

---

* This work is the first article in the fifth volume of Dr. Horsley's edition of Newton's works. The next article in the volume is entitled, " A Short Chronicle from a MS., the property of the Reverend Dr. Ekins, Dean of Carlisle;" which is nothing more than the abstract of the Chronology already printed in the same volume. We cannot even conjecture the reasons for publishing it, especially as it is less perfect than the abstract, two or three dates being wanting.

† See vol. xxxiv. p. 205, and vol. xxxv. p. 296.

sphere would indicate almost as many different epochs as it contains stars. Some of them even had not, in the time of Eudoxus, arrived at the position which had been for a long time attributed to them, and will not even reach it for three hundred years to come, and on this account he considers it impossible to deduce any chronological conclusions from such a rude mass of errors.

But however well-founded these observations may be, we agree in opinion with M. Daunou,* "that they are not sufficient to establish a new system, and we must regard the system of Newton as a great fact in the history of chronological science, and as confirming the observation of Varro, that the stage of history does not commence till the first Olympiad."

Among the chronological writings of Sir Isaac Newton we must enumerate his *letter to a person of distinction who had desired his opinion of the learned Bishop Lloyd's hypothesis concerning the form of the most ancient year.* This hypothesis was sent by the Bishop of Worcester to Dr. Prideaux. Sir Isaac remarks, that it is filled with many excellent observations on the ancient year; but he does not "find it proved that any ancient nations used a year of twelve months and 360 days without correcting it from time to time by the luminaries, to make the months keep to the course of the moon, and the year to the course of the sun, and returns of the seasons and fruits of the earth." After examining the years of all the nations of antiquity, he concludes, "that no other years are to be met with among the ancients but such as were either luni-solar, or solar or lunar, or the calendars of these years." A practical year, he adds, of 360 days is none of these. The beginning of such a year would have run round the four

* See an excellent view of this chronological controversy in an able note by M. Daunou, attached to Biot's Life of Newton in the *Biog. Universelle,* tom. xxxi. p. 180.

X

seasons in seventy years, and such a notable revolution would have been mentioned in history, and is not to be asserted without proving it.*

CHAPTER XVI.

Theological Studies of Sir Isaac—Their Importance to Christianity—Motives to which they have been ascribed—Opinions of Biot and Laplace considered—His Theological Researches begun before his supposed Mental Illness—The Date of these Works fixed—Letters to Locke—Account of his Observations on Prophecy--His Historical Account of two notable Corruptions of Scripture—His Lexicon Propheticum—His Four Letters to Dr. Bentley—Origin of Newton's Theological Studies—Analogy between the Book of Nature and that of Revelation.

THE history of the theological studies of Sir Isaac Newton will ever be regarded as one of the most interesting portions of his life. That he who among all the individuals of his species possessed the highest intellectual powers was not only a learned and profound divine, but a firm believer in the great doctrines of religion, is one of the proudest triumphs of the Christian faith. Had he distinguished himself only by an external respect for the offices and duties of religion ; and had he left merely in his last words an acknowledgment of his faith, his piety would have been regarded as a prudent submission to popular feeling, and his last aspirations would have been ascribed to the decay or to the extinction of his transcendent powers. But he had been a Christian from his youth, and though never intended for the church, yet he interchanged the study of the Scriptures with that of the laws of the material universe ; and from the examination of the works of the Supreme Creator he found it to be no abrupt

* This letter is published without any date in the *Gentleman's Magazine* for 1755, vol. xxv. p. 3. It bears internal evidence of being genuine.

transition to investigate the revelation of his will, and to contemplate the immortal destinies of mankind.

But when the religious habits of Sir Isaac Newton could not be ascribed to an ambition of popularity, to the influence of weak health, or to the force of professional impulse, it became necessary for the apostles of infidelity to refer it to some extraordinary cause. His supposed insanity was therefore eagerly seized upon by some as affording a plausible origin for his religious principles; while others, without any view of supporting the cause of skepticism, ascribed his theological researches to the habits of the age in which he lived, and to a desire of promoting political liberty, by turning against the abetters of despotism those powerful weapons which the Scriptures supplied. The anxiety evinced by M. de Laplace to refer his religious writings to a late period of his life seems to have been felt also by M. Biot, who has gone so far as to fix the very date of one of his most important works, and thus to establish the suspicions of his colleague.

" From the nature of the subject,"* says he, " and from certain indications which Newton seems to give at the beginning of his dissertation, we may conjecture with probability that he composed it at the time when the errors of Whiston, and a work of Dr. Clarke on the same subject, drew upon them the attacks of all the theologians of England, which would place the date between the years 1712 and 1719. It would then be truly a prodigy to remark, that a man of from seventy-two to seventy-five years of age was able to compose, *rapidly*, as he leads us to believe, so extensive a piece of sacred criticism, of literary history, and even of bibliography, where an erudition the most vast, the most

---

* His *Historical Account of two notable Corruptions of the Scriptures.* 50 pp. quarto.

varied, and the most ready always supports an argument well arranged and powerfully combined. * * * At this epoch of the life of Newton the reading of religious books had become one of his most habitual occupations, and after he had performed the duties of his office, they formed, along with the conversation of his friends, his principal amusement. He had then almost ceased to care for the sciences, and, as we have already remarked, since the fatal epoch of 1693, he gave to the world only three really new scientific productions."

Notwithstanding the prodigy which it involves, M. Biot has adopted 1712–1719 as the date of this critical dissertation;—it is regarded as the composition of a man of seventy-two or seventy-five;—the reading of religious works is stated to have *become* one of his most habitual occupations, and such reading is said to have been one of his principal amusements; and all this is associated with "the fatal epoch of 1693," as if his illness at that time had been the cause of his abandoning science and betaking himself to theology. Carrying on the same views, M. Biot asks, in reference to Sir Isaac's work on Prophecy, "How a mind of the character and force of Newton's, so habituated to the severity of mathematical considerations, so exercised in the observation of real phenomena, and so well aware of the conditions by which truth is to be discovered, could put together such a number of conjectures without noticing the extreme improbability of his interpretations from the infinite number of arbitrary postulates on which he has founded them ?" We would apply the same question to the reasoning by which M. Biot fixes the date of the critical dissertation; and we would ask how so eminent a philosopher could hazard such frivolous conjectures upon a subject on which he had not a single fact to guide his inquiries. The obvious tendency, though not the design, of the conclusion at which he arrives is injurious to the memory of Newton, as well as to the interests of religion; and these considerations might have checked the temerity of speculation, even if it had been founded on better data. The Newtonian interpretation of the Prophecies, and especially that part which M. Biot characterizes as unhappily stamped with the spirit of prejudice, has been adopted by men of the soundest and most unprejudiced minds; and in addition to the moral and historical evidence by which it is supported, it may yet be exhibited in all the fulness of demonstration. But the speculation of Biot respecting the date of Newton's theological works was never maintained by any other person than himself, and is capable of being disproved by the most incontrovertible evidence.

We have already seen, in the extract from Mr. Pryme's manuscript, that previous to 1692, when a shade is supposed to have passed over his gifted mind, Newton was well known by the appellation of an "excellent divine,"—a character which could not have been acquired without the devotion of many years to theological researches; but, important as this argument would have been, we are fortunately not left to so general a defence. The correspondence of Newton with Locke, recently published by Lord King, places it beyond a doubt that he had begun his researches respecting the Prophecies before the year 1691,—before the forty-ninth year of his age, and before the "fatal epoch of 1693." The following letter shows that he had previously discussed this subject with his friend :—

"Sir, *Cambridge, Feb.* 7, 1690–1.
"I am sorry your journey proved to so little purpose, though it delivered you from the trouble of the company the day after. You have obliged me by mentioning me to my friends at London, and I must thank both you and my Lady Masham for your civilities at Oates, and for not thinking that I made

X 2

a long stay there. I hope we shall meet again in due time, and then I should be glad to have your judgment upon some of my mystical fancies. The Son of Man, Dan. vii. I take to be the same with the Word of God upon the White Horse in Heaven, Apoc. xii., for both are to rule the nations with a rod of iron; but whence are you certain that the Ancient of Days is Christ? Does Christ anywhere sit upon the throne? If Sir Francis Masham be at Oates, present, I pray, my service to him, with his lady, Mrs. Cudworth, and Mrs. Masham. Dr. Covel is not in Cambridge.—I am your affectionate and humble servant,   "Is. NEWTON

"Know you the meaning of Dan. x. 21. There is none that holdeth with me in these things but Mich. the prince."

Having thus determined the date of those investigations which constitute his *observations on the prophecies of holy writ*, particularly the prophecies of Daniel and the Apocalypse, we shall proceed to fix the latest date of his *historical account of two notable corruptions of the Scripture, in a letter to a friend.*

This work seems to have been a *very early* production of our author. It was written in the form of a letter to Mr. Locke, and at that time Sir Isaac seems to have been anxious for its publication. Afraid, however, of being again led into a controversy, and dreading the intolerance to which he might be exposed, he requested Mr. Locke, who was at that time meditating a voyage to Holland, to get it translated into French, and published on the Continent. Having abandoned his design of visiting Holland, Locke transmitted the manuscript, without Newton's name, to his learned friend M. Le Clerc, in Holland; and it appears, from a letter of Le Clerc's to Locke, that he must have received it before the 11th April, 1691. M. Le Clerc delayed for a long time to take any steps regarding its publication; but in a letter dated January 20th, 1692, he announced to Locke his intention of publishing the tract in Latin. When this plan was communicated to Sir Isaac, he became alarmed at the risk of detection, and resolved to stop the publication of his manuscript. This resolution was intimated to Mr. Locke in the following letter :

" SIR, *Cambridge, Feb.* 16*th,* 1691–2.

" Your former letters came not to my hand, but this I have. I was of opinion my papers had lain still, and am sorry to hear there is news about them. Let me entreat you to stop their translation and impression so soon as you can; for I design to suppress them. If your friend hath been at any pains and charge, I will repay it, and gratify him. I am very glad my Lord Monmouth is till my friend, but intend not to give his lordship and you any farther trouble. My inclinations are to sit still. I am to beg his lordship's pardon for pressing into his company the last time I saw him. I had not done it, but that Mr. Paulin pressed me into the room. Miracles, of good credit, continued in the church for about two or three hundred years. Gregorius Thaumaturgus had his name from thence, and was one of the latest who was eminent for that gift; but of their number and frequency I am not able to give you a just account. The history of those ages is very imperfect. Mr. Paulin told me you had writ for some of Mr. Boyle's red earth, and by that I knew you had the receipt.—Your most affectionate and humble servant,

" IS. NEWTON."

Hence we see that this celebrated treatise, which Biot alleges to have been written between 1712 and 1719, was actually in the hands of Le Clerc in Holland previous to the 11th April, 1691, and consequently previous to the time of the supposed insanity

of its author. Mr. Locke lost no time in obeying the
request of his friend. Le Clerc instantly stopped the
publication of the letter, and, as he had never learned
the name of the author, he deposited the manuscript,
which was in the handwriting of Mr. Locke, in the
library of the Remonstrants, where it was afterward
found, and was published at London in 1754, under
the title of *Two letters from Sir Isaac Newton to M.
Le Clerc*,—a form which had never been given to it
by its author. The copy thus published was a very
imperfect one, wanting both the beginning* and the
end, and erroneous in many places; but Dr. Horsley
has published a genuine edition, which has the form
of a single letter to a friend, and was copied from a
manuscript in Sir Isaac Newton's handwriting, in the
possession of the Rev. Dr. Ekins, Dean of Carlisle.

Having thus determined as accurately as possible
the dates of the principal theological writings of Sir
Isaac, we shall now proceed to give some account
of their contents.

*The Observations on the Prophecies of Daniel and
the Apocalypse of St. John* were published in London
in 1733, in one volume 4to. The work is divided
into two parts, the first of which treats of the Prophecies of Daniel, and the second of the Apocalypse
of St. John. It begins with an account of the different books which compose the Old Testament; and
as the author considers Daniel to be the most distinct in the order of time, and the easiest to be understood, he makes him the key to all the prophetic
books in those matters which relate to the "last time."
He next considers the figurative language of the
prophets, which he regards as taken "from the
analogy between the world natural and an empire
or kingdom considered as a world politic;" the heavens and the things therein representing thrones and
dynasties; the earth, with the things therein, the

---

* The editor supplied the beginning down to the 13th page, where he
mentions in a note that *"thus far is not Sir Isaac's."*

inferior people; and the lowest parts of the earth the lowest parts of the earth the most miserable of the people. The sun is put for the whole race of kings, the moon for the body of the common people, and the stars for subordinate princes and rulers. In the earth, the dry land and the waters are put for the people of several nations. Animals and vegetables are also put for the people of several regions. When a beast or man is put for a kingdom, his parts and qualities are put for the analogous parts and qualities of the kingdom; and when a man is taken in a mystical sense, his qualities are often signified by his actions, and by the circumstances and things about him. In applying these principles he begins with the vision of the image composed of four different metals. This image he considers as representing a body of four great nations which should reign in succession over the earth, viz. the people of Babylonia, the Persians, the Greeks, and the Romans; while the stone cut out without hands is a new kingdom which should arise after the four, conquer all those nations, become very great, and endure to the end of time.

The vision of the four beasts is the prophecy of the four empires repeated, with several new additions. The lion with eagles' wings was the kingdom of Babylon and Media, which overthrew the Assyrian power. The beast like a bear was the Persian empire, and its three ribs were the kingdoms of Sardis, Babylon, and Egypt. The third beast, like a leopard, was the Greek empire, and its four heads and four wings were the kingdoms of Cassander, Lysimachus, Ptolemy, and Seleucus. The fourth beast, with its great iron teeth, was the Roman empire, and its ten horns were the ten kingdoms into which it was broken in the reign of Theodosius the Great.

In the fifth chapter Sir Isaac treats of the kingdoms represented by the feet of the image composed of iron and clay which did not stick to one another, and which were of different strength. These were the Gothic tribes called Ostrogoths, Visigoths, Vandals, Gepidæ, Lombards, Burgundians, Alans, &c.; all of whom had the same manners and customs, and spoke the same language, and who, about the year 416 A. C. were all quietly settled in several kingdoms within the empire, not only by conquest, but by grants of emperor.

In the sixth chapter he treats of the *ten* kingdoms represented by the ten horns of the fourth beast, into which the western empire became divided about the time when Rome was besieged and taken by the Goths.   These kingdoms were,

1. The kingdom of the Vandals and Alans in Spain and Africa.

2. The kingdom of Suevians in Spain.

3. The kingdom of the Visigoths.

4. The kingdom of the Alans in Gaul.

5. The kingdom of the Burgundians.

6. The kingdom of the Franks.

7. The kingdom of the Britains.

8. The kingdom of the Huns.

9. The kingdom of the Lombards.

10. The kingdom of Ravenna.

Some of these kingdoms at length fell, and new ones sprung up; but whatever was their subsequent number, they still retain the name of the ten kings from their first number.

The eleventh horn of Daniel's fourth beast is shown in chapter vii. to be the Church of Rome in its triple character of a seer, a prophet, and a king; and its power to change times and laws is copiously illustrated in chapter viii.

In the ninth chapter our author treats of the kingdom represented in Daniel by the ram and he-goat, the ram indicating the kingdom of the Medes and Persians from the beginning of the four empires, and the he-goat the kingdom of the Greeks to the end of them.

The prophecy of the seventy weeks, which had

hitherto been restricted to the first coming of our Saviour, is shown to be a prediction of all the main periods relating to the coming of the Messiah, the times of his birth and death, the time of his rejection by the Jews, the duration of the Jewish war by which he caused the city and sanctuary to be destroyed, and the time of his second coming.

In the eleventh chapter Sir Isaac treats with great sagacity and acuteness of the time of our Saviour's birth and passion,—a subject which had perplexed all preceding commentators.

After explaining in the twelfth chapter the last prophecy of Daniel, namely, that of the scripture of truth, which he considers as a commentary on the vision of the ram and he-goat, he proceeds in the thirteenth chapter to the prophecy of the king who did according to his will, and magnified himself above every god, and honoured Mahuzzims, and regarded not the desire of women. He shows that the Greek empire, after the division of the Roman empire into the Greek and Latin empires, became the king who in matters of religion did according to his will, and in legislation exalted and magnified himself above every god.

In the second part of his work on the Apocalypse of St. John, Sir Isaac treats, 1st, Of the time when the prophecy was written, which he conceives to have been during John's exile in Patmos, and before the epistle to the Hebrews and the epistles of Peter were written, which in his opinion have a reference to the Apocalypse; 2dly, Of the scene of the vision, and the relation which the Apocalypse has to the book of the law of Moses, and to the worship of God in the temple; and, 3dly, Of the relation which the Apocalypse has to the prophecies of Daniel, and of the subject of the prophecy itself.

Sir Isaac regards the prophecies of the Old and New Testaments, not as given to gratify men's curiosities, by enabling them to foreknow things, but that after they were fulfilled, they might be interpreted by the event, and afford convincing arguments that the world is governed by Providence. He considers that there is so much of this prophecy already fulfilled as to afford to the diligent student sufficient instances of God's providence; and he adds, that " among the interpreters of the last age, there is scarce one of note who hath not made some discovery worth knowing, and thence it seems one may gather that God is about opening these mysteries. The success of others," he continues, " put me upon considering it, and if I have done any thing which may be useful to following writers, I have my design."

Such is a brief abstract of this ingenious work, which is characterized by great learning, and marked with the sagacity of its distinguished author. The same qualities of his mind are equally conspicuous in his *Historical Account of Two Notable Corruptions of Scripture.*

This celebrated treatise relates to two texts in the Epistles of St. John and St. Paul. The first of these is in 1 John v. 7. " For there are three that bear record in heaven, the Father, the Son, and the Holy Ghost, and these three are one." This text he considers as a gross corruption of Scripture, which had its origin among the Latins, who interpreted the Spirit, Water, and Blood to be the Father, Son, and Holy Ghost, in order to prove them one. With the same view Jerome inserted the Trinity in express words in his version. The Latins marked his variations in the margins of their books; and in the twelfth and following centuries, when the disputations of the schoolmen were at their height, the variation began to creep into the text in transcribing. After the invention of printing, it crept out of the Latin into the printed Greek, contrary to the authority of all the Greek manuscripts and ancient versions; and from the Venetian press it went soon after into Greece. After proving these positions

Sir Isaac gives the following paraphrase of this re-markable passage, which is given in italics.

"*Who is he that overcometh the world, but he that believeth that Jesus is the Son of God*, that Son spoken of in the Psalms, he saith, 'thou art my Son; this day have I begotten thee.' *This is he that*, after the Jews had long expected him, *came*, first in a mortal body, *by* baptism of *water, and* then in an immortal one, by shedding his *blood* upon the cross and rising again from the dead; *not by water only, but by water and blood*; being the Son of God, as well by his resurrection from the dead (Acts xiii. 33), as by his supernatural birth of the virgin (Luke i. 35). *And it is the Spirit* also *that*, together with the water and blood, *beareth witness* of the truth of his coming; *because the Spirit is truth*; and so a fit and unexceptionable witness. *For there are three that bear record* of his coming; *the Spirit*, which he promised to send, and which has since shed forth upon us in the form of cloven tongues, and in various gifts; *the* baptism of *water*, wherein God testified 'this is my beloved Son;' *and the* shedding of his *blood*, accompanied with his resurrection, whereby he became the most faithful martyr, or witness, of this truth. *And these three*, the spirit, the baptism, and passion of Christ, *agree in* witnessing *one* and the same thing (namely, that the Son of God is come); and, therefore, their evidence is strong: for the law requires but two consenting witnesses, and here we have three: *and if we receive the witness of men, the* threefold *witness of God*, which he bare of his Son, by declaring at his baptism 'this is my beloved Son,' by raising him from the dead, and by pouring out his Spirit on us, *is greater;* and, therefore, ought to be more readily received."

While the Latin Church was corrupting the preceding text, the Greek Church was doing the same to St. Paul's 1st Epistle to Timothy iii. 16. *Great is the mystery of godliness, God manifest in the flesh.*

According to Sir Isaac, this reading was effected by changing δ into ϴC, the abbreviation of Θεος, and after proving this by a learned and ingenious examination of ancient manuscripts, he concludes that the reading should be *Great is the mystery of Godliness who* (viz. our Saviour) *was manifest in the flesh.*

As this learned dissertation had the effect of depriving the defenders of the doctrine of the Trinity of the aid of two leading texts, Sir Isaac Newton has been regarded as an Antitrinitarian; but such a conclusion is not warranted by any thing which he has published;* and he distinctly warns us, that his object was solely to " purge the truth of things spurious."   We are disposed, on the contrary, to think that he declares his belief in the doctrine of the Trinity when he says, " In the eastern nations, and for a long time in the western, the *faith* subsisted without this text; and it is rather a danger to religion than an advantage, to make *it now* lean upon a bruised reed.   There cannot be better service done to the truth than to purge it of things spurious; and therefore, knowing your prudence and calmness of temper, I am confident I shall not offend you by telling you my mind plainly; especially since it is no article of faith, no point of discipline, nothing but a criticism concerning a text of Scripture which I am going to write about."   The word faith in the preceding passage cannot mean faith in the Scriptures in general, but faith in the particular doctrine of the Trinity; for it is this article of faith only to which the author refers when he deprecates *its* leaning on a bruised reed.   But, whatever be the meaning of this passage, we know that Sir Isaac was greatly

---

* M. Biot has well remarked that there is absolutely nothing in the writings of Newton to justify, or even to authorize, the idea that he was an Antitrinitarian. This passage is strangely omitted in the English translation of Biot's Life of Newton. We do not know upon what authority Dr. Thomson states, in his History of the Royal Society, that Newton "did not believe in the Trinity," and that Dr. Horsley considered Newton's papers unfit for publication, because they contained proofs of his hostility to that doctrine.

offended at Mr. Whiston for having represented him as an Arian; and so much did he resent the conduct of his friend in ascribing to him heretical opinions, that he would not permit him to be elected a Fellow of the Royal Society while he was President.[*]

The only other religious works which were composed by Sir Isaac Newton were his *Lexicon Propheticum*, to which was added a Dissertation on the sacred cubit of the Jews, and *Four Letters addressed to Dr. Bentley, containing some arguments in proof of a Deity.*

The *Lexicon Propheticum* was left incomplete, and has not been published; but the Latin Dissertation which was appended to it, in which he shows that the cubit was about 26½ Roman unciæ, was published in 1737 among the Miscellaneous Works of Mr. John Greaves.

Upon the death of the Honourable Robert Boyle, on the 30th of December, 1691, it was found, by a codicil to his will, that he had left a revenue of 50*l*. per annum to establish a lectureship, in which eight discourses were to be preached annually in one of the churches of the metropolis, in illustration of the evidences of Christianity, and in opposition to the principles of infidelity. Dr. Bentley, though a very young man, was appointed to preach the first course of sermons, and the manner in which he discharged this important duty gave the highest satisfaction, not only to the trustees of the lectureship, but to the public in general. In the first six lectures Bentley exposed the folly of atheism even in reference to the present life, and derived powerful arguments for the existence of a Deity from the faculties of the soul, and the structure and functions of the human frame. In order to complete his plan, he proposed to devote his seventh and eighth lectures to the demonstration of a Divine Providence from the physical constitu-

* Whiston's *Memoirs of his own Life*, p. 178, 249, 250. Edit. 1753.

tion of the universe, as established in the Principia. In order to qualify himself for this task, he received from Sir Isaac written directions respecting a list of books necessary to be perused previous to the study of that work;* and having made himself master of the system which it contained, he applied it with irresistible force of argument to establish the existence of an overruling mind. Previous to the publication of these lectures, Bentley encountered a difficulty which he was not able to solve, and he prudently transmitted to Sir Isaac during 1692 a series of queries on the subject. This difficulty occurred in an argument urged by Lucretius, to prove the eternity of the world from an hypothesis of deriving the frame of it by mechanical principles from matter endowed with an innate power of gravity, and evenly scattered throughout the heavens. Sir Isaac willingly entered upon the consideration of the subject, and transmitted his sentiments to Dr. Bentley in the four letters which have been noticed in a preceding chapter.

In the first† of these letters Sir Isaac mentions that when he wrote his treatise about our system, viz. the Third Book of the Principia, "he had an eye upon such principles as might work, with considering men, for the belief of a Deity, and he expresses his happiness that it has been found useful for that purpose. In answering the first query of Dr. Bentley, the exact import of which we do not know, he states, that, if matter were evenly diffused through a finite space, and endowed with innate gravity, it would fall down into the middle of the space, and form one great spherical mass; but if it were diffused through an infinite space, some of it would collect into one mass, and some into another,

---

* Dr. Monk's *Life of Bentley*, p. 31.
† Dated December 10th, 1692. This letter is endorsed, in Bentley's hand, "Mr. Newton's answer to some queries sent by me after I had preached my two last sermons."—Monk's *Life of Bentley*, p. 34, note.

so as to form an infinite number of great masses. In this manner the sun and stars might be formed if the matter were of a lucid nature. But he thinks it inexplicable by natural causes, and to be ascribed to the counsel and contrivance of a voluntary Agent, that the matter should divide itself into two sorts, part of it composing a shining body like the sun, and part an opaque body like the planets. Had a natural and blind cause, without contrivance and design, placed the earth in the centre of the moon's orbit, and Jupiter in the centre of his system of satellites, and the sun in the centre of the planetary system, the sun would have been a body like Jupiter and the earth, that is, without light and heat, and consequently he knows no reason why there is only one body qualified to give light and heat to all the rest, but because the Author of the system thought it convenient, and because one was sufficient to warm and enlighten all the rest.

To the second query of Dr. Bentley, he replies that the motions which the planets now have could not spring from any natural cause alone, but were impressed by an intelligent Agent. "To make such a system with all its motions required a cause which understood and compared together the quantities of matter in the several bodies of the sun and planets, and the gravitating powers resulting from thence; the several distances of the primary planets from the sun, and of the secondary ones from Saturn, Jupiter, and the earth, and the velocities with which those planets could revolve about those quantities of matter in the central bodies; and to compare and adjust all these things together in so great a variety of bodies, argues that cause to be not blind and fortuitous, but very well skilled in mechanics and geometry."

In the second* letter, he admits that the spherical

* Dated Jan. 17th, 1692-3.

mass formed by the aggregation of particles would
affect the figure of the space in which the matter
was diffused, provided the matter descends directly
downwards to that body, and the body has no diurnal
rotation; but he states, that by earthquakes loosen-
ing the parts of this solid, the protuberance might
sink a little by their weight, and the mass by degrees
approach a spherical figure. He then proceeds to
correct an error of Dr. Bentley's in supposing that
all infinites are equal. He admits that gravity might
put the planets in motion, but he maintains that,
without the Divine power, it could never give them
such a circulating motion as they have about the
sun, because a proper quantity of a transverse motion is necessary for this purpose; and he concludes
that he is compelled to ascribe the frame of this
system to an intelligent Agent.

The third letter contains opinions confirming or
correcting several positions which Dr. Bentley had
laid down, and he concludes it with a curious examination of the opinion of Plato, that the motion of
the planets is such as if they had been all created
by God in some region very remote from our system, and let fall from thence towards the sun, their
falling motion being turned aside into a transverse
one whenever they arrived at their several orbits.
Sir Isaac shows that there is no common place such
as that conjectured by Plato, provided the gravitating power of the sun remains constant; but that
Plato's affirmation is true if we suppose the gravitating power of the sun to be doubled at that moment of time when they all arrive at their several
orbits. "If we suppose," says he, "the gravity of
all the planets towards the sun to be of such a quantity as it really is, and that the motions of the
planets are turned upwards, every planet will ascend
to twice its height from the sun. Saturn will ascend till he be twice as high from the sun as he is
at present, and no higher; Jupiter will ascend as

high again as at present, that is, a little above the orb of Saturn; Mercury will ascend to twice his present height, that is, to the orb of Venus; and so of the rest; and then, by falling down again from the places to which they ascended, they will arise again at their several orbs with the same velocities they had at first, and with which they now revolve.

"But if so soon as their motions by which they revolve are turned upwards, the gravitating power of the sun, by which their ascent is perpetually retarded, be diminished by one-half, they will now ascend perpetually, and all of them, at all equal distances from the sun, will be equally swift. Mercury, when he arrives at the orb of Venus, will be as swift as Venus; and he and Venus, when they arrive at the orb of the earth, will be as swift as the earth; and so of the rest. If they begin all of them to ascend at once, and ascend in the same line, they will constantly, in ascending, become nearer and nearer together, and their motions will constantly approach to an equality, and become at length slower than any motion assignable. Suppose, therefore, that they ascended till they were almost contiguous, and their motions inconsiderably little, and that all their motions were at the same moment of time turned back again, or, which comes almost to the same thing, that they were only deprived of their motions, and let fall at that time, they would all at once arrive at their several orbs, each with the velocity it had at first; and if their motions were then turned sideways, and at the same time the gravitating power of the sun doubled, that it might be strong enough to retain them in their orbs, they would revolve in them as before their ascent. But if the gravitating power of the sun was not doubled, they would go away from their orbs into the highest heavens in parabolical lines."*

* "These things," says he, "follow from my *Princip. Math.* lib. j. prop. 33, 34, 35, 36."

In the fourth letter* he states, that the hypothesis that matter is at first evenly diffused through the universe is in his opinion inconsistent with the hypothesis of innate gravity without a supernatural power to reconcile them, and therefore it infers a Deity. "For if there be innate gravity, it is impossible now for the matter of the earth and all the planets and stars to fly up from them, and become evenly spread throughout all the heavens without a supernatural power; and certainly that which can never be hereafter without a supernatural power, could never be heretofore without the same power."

These letters, of which we have endeavoured to give a brief summary, will well repay the most attentive perusal by the philosopher as well as the divine. They are written with much perspicuity of language and great power of thought, and they contain results which incontestably prove that their author was fully master of his noblest faculties, and comprehended the profoundest parts of his own writings.†

The logical acuteness, the varied erudition, and the absolute freedom from all prejudice which shine throughout the theological writings of Newton, might have protected them from the charge of having been written in his old age, and at a time when a failure of mind was supposed to have unfitted him for his mathematical investigations. But it is fortunate for his reputation, as well as for the interests of Christianity, that we have been able to prove the incorrectness of such insinuations, and to exhibit the most irrefragable evidence that *all the theological*

* Dated February 11th, 1693.
† The originals of these four letters to Bentley "were given by Dr. Richard Bentley to Cumberland, his nephew, and executor, while a student at Trinity College, and were printed by him in a separate pamphlet in 1756. This publication was reviewed by Dr. Samuel Johnson in the Literary Magazine, vol. i. p. 89. See Johnson's Works, vol. ii. p. 328. The original letters are preserved in Trinity College, to which society they were given by Cumberland a short time before his death."—*Monk's Life of Bentley*, p. 33, note.

writings of Newton were composed in the vigour of his life, and before the crisis of that bodily disorder which is supposed to have affected his reason. The able letters to Dr. Bentley were even written in the middle of that period when want of sleep and appetite had disturbed the serenity of his mind, and enable us to prove that this disturbance, whatever was its amount, never affected the higher functions of his understanding.

When a philosopher of distinguished eminence, and we believe not inimical to the Christian faith, has found it necessary to make a laboured apology for a man like Newton writing on theological subjects, and has been led to render that apology more complete by referring this class of his labours to a mind debilitated by age and weakened by its previous aberrations, it may be expected from an English biographer, and one who acknowledges the importance of revealed truth, and the paramount interest of such subjects above all secular studies, to suggest the true origin of Newton's theological inquiries.

When a mind of great and acknowledged power first directs its energies to the study of the material universe, no indications of order attract his notice, and no proofs of design call forth his admiration. In the starry firmament he sees no bodies of stupendous magnitude, and no distances of immeasurable span. The two great luminaries appear vastly inferior in magnitude to many objects around him, and the greatest distances in the heavens seem even inferior to those which his own eye can embrace on the surface of the earth. The planets, when observed with care, are seen to have a motion among the fixed stars, and to vary in their magnitude and distances, but these changes appear to follow no law. Sometimes they move to the east, sometimes to the west, sometimes towards the north, and sometimes towards the south, and at other times they are absolutely stationary. No system, in short, appears, and no general law seems to direct their motions. By the observations and inquiries of astronomers, however, during successive ages, a regular system has been recognised in this chaos of moving bodies, and the magnitudes, distances, and revolutions of every planet which composes it has been determined with the most extraordinary accuracy. Minds fitted and prepared for this species of inquiry are capable of understanding the great variety of evidence by which the truth of the planetary system is established; but thousands of individuals who are even distinguished in other branches of knowledge are incapable of such researches, and view with a skeptical eye the great and irrefragable truths of astronomy.

That the sun is stationary in the centre of our system,—that the earth moves round the sun, and round its own axis,—that the earth is 8000 miles in diameter, and the sun *one hundred and ten* times as large,—that the earth's orbit is 190 millions of miles in breadth,—and that if this immense space were filled with light, it would appear only like a luminous point at the nearest fixed star,—are positions absolutely unintelligible and incredible to all who have not carefully studied the subject. To millions of our species, then, the great book of nature is absolutely sealed, though it is in the power of all to unfold its pages, and to peruse those glowing passages which proclaim the power and wisdom of its mighty Author.

The book of revelation exhibits to us the same peculiarities as that of nature. To the ordinary eye it presents no immediate indications of its Divine origin. Events apparently insignificant—supernatural interferences seemingly unnecessary—doctrines almost contradictory—and prophecies nearly unintelligible occupy its pages. The history of the fall of man—of the introduction of moral and physical evil—the prediction of a Messiah—the actual advent of our Saviour—his instructions—his miracles—his death—his resurrection—and the subsequent propagation of his religion by the unlettered fishermen of Galilee, are each a stumblingblock to the wisdom of this world. The youthful and vigorous mind, when first summoned to peruse the Scriptures, turns from them with disappointment. It recognises in them no profound science—no secular wisdom—no Divine eloquence—no disclosures of nature's secrets—no direct impress of an Almighty hand. But, though the system of revealed truth which this book contains is, like that of the universe, concealed from common observation, yet the labours of centuries have established its Divine origin, and developed in all its order and beauty the great plan of human restoration. In the chaos of its incidents we discover the whole history of our species, whether it is delineated in events that are past or shadowed forth in those which are to come,—from the creation of man and the origin of evil, to the extinction of his earthly dynasty and the commencement of his immortal career.

The antiquity and authenticity of the books which compose the sacred canon,—the fulfilment of its prophecies,—the miraculous works of its founder,—his death and resurrection, have been demonstrated to all who are capable of appreciating the force of historical evidence; and in the poetical and prose compositions of the inspired authors we discover a system of doctrine and a code of morality traced in characters as distinct and legible as the most unerring truths in the material world. False systems of religion have indeed been deduced from the sacred record,—as false systems of the universe have sprung from the study of the book of nature,—but the very prevalence of a false system proves the existence of one that is true; and though the two classes of facts necessarily depend on different kinds of evidence, yet we scruple not to say that the Copernican system is not more demonstrably true than the system of theological truth contained in the Bible. If men of high powers, then, are still found, who are insensible to the evidence which sustains the system of the universe, need we wonder that there are others whose minds are shut against the effulgent evidence which intrenches the strongholds of our faith.

If such, then, is the character of the Christian faith, we need not be surprised that it was embraced and expounded by such a genius as Sir Isaac Newton. Cherishing its doctrines, and leaning on its promises, he felt it his duty, as it was his pleasure, to apply to it that intellectual strength which had successfully surmounted the difficulties of the material universe. The fame which that success procured him he could not but feel to be the breath of popular applause, which administered only to his personal feelings; but the investigation of the sacred mysteries, while it prepared his own mind for its final destiny, was calculated to promote the spiritual interests of thousands. This noble impulse he did not hesitate to obey, and by thus uniting philosophy with religion, he dissolved the league which genius had formed with skepticism, and added to the cloud of witnesses the brightest name of ancient or of modern times.

CHAPTER XVII.

The minor Discoveries and Inventions of Newton—His Researches on Heat—On Fire and Flame—On Elective Attraction—On the Structure of Bodies—His supposed Attachment to Alchymy—His Hypothesis respecting Ether as the Cause of Light and Gravity—On the Excitation of Electricity in Glass—His Reflecting Sextant invented before 1700—His Reflecting Microscope—His Prismatic Reflector as a Substitute for the small Speculum of Reflecting Telescopes—His Method of varying the Magnifying Power of Newtonian Telescopes—His Experiments on Impressions on the Retina.

IN the preceding chapters we have given an account of the principal labours of Sir Isaac Newton; but there still remain to be noticed several of his minor discoveries and inventions, which could not properly be introduced under any general head.

The most important of these, perhaps, are his chymical researches, which he seems to have pursued with more or less diligence from the time when he first witnessed the practical operations of chymistry during his residence at the apothecary's at Grantham. His first chymical experiments were probably made on the alloys of metals, for the purpose of obtaining a good metallic composition for the specula of reflecting telescopes. In his paper on thin plates he treats of the combinations of solids and fluids; but he enters more largely on these and other subjects in the queries published at the end of his Optics.

One of his most important chymical papers is his *Tabula quantitatum et graduum caloris*, which was published in the Philosophical Transactions. This short paper contains a comparative scale of temperature from that of melting ice to that of a small kitchen coal-fire. The following are the principal points of the scale, the intermediate

Z

degrees of heat having been determined with great care.

Degrees of Heat.	Equal Parts of Heat.	
0	0	Freezing point of water.
1	12	Blood-heat.
2	24	Heat of melting wax.
3	48	Melting point of equal parts of tin and bismuth.
4	96	Melting point of lead.
5	192	Heat of a small coal-fire.

The first column of this table contains the degrees of heat in arithmetical progression, and the second in geometrical progression,—the second degree being twice as great as the first, and so on. It is obvious from this table, that the heat at which equal parts of tin and bismuth melt is *four* times greater than that of blood-heat, the heat of melting lead *eight* times greater, and the heat of a small coal-fire *sixteen* times greater.

This table was constructed by the help of a thermometer, and of red-hot iron. By the former he measured all heats as far as that of melting tin; and by the latter he measured all the higher heats. For the heat which heated iron loses in a given time is as the total heat of the iron; and therefore, if the times of cooling are taken equal, the heats will be in a geometrical progression, and may therefore be easily found by a table of logarithms.

He found by a thermometer constructed with lin-seed oil, that if the oil, when the thermometer was placed in melting snow, occupied a space of 1000 parts, the same oil, rarefied with *one* degree of heat, or that of the human body, occupied a space of 10256; in the heat of water beginning to boil, a space of 10705; in the heat of water boiling violently, 10725; in the heat of melted tin beginning to cool, and putting on the consistency of an amalgam,

11516, and when the tin had become solid, 11496. Hence the oil was rarefied in the ratio of 40 to 39 by the heat of the human body; of 15 to 14 by the heat of boiling water; of 15 to 13 in the heat of melting tin beginning to solidify; and of 23 to 20 in the same tin when solid. The rarefaction of air was, with the same heat, *ten* times greater than that of oil, and the rarefaction of oil *fifteen* times greater than that of spirit of wine. By making the heats of oil proportional to its rarefaction, and by calling the heat of the human body 12 parts, we obtain the heat of water beginning to boil, 33; of water boiling violently, 34; of melted tin beginning to solidify, 72; and of the same become solid, 70.

Sir Isaac then heated a sufficiently thick piece of iron till it was red-hot; and having fixed it in a cold place, where the wind blew uniformly, he put upon it small pieces of different metals and other fusible bodies, and noted the times of cooling, till all the particles, having lost their fluidity, grew cold, and the heat of the iron was equal to that of the human body. Then, by assuming that the excesses of the heats of the iron and of the solidified particles of metal above the heat of the atmosphere, were in geometrical progression when the times were in arithmetical progression, all the heats were obtained. The iron was placed in a current of air, in order that the air heated by the iron might always be carried away by the wind, and that cold air might replace it with a uniform motion; for thus equal parts of the air were heated in equal times, and received a heat proportional to that of the iron. But the heats thus found had the same ratio to one another with the heats found by the thermometer; and hence he was right in assuming that the rarefactions of the oil were proportional to its heats.

Another short chymical paper by Sir Isaac Newton has been published by Dr. Horsley. It is enti-

tled *De Natura Acidorum*, but is principally occupied
with a number of brief opinions on chymical subjects. This paper was written later than 1687, as it
bears a reference to the Principia; and the most important facts which it contains seem to have been
more distinctly reproduced in the queries at the end
of the Optics.

The most important of these queries relate to fire,
flame, and electric attractions, and as they were revised in the year 1716 and 1717, they may be regarded
as containing the most matured opinions of their
author. Fire he regards as a body heated so hot as
to emit light copiously, and flame as a vapour, fume,
or exhalation heated so hot as to shine. In his long
query on elective attractions, he considers the small
particles of bodies as acting upon one another at
distances so minute as to escape observation. When
salt of tartar deliquesces, he supposes that this arises
from an attraction between the saline particles and
the aqueous particles held in solution in the atmosphere, and to the same attraction he ascribes it that
the water will not distil from the salt of tartar without great heat. For the same reason sulphuric acid
attracts water powerfully, and parts with it with
great difficulty. When this attractive force becomes
very powerful, as in the union between sulphuric
acid and water, so as to make the particles "coalesce
with violence," and rush towards one another with
an accelerated motion, heat is produced by the mixture of the two fluids. In like manner, he explains
the production of flame from the mixture of cold
fluids,—the action of fulminating powders,—the combination of iron filings with sulphur,—and all the
other chymical phenomena of precipitation, combination, solution, and crystallization, and the mechanical phenomena of cohesion and capillary attraction. He ascribes hot springs, volcanoes, fire-damps,
mineral coruscations, earthquakes, hot suffocating

exhalations, hurricanes, lightning, thunder, fiery meteors, subterraneous explosions, land-slips, ebullitions of the sea, and waterspouts, to sulphureous steams abounding in the bowels of the earth, and fermenting with minerals, or escaping into the atmosphere, where they ferment with acid vapours fitted to promote fermentation.

In explaining the structure of solid bodies, he is of opinion, "that the smallest particles of matter may cohere by the strongest attractions, and compose bigger particles of weaker virtue; and many of these may cohere and compose bigger particles whose virtue is still weaker; and so on for divers successions, until the progression end in the biggest particles, on which the operations in chymistry and the colours of natural bodies depend, and which, by adhering, compose bodies of a sensible magnitude. If the body is compact, and bends or yields inward to pression, without any sliding of its parts, it is hard and elastic, returning to its figure with a force rising from the mutual attraction of its parts. If the parts slide upon one another, the body is malleable or soft. If they slip easily, and are of a fit size to be agitated by heat, and the heat is big enough to keep them in agitation, the body is fluid; and if it be apt to stick to things, it is humid; and the drops of every fluid affect a round figure, by the mutual attraction of their parts, as the globe of the earth and sea affects a round figure, by the mutual attraction of its parts, by gravity."

Sir Isaac then supposes, that, as the attractive force of bodies can reach but to a small distance from them, "a repulsive virtue ought to succeed;" and he considers such a virtue as following from the reflection of the rays of light, the rays being repelled without the immediate contact of the reflecting body, and also from the emission of light, the ray, as soon as it is shaken off from a shining body by the vibrating motion of the parts of the body, getting beyond the reach of attraction, and being driven away with exceeding great velocity by the force of reflection.*

Many of the chymical views which Sir Isaac thus published in the form of queries were in his own lifetime illustrated and confirmed by Dr. Stephen Hales, in his book on *Vegetable Statics*,—a work of great originality, which contains the germ of some of the finest discoveries in modern chymistry.

Although there is no reason to suppose that Sir Isaac Newton was a believer in the doctrines of alchymy, yet we are informed by the Reverend Mr. Law that he had been a diligent student of Jacob Behmen's writings, and that there were found among his papers copious abstracts from them in his own handwriting.† He states also that Sir Isaac, together with one Dr. Newton, his relation, had, in the earlier part of his life, set up furnaces, and were for several months at work in quest of the philosopher's tincture. These statements may receive some confirmation from the fact, that there exist among the Portsmouth papers many sheets, in Sir Isaac's own writing, of Flammel's Explication of Hieroglyphic Figures, and in another hand, many sheets of William Yworth's *Processus Mysterii Magni Philosophicus*, and also from the manner in which Sir Isaac requests Mr. Aston to inquire after one Borry in Holland, who always went clothed in green, and who was said to possess valuable secrets; but Mr. Law has weakened the force of his own testimony, when

---

* Mr. Herschel, in his Treatise on Light, § 553, has maintained that Newton's Doctrine of Reflection is accordant with the idea that the attractive force extends beyond the repulsive or reflecting force. In the query above referred to, Sir Isaac, in the most distinct manner, places the sphere of the reflecting force without that of the attractive one.

† In a tract annexed to his *Appeal to all that doubt or disbelieve the truths of the Gospel.* See *Gent. Mag.* 1782, vol. lii. p. 227, 239.

It is stated in a letter of Mr. Law's, quoted in this magazine, that Charles I. was a diligent reader and admirer of Jacob Behmen; that he sent a well-qualified person from England to Goerlitz, in Upper Lusatia, to acquire the German language, and to collect every anecdote he could meet with there relative to this great alchymist.

he asserts that Newton borrowed the doctrine of attraction from Behmen's first three propositions of eternal nature.

On the 7th December, 1675, Sir Isaac Newton communicated to the Royal Society a paper entitled *An hypothesis explaining properties of light*, in which he, for the first time, introduces his opinions respecting ether, and employs them to explain the nature of light, and the cause of gravity. "He was induced," he says, "to do this, because he had observed the heads of some great virtuosos to run much upon hypotheses, and he therefore gave one which he was inclined to consider as the most probable, if he were obliged to adopt one."*

This hypothesis seems to have been afterward a subject of discussion between him and Mr. Boyle, to whom he promised to communicate his opinion more fully in writing. He accordingly addressed to him a long letter, dated February 28th, 1678–9, in which he explains his views respecting ether, and employs them to account for the refraction of light,—the cohesion of two polished pieces of metal in an exhausted receiver,—the adhesion of quicksilver to glass tubes, —the cohesion of the parts of all bodies,—the cause of filtration,—the phenomena of capillary attraction, —the action of menstrua on bodies,—the transmutation of gross compact substances into aerial ones, —and the cause of gravity. From the language used in this paper, we should be led to suppose that Sir Isaac had entirely forgotten that he had formerly treated the general subject of ether, and applied it to the explanation of gravity. "I shall set down," says he, "one conjecture more *which came into my mind now as I was writing this letter; it is about the cause of gravity*," which he goes on to explain ;† and

* In a letter to Dr. Halley, dated June 20th, 1686, Sir Isaac refers to this paper, and observes, that it is only to be looked upon as one of his guesses that he did not rely upon.

† See page 273.

he concludes by saying, that "he has so little fancy to things of this nature, that, *had not your encouragement moved me to it*, I should never, I think, thus far have set pen to paper about them."

These opinions, however, about the existence of ether, Newton seems to have subsequently renounced; for in the manuscript in the possession of Dr. J. C. Gregory, which we have already mentioned, and which was written previous to 1702, he states, that ether is neither obvious to our senses, nor supported by any arguments, but is a gratuitous assumption, which, if we are to trust to reason and to our senses, must be banished from the nature of things; and he goes on to establish, by various arguments, the validity of this opinion. This renunciation of his former hypothesis probably arose from his having examined more carefully some of the phenomena which he endeavoured to explain by it. Those of capillary attraction, for example, he had ascribed to the ether "standing rarer in the very sensible cavities of the capillary tubes than without them," whereas he afterward discovered their true cause, and ascribed them to the reciprocal attraction of the tube and the fluid. But, however this may be, there can be no doubt that he resumed his early opinions before the publication of his Optics, which may be considered as containing his views upon this subject.

The queries which contain these opinions are the 18th–24th, all of which appeared for the first time in the second English edition of the Optics. If a body is either heated or loses its heat when placed in vacuo, he ascribes the conveyance of the heat in both cases "to the vibration of a much subtiler medium than air;" and he considers this medium as the same with that by which light is refracted and reflected, and by whose vibrations light communicates heat to bodies, and is put into fits of easy reflection and transmission.

This ethereal medium, according to our author, is exceedingly more rare and more elastic than air. It pervades all bodies, and is expanded through all the heavens. It is much rarer within the dense bodies of the sun, stars, planets, and comets, than in the celestial spaces between them, and also more rare within glass, water, &c. than in the free and open spaces void of air and other grosser bodies. In passing out of glass, water, &c. and other dense bodies into empty space, it grows denser and denser by degrees, and this gradual condensation extends to some distance from the bodies. Owing to its great elasticity, and, consequently, its efforts to spread in all directions, it presses against itself, and, consequently, against the solid particles of bodies, so as to make them continually approach to one another, the body being impelled from the denser parts of the medium towards the rarer with all that power which we call gravity.

In employing this medium to explain the nature of light, Newton does not suppose, with Descartes, Hooke, Huygens, and others, that light is nothing more than the impression of those undulations on the retina. He regards light as a peculiar substance, composed of heterogeneous particles thrown off with great velocity, and in all directions, from luminous bodies; and he supposes that these particles while passing through the ether, excite in it vibrations or pulses which accelerate or retard the particles of light, and thus throw them into their alternate fits of easy reflection and transmission.

Hence, if a ray of light falls upon a transparent body, in which the ether consists of strata of variable density, the particles of light acted upon by the vibrations which they create will be urged with an accelerated velocity in entering the body, while their velocity will be retarded in quitting it. In this manner he conceives the phenomena of refraction to be produced, and he shows how in such a case the refraction would be regulated by the law of the sines.

In order that the ethereal medium may produce the fits of easy reflection and transmission, he conceives that its vibrations must be swifter than light. He computes its elasticity to be 490,000,000,000 times greater than that of air, in proportion to its density, and about 600,000,000 times more rare than water, from which he infers that the resistance which it would oppose to the motions of the planets would not be sensible in 10,000 years. He considers that the functions of vision and hearing may be performed chiefly by the vibrations of this medium, executed in the bottom of the eye, or in the auditory nerve by the rays of light, and propagated through the solid, pellucid, and uniform capillamenta of the optic or auditory nerves into the place of sensation; and he is of opinion that animal motion may be performed by the vibrations of the same medium, excited in the brain by the power of the will, and propagated from thence by the solid, pellucid, and uniform capillamenta of the nerves into the muscles for contracting and dilating them.

In the registers of the Royal Society there exist several letters* on the excitation of electricity in glass, which were occasioned by an experiment of this kind having been mentioned in Sir Isaac's hypothesis of light. The society had ordered the experiment to be tried at their meeting of the 16th December, 1675; but, in order to secure its success, Mr. Oldenburg wrote to Sir Isaac for a more particular account of it. Sir Isaac being thus "put upon recollecting himself a little farther about it," remembers that he made the experiment with a glass fixed at the distance of the $\frac{1}{3}$d of an inch from one end of a brass hoop, and only the $\frac{1}{8}$th of an inch from the other. Small pieces of thin paper were

* See *Newtoni Opera*, by Horsley, vol. iv. p. 375–382.

then laid upon the table; when the glass was laid above them and rubbed, the pieces of paper leaped from the one part of the glass to the other, and twirled about in the air. Notwithstanding this explicit account of the experiment, it entirely failed at the Royal Society, and the secretary was desired to request the loan of Sir Isaac's apparatus, and to inquire whether or not he had secured the papers from being moved by the air, which might have somewhere stole in. In a letter, dated 21st December, Sir Isaac recommended to the society to rub the glass "with stuff whose threads may rake its surface, and, if that will not do, to rub it with the fingers' ends to and fro, and knock them as often upon the glass." These directions enabled the society to succeed with the experiment on the 13th January, 1676, when they used a scrubbing brush of short hog's bristles, and the heft of a knife made with whalebone.

Among the minor inventions of Sir Isaac Newton, we must enumerate his reflecting instrument for observing the moon's distance from the fixed stars at sea. The description of this instrument was communicated to Dr. Halley in the year 1700; but, either from having mislaid the manuscript, or from attaching no value to the invention, he never communicated it to the Royal Society, and it remained among his papers till after his death in 1742, when it was published in the Philosophical Transactions. The following is Sir Isaac's own description of it as communicated to Dr. Halley.

"In the annexed figure PQRS denotes a plate of brass, accurately divided in the limb DQ, into $\frac{1}{2}$ degrees, $\frac{1}{2}$ minutes, and $\frac{1}{12}$ minutes, by a diagonal scale; and the $\frac{1}{2}$ degrees, and $\frac{1}{2}$ minutes, and $\frac{1}{12}$ minutes, counted for degrees, minutes, and $\frac{1}{6}$ minutes. AB is a telescope three or four feet long, fixed on the edge of that brass plate. G is a speculum fixed

on the brass plate perpendicularly as near as
may be to the object-glass of the telescope, so as

Fig. 12.

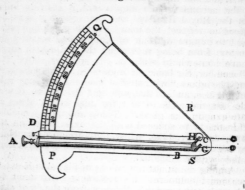

to be inclined forty-five degrees to the axis of
the telescope, and intercept half the light which
would otherwise come through the telescope to the
eye. CD is a moveable index turning about the
centre C, and, with its fiducial edge, showing the
degrees, minutes, and $\frac{1}{8}$ minutes on the limb of the
brass plate PQ; the centre C must be over against
the middle of the speculum G. H is another speculum, parallel to the former, when the fiducial edge
of index falls on 0° 0′ 0″; so that the same star may
then appear through the telescope in one and the
same place, both by the direct rays and by the reflexed ones; but if the index be turned, the star shall
appear in two places, whose distance is showed on
the brass limb by the index.

"By this instrument the distance of the moon
from any fixed star is thus observed: view the star

through the perspicil by the direct light, and the moon by the reflexed (or on the contrary); and turn the index till the star touch the limb of the moon, and the index shall show on the brass limb of the instrument the distance of the star from the moon's limb; and though the instrument shake by the motion of the ship at sea, yet the moon and star will move together as if they did really touch one another in the heavens; so that an observation may be made as exactly at sea as at land.

"And by the same instrument may be observed exactly the altitudes of the moon and stars, by bringing them to the horizon; and thereby the latitude and times of observation may be determined more exactly than by the ways now in use.

"In the time of the observation, if the instrument move angularly about the axis of the telescope, the star will move in a tangent of the moon's limb, or of the horizon; but the observation may notwithstanding be made exactly, by noting when the line described by the star is a tangent to the moon's limb, or to the horizon.

"To make the instrument useful, the telescope ought to take in a large angle; and to make the observation true, let the star touch the moon's limb, not on the outside, but on the inside."

This ingenious contrivance is obviously the very same invention as that which Mr. Hadley produced in 1731, and which, under the name of Hadley's Quadrant, has been of so great service in navigation. The merit of its first invention must therefore be transferred to Sir Isaac Newton.

In the year 1672, Sir Isaac communicated to Mr. Oldenburg his design for a microscope, which he considered to be as capable of improvement as the telescope, and perhaps more so, because it requires only one speculum. This microscope is shown in the annexed diagram, where AB is the object-metal, CD the eye-glass, F their common

focus, and O the other focus of the metal in which
the object is placed.   This ingenious idea has been

Fig. 13.

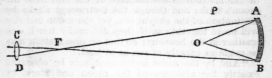

greatly improved in modern times by Professor
Amici, who makes AB a portion of an ellipsoid,
whose foci are O and F, and who places a small
plain speculum between O and AB, in order to reflect the object, which is placed on one side AP, for
the purpose of being illuminated.

In another letter to Mr. Oldenburg, dated July
11th in the same year, he suggests another improvement in microscopes, which is to "illuminate the
object in a darkened room with the light of any
convenient colour not too much compounded : for
by that means the microscope will, with distinctness, bear a deeper charge and larger aperture,
especially if its construction be such as I may hereafter describe."*   This happy idea I have some
years ago succeeded in realizing, by illuminating
microscopic objects with the light of a monochro-
matic lamp, which discharges a copious flame of
pure yellow light of definite refrangibility.†

In order to remedy the evils arising from the
weak reflecting power of speculum metal, and from
its tarnishing by exposure to the air, Sir Isaac proposed to substitute for the small oval speculum a
triangular prism of glass or crystal ABC.   Its side

---

* Sir Isaac does not seem to have afterward described this construction.

† See *Edinburgh Transactions*, vol. ix. p. 433, and the *Edinburgh
Journal of Science*, July, 1829, No. I. New Series, p. 108.

AB *ba* he supposes to perform the office of that metal, by reflecting towards the eye-glass the light which comes from the concave speculum DF, *fig*. 13, whose light he supposes to enter into this prism at its side CB *bc*, and lest any colours should be produced by the refraction of these planes, it is requisite that the angles of the prism at A*a* and B*b* be precisely equal. This may be done most conveniently, by making them half right angles, and consequently the third angle at C*c* a right one. The plane AB *ba* will reflect all the light incident upon it ; but in order to exclude unnecessary light, it will be proper to cover

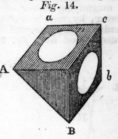

Fig. 14.

it all over with some black substance excepting two circular spaces of the planes A*c* and B*c*, through which the useful light may pass. The length of the

Fig. 15

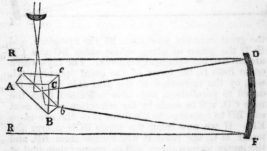

prism should be such that its sides A*c* and B*c* may be square, and so much of the angles B and *b* as are

superfluous ought to be ground off, to give passage
for as much light as is possible from the object to
the speculum.

One great advantage of this prism, which cannot
be obtained from the oval metal, is, that without
using two glasses the object may be erected, and
the magnifying power of the telescope varied at
pleasure, by merely varying the distances of the
speculum, the prism, and the eye-glass. This will
be understood from *fig.* 16, where AI represents

Fig. 16.

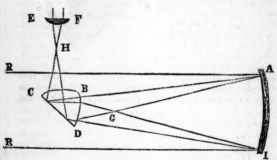

the great concave speculum, EF the eye-glass, and
BCD the prism of glass, whose sides BC and CD
are not flat, but spherically convex. The rays which
come from G, the focus of the great speculum AI,
will, by the refraction of the first side BC, be reduced to parallelism, and after reflection from the
base CD, will be made by the refraction of the next
side BD to converge to the focus H of the eye-glass
EF. If we now bring the prism BCD nearer the
image at G, the point H will recede from BD, and
the image formed there will be greater than that at
G, and if we remove the prism BCD from G, the
point H will approach to BD, and the image at H

will be less than that at G. The prism BCD performs the same part as a convex lens, G and H being its conjugate foci, and the relative size of the images formed at these points being proportional to their distance from the lens. This construction would be a good one for varying optically the angular distance of a pair of wires placed in the focus of the eye-glass EF; and by bisecting the lenticular prism BCD, and giving the halves a slight inclination, we should be able to separate and to close the two images or disks which would thus be produced, and thus form a double image micrometer.

Among the minor and detached labours of Sir Isaac, we must not omit his curious experiments on the action of light upon the retina. Locke seems to have wished his opinion respecting a fact stated in Boyle's Book on Colours, and in a letter from Cambridge, dated June 30th, 1691, he communicated to his friend the following very remarkable observations made by himself.

" The observation you mention in Mr. Boyle's book of colours I once made upon myself with the hazard of my eyes. The manner was this; I looked a very little while upon the sun in the looking-glass with my right eye, and then turned my eyes into a dark corner of my chamber, and winked, to observe the impression made, and the circles of colours which encompassed it, and how they decayed by degrees, and at last vanished. This I repeated a second and a third time. At the third time, when the phantasm of light and colours about it were almost vanished, intending my fancy upon them to see their last appearance, I found, to my amazement, that they began to return, and by little and little to become as lively and vivid as when I had newly looked upon the sun. But when I ceased to intend my fancy upon them, they vanished again. After this, I found, that as often as I went into the dark, and intended my mind upon them, as when a man looks earnestly to see any thing which is difficult to be seen, I could make the phantasm return without looking any more upon the sun; and the oftener I made it return, the more easily I could make it return again. And at length, by repeating this without looking any more upon the sun, I made such an impression on my eye, that, if I looked upon the clouds, or a book, or any bright object, I saw upon it a round bright spot of light like the sun, and, which is still stranger, though I looked upon the sun with my right eye only, and not with my left, yet my fancy began to make an impression upon my left eye, as well as upon my right. For if I shut my right eye, or looked upon a book or the clouds with my left eye, I could see the spectrum of the sun almost as plain as with my right eye, if I did but intend my fancy a little while upon it; for at first, if I shut my right eye, and looked with my left, the spectrum of the sun did not appear till I intended my fancy upon it; but by repeating, this appeared every time more easily. And now, in a few hours' time, I had brought my eyes to such a pass, that I could look upon no bright object with either eye but I saw the sun before me, so that I durst neither write nor read; but to recover the use of my eyes, shut myself up in my chamber made dark, for three days together, and used all means to divert my imagination from the sun. For if I thought upon him, I presently saw his picture, though I was in the dark. But by keeping in the dark, and employing my mind about other things, I began in three or four days to have some use of my eyes again; and, by forbearing to look upon bright objects, recovered them pretty well, though not so well but that, for some months after, the spectrum of the sun began to return as often as I began to meditate upon the phenomena, even though I lay in bed at midnight with my curtains drawn. But now I have been very well for many years, though I am apt to think, if I durst venture my eyes, I could still make the phantasm return by the power of my fancy. This story I tell you, to let you understand, that in the observation related by Mr. Boyle, the man's fancy probably concurred with the impression made by the sun's light to produce that phantasm of the sun which he constantly saw in bright objects. And so your question about the cause of this phantasm involves another about the power of fancy, which I must confess is too hard a knot for me to untie. To place this effect in a constant motion is hard, because the sun ought then to appear perpetually. It seems rather to consist in a disposition of the sensorium to move the imagination strongly, and to be easily moved, both by the imagination and by the light, as often as bright objects are looked upon."

These observations possess in many respects a high degree of interest. The fact of the transmission of the impression from the retina of the one eye to that of the other is particularly important; and it deserves to be remarked, as a singular coincidence, that I had occasion to observe and to describe the same phenomena above twenty years ago,* and long before the observations of Sir Isaac were communicated to the scientific world.

* Art. *Accidental Colours* in the *Edinburgh Encyclopædia.*

CHAPTER XVIII.

ABOUT the year 1722, Sir Isaac was desirous of publishing a third edition of his Principia, and the premature death of Mr. Cotes having deprived him of his valuable aid, he had the good fortune to become acquainted with Dr. Henry Pemberton, a young and accomplished physician, who had cultivated mathematical learning with considerable success. M. Poleni, an eminent professor in the University of Padua, having endeavoured, on the authority of a new experiment, to overturn the common opinion respecting the force of bodies in motion, and to establish that of Leibnitz in its place, Dr. Pemberton transmitted to Dr. Mead a demonstration of its inaccuracy. Dr. Mead communicated this paper to Sir Isaac, who not only highly approved of it, but added a demonstration of his own, drawn from another consideration of the subject; and this was printed without his name, as a postscript to Pemberton's paper, when it appeared in the Transactions.*

In a short time after the commencement of their acquaintance, Sir Isaac engaged Dr. Pemberton to superintend the new edition of the Principia. In discharging this duty, Dr. Pemberton had occasion to make many remarks on this work, which Sir Isaac

* See *Phil. Trans.* 1722, vol. xxxiii. p. 57.

always received with the utmost goodness, and the new edition appeared with numerous alterations in 1726. On the occasions upon which he had personal intercourse with Sir Isaac, and which were necessarily numerous, he endeavoured to learn his opinions on various mathematical subjects, and to obtain some historical information respecting his inventions and discoveries. Sir Isaac entered freely into all these topics; and during the conversations which took place, and while they were reading together Dr. Pemberton's popular account of Sir Isaac's discoveries, he obtained the most perfect evidence that, though his memory was much decayed, yet he was fully able to understand his own writings.

During the last twenty years of his life, which he spent in London, the charge of his domestic concerns devolved upon his beautiful and accomplished niece, Mrs. Catharine Barton, the wife of Colonel Barton, for whom, as we have already seen, the Earl of Halifax had conceived the warmest affection. This lady, who had been educated at her uncle's expense, married Mr. Conduit, and continued to reside with her husband in Sir Isaac's house till the time of his death.

In the year 1722, when he had reached the eightieth year of his age, he was seized with an incontinence of urine, which was ascribed to stone in the bladder, and was considered incurable. By means of a strict regimen, however, and other precautions, he was enabled to alleviate his complaint, and to procure long intervals of ease. At this time he gave up the use of his carriage, and always went out in a chair. He declined all invitations to dinner, and at his own house he had only small parties. In his diet he was extremely temperate. Though he took a little butcher meat, yet the principal articles of his food were broth, vegetables, and fruit, of which he always ate very heartily. In spite of all his precautions, however, he experienced a return of his old complaint, and in August, 1724, he passed a stone the size of a pea, which came away in two pieces, the one at the distance of two days from the other. After some months of tolerable good health, he was seized in January, 1725, with a violent cough and inflammation of the lungs; and in consequence of this attack, he was prevailed upon, with some difficulty, to take up his residence at Kensington, where his health experienced a decided improvement. In February, 1725, he was attacked in both his feet with a fit of the gout, of which he had received a slight warning a few years before, and the effect of this new complaint was to produce a great and beneficial change in his general health. On Sunday the 7th March, when his head was clearer and his memory stronger than Mr. Conduit had known it to be for some time, he entered into a long conversation on various subjects in astronomy. He explained to Mr. Conduit how comets might be formed out of the light of vapours discharged from the sun and the fixed stars as the centres of systems. He conceived that these luminaries were replenished by the same comets being again returned to them; and upon this principle he explained the extraordinary lights which were seen among the fixed stars by Hipparchus, Tycho Brahe, and Kepler's disciples, and which he supposed to arise from the additional fuel which they received.*

Notwithstanding the improvement which his health had experienced, his indisposition was still sufficiently severe to unfit him for the discharge of his duties at the mint; and as his old deputy was confined with the dropsy, he was desirous in 1725 of resigning his office to Mr. Conduit. Difficulties probably were experienced in making this arrangement, but his nephew discharged for him all the

---

* This conversation, originally copied from Mr. Conduit's handwriting, is given in the Appendix, No. iii. p. 320.

duties of his office; and during the last year of his life he hardly ever went to the mint.

But though every kind of motion was calculated to aggravate his complaint, and though he had derived from absolute rest and from the air at Kensington the highest benefit, yet great difficulty was experienced in preventing him from occasionally going to town. Feeling himself able for the journey, he went to London on Tuesday the 28th of February, 1727, to preside at a meeting of the Royal Society. On the following day Mr. Conduit considered him better than he had been for many years, and Sir Isaac was himself so sensible of this improvement in his health, that he assured his nephew that on the Sunday preceding, he had slept from cleven o'clock at night till eight o'clock next morning without waking. He had undergone, however, great fatigue in attending the meeting of the Royal Society, and in paying and receiving visits, and the consequence of this was a violent return of his former complaint. He returned to Kensington on Saturday the 4th March, and was attended by Dr. Mead and Dr. Cheselden, who pronounced his disease to be stone, and held out no hopes of his recovery. From the time of his last journey to London he had experienced violent fits of pain with very short intermissions; and though the drops of sweat ran down his face during these severe paroxysms, yet he never uttered a cry or a complaint, or displayed the least marks of peevishness or impatience; but during the short intervals of relief which occurred, he smiled and conversed with his usual gayety and cheerfulness. On Wednesday the 15th of March he seemed a little better; and slight, though groundless hopes were entertained of his recovery. On the morning of Saturday the 18th he read the newspapers, and carried on a pretty long conversation with Dr. Mead, when all his senses and faculties were strong and vigorous; but at six o'clock of the same evening he became insensible, and he continued in that state during the whole of Sunday, and till Monday the 20th, when he expired between one and two o'clock in the morning, in the eighty-fifth year of his age.

His body was removed from Kensington to London, and on Tuesday the 28th March it lay in state in the Jerusalem Chamber, and was thence conveyed to Westminster Abbey, where it was buried near the entrance into the choir on the left-hand. The pall was supported by the Lord High Chancellor, the Dukes of Roxburghe and Montrose, and the Earls of Pembroke, Sussex, and Macclesfield, who were Fellows of the Royal Society. The Hon. Sir Michael Newton, Knight of the Bath, was chief mourner, and was followed by some other relations, and several distinguished characters who were intimately acquainted with the deceased. The funeral service was performed by the Bishop of Rochester, attended by the prebend and choir.

Sensible of the high honour which they derived from their connexion with so distinguished a philosopher, the relations of Sir Isaac Newton who inherited his personal estate,* agreed to devote 500l. to the erection of a monument to his memory, and the dean and chapter of Westminster appropriated for it a place in the most conspicuous part of the Abbey, which had often been refused to the greatest of our nobility. This monument was erected in 1731. On the front of a sarcophagus resting on a pedestal are sculptured in basso-relievo youths bearing in their hands the emblems of Sir Isaac's principal discoveries. One carries a prism, another a reflecting telescope, a third is weighing the sun and

---

* These were the three children of his half-brother Smith, the three children of his half-sister Pilkington, and the two daughters of his half-sister Barton, all of whom survived Sir Isaac. *New Anecdotes of Sir Isaac Newton, by J. H., a Gentleman of his Mother's Family.* See *Annual Register*, 1776, vol. xix. p. 25 of Characters. The author of this paper was James Hutton, Esq. of Pimlico.

planets with a steelyard, a fourth is employed about a furnace, and two others are loaded with money newly coined. On the sarcophagus is placed the figure of Sir Isaac in a cumbent posture, with his elbow resting on several of his works. Two youths stand before him with a scroll, on which is drawn a remarkable diagram relative to the solar system, and above that is a converging series. Behind the sarcophagus is a pyramid, from the middle of which rises a globe in mezzo-relievo, upon which several of the constellations are drawn, in order to show the path of the comet of 1681, whose period Sir Isaac had determined, and also the position of the solstitial colure mentioned by Hipparchus, and by means of which Sir Isaac had, in his Chronology, fixed the time of the Argonautic expedition. A figure of Astronomy as Queen of the Sciences sits weeping on the Globe with a sceptre in her hand, and a star surmounts the summit of the pyramid. The following epitaph is inscribed on the monument.

Hic situs est
Isaacus Newton, Eques Auratus,
Qui Animi Vi prope divina,
Planetarum Motus, Figuras,
Cometarum Semitas, Oceanique Æstus,
Sua Mathesi facem preferente,
Primus demonstravit.
Radiorum Lucis dissimilitudines,
Colorumque inde nascentium Proprietates,
Quas nemo antea vel suspicatus erat, pervestigavit.
Naturæ, Antiquitates, S. Scripturæ,
Sedulus, sagax, fidus Interpres,
Dei Opt. Max. Majestatem Philosophia asseruit,
Evangelii simplicitatem moribus expressit.
Sibi gratulentur Mortales, tale tantumque extitisse,
Humani Generis Decus.
Natus xxv. Decemb. MDCXLII. Obiit. xx. Mar.
MDCCXXVII.

Of which the following is a literal translation:

Here lies
Isaac Newton, Knight,
Who, by a Vigour of Mind almost supernatural,
First demonstrated
The Motions and Figures of the Planets,

B b

> The Paths of the Comets, and the Tides of the Ocean.
>   He diligently investigated
> The different Refrangibilities of the Rays of Light,
> And the Properties of the Colours to which they give rise.
>   An assiduous, sagacious, and faithful Interpreter
> Of Nature, Antiquity, and the Holy Scriptures,
> He asserted in his Philosophy the Majesty of God,
> And exhibited in his conduct the Simplicity of the Gospel.
>   Let Mortals rejoice
>   That there has existed such and so great
>   AN ORNAMENT OF HUMAN NATURE.
>   Born 25th Dec. 1642, Died 20th March, 1727.

In the beginning of 1731, a medal was struck at the Tower in honour of Sir Isaac Newton. It had on one side the head of the philosopher, with the motto, *Felix cognoscere causas*, and on the reverse a figure representing the mathematics.

On the 4th February, 1755, a magnificent full-length statue of Sir Isaac Newton in white marble was erected in the antechapel of Trinity College. He is represented standing on a pedestal in a loose gown, holding a prism, and looking upwards with an expression of the deepest thought. On the pedestal is the inscription,

> Qui genus humanum ingenio superavit.
>   Who surpassed all men in genius.

This statue, executed by Roubiliac, was erected at the expense of Dr. Robert Smith, the author of the *Compleat System of Optics*, and professor of astronomy and experimental philosophy at Cambridge. —It has been thus described by a modern poet:

> Hark where the organ, full and clear,
> With loud hosannas charms the ear;
> Behold, a prism within his hands,
> Absorbed in thought great Newton stands
> Such was his brow, and looks serene,
> His serious gait and musing mien,
> When taught on eagle wings to fly,
> He traced the wonders of the sky;
> The chambers of the sun explored,
> Where tints of thousand hues were stored.

Dr. Smith likewise bequeathed the sum of 500*l.*

for executing a painting on glass for the window at the south end of Trinity College, Cambridge. The subject represents the presentation of Sir Isaac Newton to his majesty George III., who is seated under a canopy with a laurel chaplet in his hand, and attended by the British Minerva, apparently advising him to reward merit in the person of the great philosopher. Below the throne, the Lord Chancellor Bacon is proposing to register the reward about to be conferred upon Sir Isaac. The original drawing of this absurd picture was executed by Cypriani, and cost one hundred guineas.

The personal estate of Sir Isaac Newton, which was worth about 32,000*l.*, was divided among his four nephews and four nieces of the half-blood, the grandchildren of his mother by the Reverend Mr. Smith. The family estates of Woolsthorpe and Sustern he bequeathed to John Newton, the heir-at-law, whose great-grandfather was Sir Isaac's uncle. This gentleman does not seem to have sufficiently valued the bequest, for he sold them in 1732, to Edmund Turnor of Stoke Rocheford.* A short time before his death, Sir Isaac gave away an estate in Berkshire to the sons and daughter of a brother of Mrs. Conduit, who, in consequence of their father dying before Sir Isaac, had no share in the personal estate; and he also gave an estate of the same value, which he bought at Kensington, to Catharine, the only daughter of Mr. Conduit, who afterward married Mr. Wallop, the eldest son of Lord Lymington. This lady was afterward Viscountess Lymington, and the estate of Kensington descended to the late Earl of Portsmouth, by whom it was sold. Sir Isaac was succeeded as master and warden in the mint by his nephew, John Conduit, Esq., who wrote a treatise on the gold and silver coin, and who died in 1737, leaving behind him his wife and daughter, the former of whom died in 1739, in the 59th year of her age.

* Turnor's *Collections*, &c. p. 158. See APPENDIX, p. 316.

CHAPTER XIX.

Permanence of Newton's Reputation—Character of his Genius—His Methods of Investigation similar to that used by Galileo—Error in ascribing his Discoveries to the Use of the Methods recommended by Lord Bacon—The Pretensions of the Baconian Philosophy examined —Sir Isaac Newton's social Character—His great Modesty—The Simplicity of his Character—His religious and moral Character— His Hospitality and Mode of Life—His Generosity and Charity— His Absence—His personal Appearance—Statues and Pictures of him—Memorials and Recollections of him.

SUCH were the last days of Sir Isaac Newton, and such the last laurels which were shed over his grave. A century of discoveries has since his day been added to science; but brilliant as these discoveries are, they have not obliterated the minutest of his labours, and have served only to brighten the halo which encircles his name. The achievements of genius, like the source from which they spring, are indestructible. Acts of legislation and deeds of war may confer a high celebrity, but the reputation which they bring is only local and transient; and while they are hailed by the nation which they benefit, they are reprobated by the people whom they ruin or enslave. The labours of science, on the contrary, bear along with them no counterpart of evil. They are the liberal bequests of great minds to every individual of their race, and wherever they are welcomed and honoured they become the solace of private life, and the ornament and bulwark of the commonwealth.

The importance of Sir Isaac Newton's discoveries has been sufficiently exhibited in the preceding chapters: the peculiar character of his genius, and the method which he pursued in his inquiries, can be gathered only from the study of his works, and from the history of his individual labours. Were we to judge of the qualities of his mind from the early age at which he made his principal discoveries, and from the rapidity of their succession, we should be led to ascribe to him that quickness of penetration, and that exuberance of invention, which is more characteristic of poetical than of philosophical genius. But we must recollect that Newton was placed in the most favourable circumstances for the development of his powers. The flower of his youth and the vigour of his manhood were entirely devoted to science. No injudicious guardian controlled his ruling passion, and no ungenial studies or professional toils interrupted the continuity of his pursuits. His discoveries were, therefore, the fruit of persevering and unbroken study; and he himself declared, that whatever service he had done to the public was not owing to any extraordinary sagacity, but solely to industry and patient thought.

Initiated early into the abstractions of geometry, he was deeply imbued with her cautious spirit; and if his acquisitions were not made with the rapidity of intuition, they were at least firmly secured; and the grasp which he took of his subject was proportional to the mental labour which it had exhausted. Overlooking what was trivial, and separating what was extraneous, he bore down with instinctive sagacity on the prominences of his subject, and having thus grappled with its difficulties, he never failed to intrench himself in its strongholds.

To the highest powers of invention Newton added, what so seldom accompanies them, the talent of simplifying and communicating his profoundest speculations.* In the economy of her distributions, nature is seldom thus lavish of her intellectual gifts. The inspired genius which creates is rarely con-

* This valuable faculty characterizes all his writings, whether theological, chymical, or mathematical; but it is peculiarly displayed in his treatise on Universal Arithmetic, and in his Optical Lectures.

ferred along with the matured judgment which combines, and yet without the exertion of both the fabric of human wisdom could never have been reared. Though a ray from heaven kindled the vestal fire, yet an humble priesthood was required to keep alive the flame.

The method of investigating truth by observation and experiment, so successfully pursued in the Principia, has been ascribed by some modern writers of great celebrity to Lord Bacon; and Sir Isaac Newton is represented as having owed all his discoveries to the application of the principles of that distinguished writer. One of the greatest admirers of Lord Bacon has gone so far as to characterize him as a man who has had no rival in the times which are past, and as likely to have none in those which are to come. In a eulogy so overstrained as this, we feel that the language of panegyric has passed into that of idolatry; and we are desirous of weighing the force of arguments which tend to depose Newton from the high-priesthood of nature, and to unsettle the proud destinies of Copernicus, Galileo, and Kepler.

That Bacon was a man of powerful genius, and endowed with varied and profound talent,—the most skilful logician,—the most nervous and eloquent writer of the age which he adorned, are points which have been established by universal suffrage. The study of ancient systems had early impressed him with the conviction that experiment and observation were the only sure guides in physical inquiries; and, ignorant though he was of the methods, the principles, and the details of the mathematical sciences, his ambition prompted him to aim at the construction of an artificial system by which the laws of nature might be investigated, and which might direct the inquiries of philosophers in every future age. The necessity of experimental research, and of advancing gradually from the study of facts to the determination of their cause, though the groundwork of Bacon's method, is a doctrine which was not only inculcated but successfully followed by preceding philosophers. In a letter from Tycho Brahe to Kepler, this industrious astronomer urges his pupil " to lay a solid foundation for his views by actual observation, and then by ascending from these to strive to reach the causes of things;" and it was no doubt under the influence of this advice that Kepler submitted his wildest fancies to the test of observation, and was conducted to his most splendid discoveries. The reasonings of Copernicus, who preceded Bacon by more than a century, were all founded upon the most legitimate induction. Dr. Gilbert had exhibited in his treatise on the magnet* the most perfect specimen of physical research. Leonardo da Vinci had described in the clearest manner the proper method of philosophical investigation;† and the whole scientific career of Galileo was one continued example of the most

---

* *De Magnete*, p. 42, 52, 169, and Pref. p. 30.

† The following passages from Leonardo da Vinci are very striking:
" Theory is the general, and practice the soldiers.

" Experiment is the interpreter of the artifices of nature. It never deceives us ; it is our judgment itself which sometimes deceives us, because we expect from it effects which are contrary to experiment. We must consult experiment by varying the circumstances till we have deduced from it general laws ; for it is it which furnishes true laws.

" In the study of the sciences which depend on mathematics, those who do not consult nature, but authors, are not the children of nature ; they are only her grandchildren. Nature alone is the master of true genius.

"In treating any particular subject, I would first of all make some experiments, because my design is first to refer to experiment, and then to demonstrate why bodies are constrained to act in such a manner. This is the method which we ought to follow in investigating the phenomena of nature. It is very true that nature begins by reasoning and ends with experiment ; but it matters not, *we must take the opposite course ; as I have said, we must begin by experiment,* and endeavour by its means to discover general principles." Thus, says Ventusi, spoke Leonard a century before Bacon, and thus, we add, did Leonard tell philosophers all that they required for the proper investigation of general laws. See *Essai sur les œuvrages physico-mathematiques de Leonard de Vinci*, par J. B. Venturi. Paris, 1799, p. 32, 33, &c. See also Carlo Amoretti's *Memorie storiche su la vita gli studi e le Opere de Leonardo da Vinci.* Milano, 1804.

sagacious application of observation and experiment
to the discovery of general laws. The names of
Paracelsus, Van Helmont, and Cardan have been
ranged in opposition to this constellation of great
names, and while it is admitted that even they had
thrown off the yoke of the schools, and had succeeded in experimental research, their credulity and
their pretensions have been adduced as a proof that
to the "bulk of philosophers" the method of induction was unknown. The fault of this argument consists in the conclusion being infinitely more general
than the fact. The errors of these men were not
founded on their ignorance, but on their presumption. They wanted the patience of philosophy and
not her methods. An excess of vanity, a wayward-
ness of fancy, and an insatiable appetite for that
species of passing fame which is derived from eccen-
tricity of opinion, moulded the reasonings and dis-
figured the writings of these ingenious men; and it
can scarcely admit of a doubt, that, had they lived
in the present age, their philosophical character
would have received the same impress from the
peculiarity of their tempers and dispositions. This
is an experiment, however, which cannot now be
made; but the history of modern science supplies
the defect, and the experience of every man furnishes a proof that in the present age there are
many philosophers of elevated talents and inventive
genius who are as impatient of experimental research as Paracelsus, as fanciful as Cardan, and as
presumptuous as Van Helmont.

Having thus shown that the distinguished philosophers who flourished before Bacon were perfect
masters both of the principles and practice of inductive research, it becomes interesting to inquire
whether or not the philosophers who succeeded
him acknowledged any obligation to his system, or
derived the slightest advantage from his precepts.
If Bacon constructed a method to which modern

science owes its existence, we shall find its cultiva-
tors grateful for the gift, and offering the richest
incense at the shrine of a benefactor whose generous labours conducted them to immortality. No
such testimonies, however, are to be found. Nearly
two hundred years have gone by, teeming with
the richest fruits of human genius, and no grateful
disciple has appeared to vindicate the rights of the
alleged legislator of science. Even Newton, who
was born and educated after the publication of the
Novum Organon, never mentions the name of Bacon
or his system, and the amiable and indefatigable
Boyle treated him with the same disrespectful
silence. When we are told, therefore, that Newton
owed all his discoveries to the method of Bacon,
nothing more can be meant than that he proceeded
in that path of observation and experiment which
had been so warmly recommended in the Novum
Organon ; but it ought to have been added, that the
same method was practised by his predecessors,—
that Newton possessed no secret that was not used
by Galileo and Copernicus,—and that he would
have enriched science with the same splendid discoveries if the name and the writings of Bacon had
never been heard of.

From this view of the subject we shall now proceed to examine the Baconian process itself, and
consider if it possesses any merit as an artificial
method of discovery; or if it is at all capable of being
employed, for this purpose, even in the humblest
walks of scientific inquiry.

The process of Lord Bacon was, we believe, never
tried by any philosopher but himself. As the subject of its application, he selected that of heat. With
his usual erudition, he collected all the facts which
science could supply,—he arranged them in tables,—
he cross-questioned them with all the subtlety of a
pleader,—he combined them with all the sagacity
of a judge,—and he conjured with them by all the

magic of his exclusive processes. But, after all this
display of physical logic, nature thus interrogated
was still silent. The oracle which he had himself
established refused to give its responses, and the
ministering priest was driven with discomfiture from
his own shrine. This example, in short, of the application of his system, will remain to future ages
as a memorable instance of the absurdity of attempting to fetter discovery by any artificial rules.

Nothing even in mathematical science can be
more certain than that a collection of scientific facts
are of themselves incapable of leading to discovery,
or to the determination of general laws, unless they
contain the predominating fact or relation in which
the discovery mainly resides. A vertical column of
arch-stones possesses more strength than the same
materials arranged in an arch without the key-stone.
However nicely they are adjusted, and however nobly the arch may spring, it never can possess either
equilibrium or stability. In this comparison all the
facts are supposed to be necessary to the final result; but, in the inductive method, it is impossible
to ascertain the relative importance of any facts, or
even to determine if the facts have any value at all,
till the master-fact which constitutes the discovery
has crowned the zealous efforts of the aspiring philosopher. The mind then returns to the dark and
barren waste over which it has been hovering; and
by the guidance of this single torch it embraces,
under the comprehensive grasp of general principles, the multifarious and insulated phenomena which
had formerly neither value nor connexion. Hence
it must be obvious to the most superficial thinker,
that discovery consists either in the detection of
some concealed relation—some deep-seated affinity
which baffles ordinary research, or in the discovery
of some simple fact which is connected by slender
ramifications with the subject to be investigated;
but which, when once detected, carries us back by

its divergence to all the phenomena which it embraces and explains.

In order to give additional support to these views, it would be interesting to ascertain the general character of the process by which a mind of acknowledged power actually proceeds in the path of successful inquiry. The history of science does not furnish us with much information on this head, and if it is to be found at all, it must be gleaned from the biographies of eminent men. Whatever this process may be in its details, if it has any, there cannot be the slightest doubt that in its generalities at least it is the very reverse of the method of induction. The impatience of genius spurns the restraints of mechanical rules, and never will submit to the plodding drudgery of inductive discipline. The discovery of a new fact unfits even a patient mind for deliberate inquiry. Conscious of having added to science what had escaped the sagacity of former ages, the ambitious spirit invests its new acquisition with an importance which does not belong to it. He imagines a thousand consequences to flow from his discovery: he forms innumerable theories to explain it, and he exhausts his fancy in trying all its possible relations to recognised difficulties and unexplained facts. The reins, however, thus freely given to his imagination, are speedily drawn up. His wildest conceptions are all subjected to the rigid test of experiment, and he has thus been hurried by the excursions of his own fancy into new and fertile paths, far removed from ordinary observation. Here the peculiar character of his own genius displays itself by the invention of methods of trying his own speculations, and he is thus often led to new discoveries far more important and general than that by which he began his inquiry. For a confirmation of these views, we may refer to the History of Kepler's Discoveries; and if we do not recognise them to the same extent in the labours of

Newton, it is because he kept back his discoveries till they were nearly perfected, and therefore withheld the successive steps of his inquiries.

The social character of Sir Isaac Newton was such as might have been expected from his intellectual attainments. He was modest, candid, and affable, and without any of the eccentricities of genius, suiting himself to every company, and speaking of himself and others in such a manner that he was never even suspected of vanity. "But this," says Dr. Pemberton, "I immediately discovered in him, which at once both surprised and charmed me. Neither his extreme great age nor his universal reputation had rendered him stiff in opinion, or in any degree elated. Of this I had occasion to have almost daily experience. The remarks I continually sent him by letters on the Principia were received with the utmost goodness. These were so far from being any ways displeasing to him, that on the contrary it occasioned him to speak many kind things of me to my friends, and to honour me with a public testimony of his good opinion."

The modesty of Sir Isaac Newton in reference to his great discoveries was not founded on any indifference to the fame which they conferred, or upon any erroneous judgment of their importance to science. The whole of his life proves, that he knew his place as a philosopher, and was determined to assert and vindicate his rights. His modesty arose from the depth and extent of his knowledge, which showed him what a small portion of nature he had been able to examine, and how much remained to be explored in the same field in which he had himself laboured. In the magnitude of the comparison he recognised his own littleness; and a short time before his death he uttered this memorable sentiment:—"I do not know what I may appear to the world; but to myself I seem to have been only like a boy playing on the seashore, and diverting myself in now and then finding a smoother pebble or a prettier shell than ordinary, while the great ocean of truth lay all undiscovered before me." What a lesson to the vanity and presumption of philosophers, —to those especially who have never even found the smoother pebble or the prettier shell! What a preparation for the latest inquiries, and the last views of the decaying spirit,—for those inspired doctrines which alone can throw a light over the dark ocean of undiscovered truth!

The native simplicity of Sir Isaac Newton's mind is finely portrayed in the affecting letter in which he acknowledges to Locke that he had thought and spoken of him uncharitably; and the humility and candour in which he asks forgiveness could have emanated only from a mind as noble as it was pure.

In the religious and moral character of our author there is much to admire and to imitate. While he exhibited in his life and writings an ardent regard for the general interests of religion, he was at the same time a firm believer in revelation. He was too deeply versed in the Scriptures, and too much imbued with their spirit, to judge harshly of other men who took different views of them from himself. He cherished the great principles of religious toleration, and never scrupled to express his abhorrence of persecution, even in its mildest form. Immorality and impiety he never permitted to pass unreproved; and when Dr. Halley* ventured to say any thing disrespectful to religion, he invariably checked him, and said, "I have studied these things,—you have not."†

After Sir Isaac Newton took up his residence in London, he lived in a very handsome style, and kept his carriage, with an establishment of three male

---

* Mr. Hearne, in a memorandum dated April 4th, 1726, states, that a great quarrel happened between Sir Isaac Newton and Mr. Halley. If this is true, the difference is likely to have originated in Halley's impiety.

† Professor Rigaud of Oxford heard this anecdote from Dr. Maskelyne.

C c

and three female servants. In his own house he was hospitable and kind, and on proper occasions he gave splendid entertainments, though without ostentation or vanity. His own diet was frugal, and his dress was always simple; but on one occasion, when he opposed the Honourable Mr. Annesley in 1705, as a candidate for the university, he is said to have put on a suit of laced clothes.

His generosity and charity had no bounds, and he used to remark, that they who gave away nothing till they died never gave at all. Though his wealth had become considerable by a prudent economy, yet he had always a contempt for money, and he spent a considerable part of his income in relieving the poor, in assisting his relations, and in encouraging ingenuity and learning. The sums which he gave to his relations at different times were enormous;* and in 1724 he wrote a letter to the Lord Provost of Edinburgh, offering to contribute 20l. per annum to a provision for Mr. Maclaurin, provided he accepted the situation of assistant to Mr. James Gregory, who was professor of mathematics in the university.

The habits of deep meditation which Sir Isaac Newton had acquired, though they did not show themselves in his intercourse with society, exercised their full influence over his mind when in the midst of his own family. Absorbed in thought he would often sit down on his bedside after he rose, and remain there for hours without dressing himself, occupied with some interesting investigation which had fixed his attention. Owing to the same absence of mind, he neglected to take the requisite quantity

---

* "He was very kind to all the Ayscoughs. To one he gave 800l., to another 200l., and to a third 100l., and many other sums; and other engagements did he enter into also for them. He was the ready assistant of all who were any way related to him,—to their children and grandchildren."—*Annual Register*, 1776, vol. xix. p. 25. Sir Isaac gave some donations to the chapel and parish of Colsterworth. Hearne says "that he promised to become a benefactor to the Royal Society, but failed"

of nourishment, and it was therefore often necessary to remind him of his meals.*

Sir Isaac Newton is supposed to have had little knowledge of the world, and to have been very ignorant of the habits of society. This opinion has, we think, been rashly deduced from a letter which he wrote in the twenty-seventh year of his age to his young friend, Francis Aston, Esq., who was about to set out on his travels. This letter is a highly interesting production; and while it shows much knowledge of the human heart, it throws a strong light upon the character and opinions of its author.

In his personal appearance, Sir Isaac Newton was not above the middle size, and in the latter part of his life was inclined to be corpulent. According to Mr. Conduit " he had a very lively and piercing eye, a comely and gracious aspect, with a fine head of hair as white as silver, without any baldness, and when his peruke was off was a venerable sight." Bishop Atterbury asserts,† on the other hand, that the lively and piercing eye did not belong to Sir Isaac during the last twenty years of his life. " Indeed," says he, " in the whole air of his face and make there was nothing of that penetrating sagacity which appears in his compositions. He had something rather languid in his look and manner which did not raise any great expectation in those who did not know him." This opinion of Bishop Atterbury is confirmed by an observation of Mr. Thomas

---

* The following anecdote of Sir Isaac's absence has been published, but I cannot vouch for its authenticity. His intimate friend Dr. Stukely, who had been deputy to Dr. Halley as secretary to the Royal Society, was one day shown into Sir Isaac's dining-room, where his dinner had been for some time served up. Dr. Stukely waited for a considerable time, and getting impatient, he removed the cover from a chicken, which he ate, replacing the bones under the cover. In a short time Sir Isaac entered the room, and after the usual compliments sat down to his dinner, but on taking off the cover, and seeing nothing but bones, he remarked, " How absent we philosophers are. I really thought that I had not dined."

† *Epistolary Correspondence*, vol. i. p. 180, sec. 77.

Hearne,* who says " that Sir Isaac was a man of no
very promising aspect. He was a short, well-set
man. He was full of thought, and spoke very little in
company, so that his conversation was not agreeable.
When he rode in his coach, one arm would be out
of his coach on one side and the other on the other."
Sir Isaac never wore spectacles, and never " lost
more than one tooth to the day of his death."

Besides the statue of Sir Isaac Newton executed
by Roubiliac, there is a bust of him by the same
artist in the library of Trinity College, Cambridge.
Several good paintings of him are extant. Two
of these are in the hall of the Royal Society of
London, and have, we believe, been often engraved.
Another, by Vanderbank, is in the apartments of
the Master's lodge in Trinity College, and has been
engraved by Vertue. Another, by Valentine Ritts,
is in the landing-place near the entrance to Trinity
College library; but the best, from which our engraving is copied, was painted by Sir Godfrey Knel-
ler, and is in the possession of Lord Egremont at
Petworth. In the university library there is preserved a cast taken from his face after death.

Every memorial of so great a man as Sir Isaac
Newton has been preserved and cherished with peculiar veneration. His house at Woolsthorpe, of which
we have given an engraving, has been religiously
protected by Mr. Turnor of Stoke Rocheford, the
proprietor. Dr. Stukeley, who visited it in Sir
Isaac's lifetime, on the 13th October, 1721, gives the
following description of it in his letter to Dr. Mead,
written in 1727: " 'Tis built of stone as is the way
of the country hereabouts, and a reasonable good
one. They led me up stairs and showed me Sir
Isaac's study, where I suppose he studied when in
the country in his younger days, or perhaps when
he visited his mother from the university. I observed the shelves were of his own making, being
pieces of deal boxes which probably he sent his

* MS. Memoranda in the Bodleian Library.

books and clothes down in on those occasions. There were some years ago two or three hundred books in it of his father-in-law, Mr. Smith, which Sir Isaac gave to Dr. Newton of our town."*

When the house was repaired in 1798, a tablet of white marble was put up by Mr. Turnor in the room where Sir Isaac was born, with the following inscription:

"Sir Isaac Newton, son of John Newton, Lord of the manor of Woolsthorpe, was born in this room on the 25th December, 1642."

> Nature and Nature's laws lay hid in night,
> God said, "Let Newton be," and all was light.

The following lines have been written upon the house:

> Here Newton dawned, here lofty wisdom woke,
> And to a wondering world divinely spoke.
> If Tully glowed, when Phædrus' steps he trode,
> Or fancy formed Philosophy a god;
> If sages still for Homer's birth contend
> The Sons of Science at this dome must bend.
> All hail the shrine! All hail the natal day,
> Cam boasts his noon,—This *Cot* his morning ray.

The house is now occupied by a person of the name of John Wollerton. It still contains the two dials made by Newton, but the styles of both are wanting. The celebrated apple-tree, the fall of one of the apples of which is said to have turned the attention of Newton to the subject of gravity, was destroyed by wind about four years ago; but Mr. Turnor has preserved it in the form of a chair.†

The chambers which Sir Isaac inhabited at Cambridge are known by tradition. They are the apartments next to the great gate of Trinity College, and it is believed that they then communicated by a staircase with the observatory in the Great Tower,

---

* Turnor's *Collections*, p. 176.

† The anecdote of the falling apple is mentioned neither by Dr. Stukely nor by Mr. Conduit, and as I have not been able to find any authority for it whatever, I did not feel myself at liberty to use it.

—an observatory which was furnished by the contributions of Newton, Cotes, and others. His telescope, represented in *fig.* 1, page 41, is preserved in the library of the Royal Society of London, and his globe, his universal ring-dial, quadrant, compass, and a reflecting telescope said to have belonged to him, in the library of Trinity College. There is also in the same collection a long and curled lock of his silver white hair. The door of his bookcase is in the Museum of the Royal Society of Edinburgh.

The manuscripts, letters, and other papers of Newton have been preserved in different collections. His correspondence with Cotes relative to the second edition of the Principia, and amounting to between sixty and a hundred letters, a considerable portion of the manuscript of that work, and two or three letters to Dr. Keill on the Leibnitzian controversy, are preserved in the library of Trinity College, Cambridge. Newton's letters to Flamstead, about thirty-four in number, are deposited in the library of Corpus Christi College, Oxford.* Several letters of Newton, and, we believe, the original specimen which he drew up of the Principia, exist among the papers of Mr. William Jones (the father of Sir William Jones), which are preserved at Shirburn Castle, in the library of Lord Macclesfield. But the great mass of Newton's papers came into the possession of the Portsmouth family through his niece, Lady Lymington, and have been safely preserved by that noble family. There is reason to believe that they contain nothing which could be peculiarly interesting to science; but as the correspondence of Newton with contemporary philosophers must throw considerable light on his personal history, we trust that it will ere long be given to the public.

* In the Monthly Review for August, 1829, p. 593, it is stated, that the correspondence between Newton and Flamstead, from 1680 to 1698, exists in the Sloane collection of Manuscripts in the British Museum. Professor Rigaud, however, has had the kindness to inquire into the accuracy of this statement, and he has ascertained that these letters are merely copies, which Dr. Birch had made from the originals at Oxford.

APPENDIX.

No. I.

IN the year 1705, Sir Isaac gave into the Herald's Office an elaborate pedigree, stating upon oath *that he had reason to believe* that John Newton of Westby, in the county of Lincoln, was his great-grandfather's father, and that this was the same John Newton who was buried in Basingthorpe church, on the 22d December, 1563. This John Newton had four sons, John, Thomas, Richard, and William Newton of Gunnerly, the last of whom was great-grandfather to Sir John Newton, Bart., of Hather. Sir Isaac considered himself as descended from the eldest of these, *he having, by tradition from his kindred ever since he can remember, reckoned himself next of kin (among the Newtons) to Sir John Newton's family.*

The pedigree, founded upon these and other considerations, was accompanied by a certificate from Sir John Newton, of Thorpe, Bart., who states that he had heard his father speak of Sir Isaac Newton *as of his relation and kinsman*, and that *he himself believed that Sir Isaac was descended from John Newton, son to John Newton of Westby, but knoweth not in what particular manner.*

The pedigree of Sir Isaac, as entered at the Herald's Office, does not seem to have been satisfactory either to himself or to his successors, as it could not be traced with certainty beyond his grandfather; and it will be seen from the following interesting correspondence, that upon making further researches, he had found some reason to believe that he was of Scotch extraction.

Extract of a Letter from the Reverend Dr. Reid of Glasgow to Dr. Gregory of Edinburgh, dated 14th March, 1784.

"I send you on the other page an anecdote respecting Sir Isaac Newton, which I do not remember whether I ever happened to mention to you in conversation. If his descent be not clearly ascertained (as I think it is not in the books I have seen), might it not be worth while to inquire if evidence can be found to confirm the account which he is said to have given of himself. Sheriff Cross was very zealous about it when death put a stop to his inquiries.

"When I lived in old Aberdeen above twenty years ago, I happened to be conversing over a pipe of tobacco with a gentleman of that country, who had been lately at Edinburgh. He told me that he had been often in company with Mr. Hepburn of Keith, with whom I had the honour of some acquaintance. He said that, speaking of Sir Isaac Newton, Mr. Hepburn mentioned an anecdote, which he had from Mr. James Gregory, professor of mathematics at Edinburgh, which was to this purpose:

"Mr. Gregory, being at London for some time after he resigned the mathematical chair, was often with Sir Isaac Newton. One day Sir Isaac said to him, 'Gregory, I believe you don't know that I am connected with Scotland.'—'Pray how, Sir Isaac?' said Gregory. Sir Isaac said he was told that his grandfather was a gentleman of East Lothian; that he came to London with King James at his accession to the crown of England, and there spent his fortune, as many more did at that time, by which his son (Sir Isaac's father) was reduced to mean circumstances. To this Gregory bluntly replied, 'Newton a gentleman of East Lothian, I never heard of a gentleman of East Lothian of that name.' Upon this Sir Isaac said, 'that being very young when his father died, he had it only by tradition, and it might be a mistake;' and immediately turned the conversation to another subject.

" I confess I suspected that the gentleman who was my author had given some colouring to this story, and therefore I never mentioned it for a good many years.

" After I removed to Glasgow, I came to be very intimately acquainted with Mr. Cross, then sheriff of Lanark, and one day at his own house mentioned this story, without naming my author, of whom I expressed some diffidence.

" The sheriff immediately took it up as a matter worth being inquired into. He said he was well acquainted with Mr. Hepburn of Keith (who was then alive), and that he would write him to know whether he ever heard Mr. Gregory say that he had such a conversation with Sir Isaac Newton. He said he knew that Mr. Keith, the ambassador, was also intimate with Mr. Gregory, and that he would write him to the same purpose.

" Some time after, Mr. Cross told me that he had answers from both the gentlemen above mentioned, and that both remembered to have heard Mr. Gregory mention the conversation between him and Sir Isaac Newton, to the purpose above narrated, and at the same time acknowledged that they had made no further inquiry about the matter.

" Mr. Cross, however, continued the inquiry, and a short time before his death told me that all he had learned was, that there is, or was lately, a baronet's family of the name of Newton in West Lothian or Mid Lothian (I have forgot which): that there is a tradition in that family that Sir Isaac Newton wrote a letter to the old knight that then was (I think Sir John Newton of Newton was his name), desiring to know what children, and particularly what sons he had, their age, and what professions they intended: that the old baronet never deigned to return an answer to this letter, which his family was sorry for, as they thought Sir Isaac might have intended to do something for them."

Several years after this letter was written, a Mr. Barron, a relation of Sir Isaac Newton, seems to have been making inquiries respecting the family of his ancestor, and in consequence of this the late Professor Robison applied to Dr. Reid, to obtain from him a more particular account of the remarkable conversation between Sir Isaac and Mr. James Gregory referred to in the preceding letter. In answer to this request, Dr. Reid wrote the following letter, for which I was indebted to John Robison, Esq. Sec. R. S. E., who found it among his father's manuscripts.

Letter from Dr. Reid to Professor Robison respecting the Family of Sir Isaac Newton.

" DEAR SIR,
"I am very glad to learn by yours of April 4, that a Mr. Barron, a near relation of Sir Isaac Newton, is anxious to inquire into the descent of that great man, as the family cannot trace it farther, with any certainty, than his grandfather. I therefore, as you desire, send you a precise account of all I know; and am glad to have this opportunity, before I die, of putting this information in hands that will make the proper use of it, if it shall be found of any use.
"Several years before I left Aberdeen (which I did in 1764), Mr. Douglas of Feckel, the father of Sylvester Douglas, now a barrister at London, told

me, that having been lately at Edinburgh, he was often in company with Mr. Hepburn of Keith, a gentleman of whom I had some acquaintance, by *his lodging a night at my house at New Machar,* when he was in the rebel army in 1745. That Mr. Hepburn told him that he had heard Mr. James Gregory, professor of mathematics, Edinburgh, say, that being one day in familiar conversation with Sir Isaac Newton at London, Sir Isaac said, 'Gregory, I believe you don't know that I am a Scotchman.'—'Pray, how is that?' said Gregory. Sir Isaac said he was informed that his grandfather (or great-grandfather) was a gentleman of East (or West) Lothian: that he went to London with King James the I. at his accession to the crown of England: and that he attended the court in expectation, as many others did, until he spent his fortune, by which means his family was reduced to low circumstances. At the time this was told me Mr. Gregory was dead, otherwise I should have had his own testimony, for he was my mother's brother. I likewise thought at that time that it had been certainly known that Sir Isaac had been descended from an old English family, as I think is said in his *eloge* before the Academy of Sciences at Paris, and therefore I never mentioned what I had heard for many years, believing that there must be some mistake in it.

"Some years after I came to Glasgow, I mentioned (I believe for the first time) what I had heard to have been said by Mr. Hepburn to Mr. Cross, late sheriff of this county, whom you will remember. Mr. Cross was moved by this account, and immediately said, 'I know Mr. Hepburn very well, and I know he was intimate with Mr. Gregory: I shall write him this same night, to know whether he heard Mr. Gregory say so or not.' After some reflection, he added, 'I know that Mr. Keith, the ambassador, was also an intimate acquaintance of Mr. Gregory, and as he is at present in Edinburgh, I shall likewise write to him this night.'

"The next time I waited on Mr. Cross he told me that he had wrote both to Mr. Hepburn and Mr. Keith, and had an answer from both, and that both of them testified that they had several times heard Mr. James Gregory say, that Sir Isaac Newton told him what is above expressed, but that neither they nor Mr. Gregory, as far as they knew, ever made any further inquiry into the matter. This appeared very strange both to Mr. Cross and me, and he said he would reproach them for their indifference, and would make inquiry as soon as he was able.

"He lived but a short time after this, and in the last conversation I had with him upon the subject, he said, that all he had yet learned was, that there was a Sir John Newton of Newton in one of the counties of Lothian (but I have forgot which), some of whose children were yet alive: that they reported that their father, Sir John, had a letter from Sir Isaac Newton, desiring to know the state of his family, what children he had, particularly what sons, and in what way they were. The old knight never returned an answer to this letter, thinking probably that Sir Isaac was some upstart, who wanted to claim a relation to his worshipful house. This omission the children regretted, conceiving that Sir Isaac might have had a view of doing something for their benefit.

"After this I mentioned occasionally in conversation what I knew, hoping that these facts might lead to some more certain discovery, but I found more coldness about the matter than I thought it deserved. I wrote an account of it to Dr. Gregory, your colleague, that he might impart it to any member of the Antiquarian Society who he judged might have the curiosity to trace the matter further.

"In the year 1787, my colleague, Mr. Patrick Wilson, professor of astronomy, having been in London, told me on his return that he had met accidentally with a James Hutton, Esq. of Pimlico,

Westminster, a near relation of Sir Isaac Newton,* to whom he mentioned what he had heard from me with respect to Sir Isaac's descent, and that I wished much to know something more decisive on that subject. Mr. Hutton said, if I pleased to write to him he would give me all the information he could give. I wrote him accordingly, and had a very polite answer, dated at Bath, 25th December, 1787, which is now before me. He says, 'I shall be glad when I return to London, if I can find in some old notes of my mother any thing that may fix the certainty of Sir Isaac's descent. If he spoke so to Mr. James Gregory, it is most certain he spoke truth. But Sir Isaac's grandfather, not his great-grandfather, must be the person who came from Scotland with King James I. If I find any thing to the purpose, I will take care it shall reach you.'

"In consequence of this letter I expected another from Mr. Hutton when he should return to London, but have never had any. Mr. Wilson told me he was a very old man, and whether he be dead or alive I know not.

"This is all I know of the matter, and for the facts above mentioned I pledge my veracity. I am much obliged to you, dear sir, for the kind expressions of your affection and esteem, which, I assure you, are mutual on my part, and I sincerely sympathize with you on your afflicting state of health, which makes you consider yourself as out of the world, and despair of seeing me any more.

"I have been long out of the world by deafness and extreme old age. I hope, however, if we should not meet again in this world, that we shall meet and renew our acquaintance in another. In the mean time, I am with great esteem, dear sir, yours affectionately, "THO. REID.

"*Glasgow College,*
"*12th April,* 1792."

* See page 288, note.

D d

This curious letter I published in the Ed. Phil. Journal for October1, 1820. It excited the particular attention of the late George Chalmers, Esq., who sent me an elaborate letter upon the subject; but as I was at that time in the expectation of obtaining some important information through other channels, this letter was not published. This hope, however, has been disappointed. A careful search has been made through the charter-chest of the Newtons of Newton in East Lothian, by Mr. Richard Hay Newton, the representative of that family, but no document whatever has been found that can throw the least light upon the matter. It deserves to be remarked, however, that Sir Richard Newton, the alleged correspondent of Sir Isaac, appears to have destroyed his correspondence; for though the charter-chest contains the letters of his predecessors for some generations, yet there is not a single epistolary document either of his own or of his lady's.

Hitherto the evidence of Sir Isaac's Scottish descent has been derived chiefly from his conversation with Mr. James Gregory; but I am enabled, by the kindness of Mr. Robison, to corroborate this evidence by the following information, derived, as will be seen, from the family of the Newtons of Newton. Among various memoranda in the handwriting of Professor Robison, who at one time proposed to write the life of Sir Isaac, are the following:—

" 1st, Lord Henderland informed me in a letter dated March, 1794, that he had heard from his infancy that Sir Isaac considered himself as descended from the family of Newton of Newton. This he heard from his uncle Richard Newton of Newton (who was third son of Lord William Hay of Newhall):" " He said that Sir Isaac wrote to Scotland to learn whether any descendants of that family remained, and this (it was thought) with the view to leave some of his fortune to the family possessing the estate with the title of baronet. Mr. Newton, not having this honour, and being a shy man, did not encourage the correspondence, because he did not consider *himself* as of kin to Sir Isaac, &c."

"2d, Information communicated to me by Hay Newton, Esq., of that ilk, 18th August, 1800."

"The late Sir Richard Newton of Newton, Bart., chief of that name, having no male children, settled the estate and barony of Newton in East Lothian county upon his relation Richard Hay Newton, Esq., son of Lord William Hay."*—"It cannot be discovered how long the family of Newton have been in possession of the barony, there being no tradition concerning that circumstance further than that they came originally from England at a very distant period, and settled on these lands."—"The celebrated Sir Isaac Newton was a distant relation of the family, and corresponded with the last baronet, the above-mentioned Sir Richard Newton."

The preceding documents furnish the most complete evidence that the conversation respecting Sir Isaac Newton's family took place between him and Mr. Gregory; and the testimony of Lord Henderland proves that his own uncle, Richard Newton of Newton, the immediate successor of Sir Richard Newton, with whom Sir Isaac corresponded, was perfectly confident that such a correspondence took place.

All these circumstances prove that Sir Isaac Newton could not trace his pedigree with any certainty beyond his grandfather, and that there were two different traditions in his family,—one which referred his descent to John Newton of Westby, and the other to a gentleman of East Lothian who accompanied King James VI. to England. In the first of these traditions he seems to have placed most confidence in 1705, when he drew out his traditionary pedigree; but as the conversation with Professor James Gregory respecting his Scotch extraction

* This entail was executed in 1724, a year or two before Sir Richard's death.—D. B.

took place *twenty years* afterward, namely, between 1725 and 1727, it is probable that he had discovered the incorrectness of his first opinions, or at least was disposed to attach more importance to the other tradition respecting his descent from a Scotch family.

In the letter addressed to me by the learned George Chalmers, Esq. I find the following observations respecting the immediate relations of Sir Isaac. " The Newtons of Woolsthorpe," says he, " who were merely yeomen farmers, were not by any means opulent. The son of Sir Isaac's father's brother was a carpenter called John. He was afterward appointed gamekeeper to Sir Isaac, as lord of the manor, and died at the age of sixty in 1725. This John had a son, Robert, (John ?) who was Sir Isaac's second cousin, and who became possessed of the whole land estates at and near Woolsthorpe, which belonged to the great Newton, as his heir-at-law.* Robert (John ?) became a worthless and dissolute person, who very soon wasted this ancient patrimony, and falling down with a tobacco-pipe in his mouth when he was drunk, it broke in his throat, and put an end to his life at the age of thirty years, in 1737."

No. II.

LETTER FROM SIR ISAAC NEWTON TO FRANCIS ASTON, ESQ., A YOUNG FRIEND WHO WAS ON THE EVE OF SETTING OUT UPON HIS TRAVELS.

Mr. Aston was elected a Fellow of the Royal Society in 1678. He held the office of Secretary between 1681 and 1685; and he was the author of some observations on certain unknown ancient characters, which were published in the Philosophical Transactions for 1693.

* See p. 291.

This letter has been referred to in pages 270 and 303, and was written when Newton was only twenty-six years of age. It is in every respect an interesting document.

"*Trinity College, Cambridge,*
"SIR, *May 18, 1669.*

"Since in your letter you give mee so much liberty of spending my judgement about what may be to your advantage in travelling, I shall do it more freely than perhaps otherwise would have been decent. First, then, I will lay down some general rules, most of which, I believe, you have considered already; but if any of them be new to you, they may excuse the rest; if none at all, yet is my punishment more in writing than yours in reading.

"When you come into any fresh company, 1. Observe their humours. 2. Suit your own carriage thereto, by which insinuation you will make their converse more free and open. 3. Let your discours be more in querys and doubtings than peremptory assertions or disputings, it being the designe of travellers to learne, not to teach. Besides, it will persuade your acquaintance that you have the greater esteem of them, and soe make them more ready to communicate what they know to you; whereas nothing sooner occasions disrespect and quarrels than peremptorinesse. You will find little or no advantage in seeming wiser or much more ignorant than your company. 4. Seldom discommend any thing though never so bad, or doe it but moderately, lest you bee unexpectedly forced to an unhansom retraction. It is safer to commend any thing more than it deserves, than to discommend a thing soe much as it deserves; for commendations meet not soe often with oppositions, or, at least, are not usually soe ill resented by men that think otherwise, as discommendations; and you will insinuate into

men's favour by nothing sooner than seeming to
approve and commend what they like; but beware
of doing it by a comparison.   5. If you bee affronted,
it is better, in a forraine country, to pass it by in
silence, and with a jest, though with some dishonour,
than to endeavour revenge; for, in the first case,
your credit's ne'er the worse when you return into
England, or come into other company that have not
heard of the quarrell.   But, in the second case, you
may beare the marks of the quarrell while you live,
if you outlive it at all.   But, if you find yourself un-
avoidably engaged, 'tis best, I think, if you can command your passion and language, to keep them
pretty evenly at some certain moderate pitch, not
much hightning them to exasperate your adversary,
or provoke his friends, nor letting them grow over-
much dejected to make him insult.   In a word, if
you can keep reason above passion, that and watch-
fullnesse will be your best defendants.   To which
purpose you may consider, that, though such excuses
as this,—He provok't mee so much I could not for-
bear,—may pass among friends, yet amongst stran-
gers they are insignificant, and only argue a traveller's weaknesse.

   " To these I may add some general heads for in-
quirys or observations, such as at present I can
think on.   As, 1. To observe the policys, wealth,
and state-affairs of nations, so far as a solitary
traveller may conveniently doe.   2. Their imposi-
tions upon all sorts of people, trades, or commoditys,
that are remarkable.   3. Their laws and customs,
how far they differ from ours.   4. Their trades and
arts wherein they excell or come short of us in
England.   5. Such fortifications as you shall meet
with, their fashion, strength, and advantages for defence, and other such military affairs as are considerable.   6. The power and respect belonging to their
degrees of nobility or magistracy.   7. It will not be
time mispent to make a catalogue of the names and

excellencys of those men that are most wise, learned, or esteemed in any nation. 8. Observe the mechanisme and manner of guiding ships. 9. Observe the products of nature in several places, especially in mines, with the circumstances of mining and of extracting metals or minerals out of their oare, and of refining them ; and if you meet with any transmutations out of their own species into another (as out of iron into copper, out of any metall into quicksilver, out of one salt into another, or into an insipid body, &c.), those, above all, will be worth your noting, being the most luciferous, and many times lucriferous experiments too, in philosophy. 10. The prices of diet and other things. 11. And the staple commoditys of places.

"These generals (such as at present I could think of), if they will serve for nothing else, yet they may assist you in drawing up a modell to regulate your travells by. As for particulars, these that follow are all that I can now think of, viz. Whether at Schemnitium, in Hungary (where there are mines of gold, copper, iron, vitrioll, antimony, &c.), they change iron into copper by dissolving it in a vitriolate water, which they find in cavitys of rocks in the mines, and then melting the slimy solution in a strong fire, which in the cooling proves copper. The like is said to be done in other places, which I cannot now remember ; perhaps, too, it may be done in Italy. For about twenty or thirty years agone there was a certain vitrioll came from thence (called Roman vitrioll), but of a nobler virtue than that which is now called by that name ; which vitrioll is not now to be gotten, because, perhaps, they make a greater gain by some such trick as turning iron into copper with it than by selling it. 2. Whether, in Hungary, Sclavonia, Bohemia, near the town Eila, or at the mountains of Bohemia near Silesia, there be rivers whose waters are impregnated with gold ; perhaps, the gold being dissolved by some corrosive waters like *aqua regis*, and the solution carried along with the streame, that runs through the mines. And whether the practice of laying mercury in the rivers, till it be tinged with gold, and then straining the mercury through leather, that the gold may stay behind, be a secret yet, or openly practised. 3. There is newly contrived, in Holland, a mill to grind glasses plane withall, and I think polishing them too ; perhaps it will be worth the while to see it. 4. There is in Holland one —— Borry, who some years since was imprisoned by the Pope, to have extorted from him secrets (as I am told) of great worth, both as to medicine and profit, but he escaped into Holland, where they have granted him a guard. I think he usually goes clothed in green. Pray inquire what you can of him, and whether his ingenuity be any profit to the Dutch. You may inform yourself whether the Dutch have any tricks to keep their ships from being all worm-eaten in their voyages to the Indies. Whether pendulum clocks do any service in finding out the longitude, &c.

" I am very weary, and shall not stay to part with a long compliment, only I wish you a good journey, and God be with you.

" Is. NEWTON,

" Pray let us hear from you in your travells. I have given your two books to Dr. Arrowsmith."

No. III.

" A REMARKABLE AND CURIOUS CONVERSATION BETWEEN SIR ISAAC NEWTON AND MR. CONDUIT."

" I WAS on Sunday night, the 7th of March, 1724–5, at Kensington with Sir Isaac Newton, in his lodgings, just after he was come out of a fit of the gout, which he had had in both his feet, for the first time, in the eighty-third year of his age. He was better after it, and his head clearer, and memory stronger than I had known them for some time. He then repeated to me, by way of discourse, very distinctly, though rather in answer to my queries than in one continued narration, what he had often hinted to me before, viz. that it was his conjecture (he would affirm nothing) that there was a sort of revolution in the heavenly bodies; that the vapours and light emitted by the sun, which had their sediment as water and other matter, had gathered themselves by degrees into a body, and attracted more matter from the planets, and at last made a secondary planet (viz. one of those that go round another planet and then by gathering to them, and attracting more matter, became a primary planet; and then by increasing still became a comet, which after certain revolutions, by coming nearer and nearer to the sun, had all its volatile parts condensed, and became a matter fit to recruit and replenish the sun (which must waste by the constant heat and light it emitted) as a fagot would this fire if put into it (we were sitting by a wood fire), and that that would probably be the effect of the comet of 1680, sooner or later, for, by the observations made upon it, it appeared, before it came near the sun, with a tail only two or three degrees long; but by the heat it contracted in going so near the sun, it seemed to have a tail of thirty or forty degrees when it went from it; that he could not say when this comet would drop into the sun; it might perhaps have five or six revolutions more first, but whenever it did it would so much increase the heat of the sun that this earth would be burnt, and no animals in it could live. That he took the three phenomena seen by Hipparchus, Tycho Brahe, and Kepler's disciples to have been of this kind, for he could not otherwise account for an extraordinary light as those were, appearing all at once among the fixed stars (all which he took to be suns enlightening other planets as our sun does ours) as big as Mercury or Venus seems to us, and gradually diminishing for sixteen months, and then sinking into nothing. He seemed to doubt whether there were not intelligent beings superior to us who superintended these revolutions of the heavenly bodies by the direction of the Supreme Being. He appeared also to be very clearly of opinion that the inhabitants of this world were of a short date, and alleged as one reason for that opinion, that all arts, as letters, ships, printing, needle, &c., were discovered within the memory of history, which could not have happened if the world had been eternal; and that there were visible marks of ruin upon it which could not be effected by a flood only. When I asked him how this earth could have been repeopled if ever it had undergone the same fate it was threatened with hereafter by the comet of 1680, he answered, that required the power of a Creator. He said he took all the planets to be composed of the same matter with this earth, viz. earth, water, stones, &c., but variously concocted. I asked him why he would not publish his conjectures as conjectures, and instanced that Kepler had communicated his; and though he had not gone near so far as Kepler, yet Kepler's guesses were so just and happy that they had been proved and demonstrated by him. His answer was, 'I do not deal in conjectures.' But upon my talking to him about the four observations that had been made of the comet of 1680, at 574 years' distance, and asking him the particular times, he opened his *Principia*, which laid on the table, and showed me there the particular periods, viz. 1st, the Julium Sidus, in the time of Justinian, in 1106, in 1680.

And I, observing that he said there of that comet, 'incidet in corpus solis,' and in the next paragraph adds, 'stellæ fixæ refici possunt,' told him I thought he owned there what we had been talking about, viz.

that the comet would drop into the sun, and that fixed stars were recruited and replenished by comets when they dropped into them; and, consequently, that the sun would be recruited too; and asked him why he would not own as freely what he thought of the sun as well as what he thought of the fixed stars. He said, 'that concerned us more;' and, laughing, added, 'that he had said enough for people to know his meaning.'"

The preceding paper, with the title prefixed to it, was first published by Mr. Turnor in his *Collections, &c.* p. 172. It was found among the Portsmouth manuscripts, in the handwriting of Mr. Conduit.

THE END.